Lasers
**Principles
and Applications**

Lasers
Principles
and Applications

J. Wilson
J. F. B. Hawkes
School of Physics
Newcastle upon Tyne Polytechnic

Prentice Hall
New York   London   Sydney   Tokyo

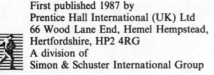

First published 1987 by
Prentice Hall International (UK) Ltd
66 Wood Lane End, Hemel Hempstead,
Hertfordshire, HP2 4RG
A division of
Simon & Schuster International Group

© 1987 Prentice Hall International (UK) Ltd

Printed and bound in Great Britain by
A. Wheaton and Co. Ltd, Exeter

Library of Congress Cataloging-in-Publication Data

Wilson, J. (John), 1939–
   Lasers: principles and applications.
   (Prentice Hall international series in
   optoelectronics)
   Includes bibliographies and index.
   1. Lasers. I. Hawkes, J. F. B., 1942–
   II. Title. III. Series.
   TA1675.W55   1988   621.36'6   87-18683

   ISBN 0-13-523705-X

British Library Cataloguing in Publication Data

Wilson, J.
   Lasers: principles and applications.—
   (Prentice Hall International Series in
   Optoelectronics).
   1. Lasers
   I. Title   II. Hawkes, J. F. B.
   621.36'6   TA1675

   ISBN 0-13-523705-X
   ISBN 0-13-523697-5 Pbk

5 6 7 8 96 95 94 93 92

0-13-523705-X
0-13-523697-5 PBK

Contents

Preface

It is now just over twenty-five years since laser action was first successfully demonstrated using a crystal of ruby as the laser medium. In the time since then not only has the term *laser* been adopted into our everyday speech but the laser has grown from the status of a scientific curiosity with a few potential applications to that of being one of the most important inventions of our time. It is now a vital tool for areas as diverse as manufacturing industries and medicine, an essential component of communication and holographic systems and the basis of many scientific measurements and research programs.

The term laser is used here in a general way for there are many different types of laser with quite different characteristics. All lasers, however, emit radiation with special properties which enables the laser to be used in a much wider range of applications than conventional light sources.

In view of the very wide range of applications, there is clearly a need for those other than physicists to have a good working knowledge of lasers so that they may better understand the particular application they are interested in and also appreciate the advantages and limitations of using lasers. This knowledge will hopefully enable them to make informed judgments on the purchase of appropriate lasers and associated components. Such people might include mechanical, electronic, civil and telecommunications engineers, chemists, life scientists, surgeons, military personnel and artists.

In writing this book, we have attempted to present a treatment of lasers appropriate to the needs of such a wide range of people. It is at an academic level equivalent to about the second year of a degree program and should also prove useful to students taking an introductory course in lasers. The text falls short of a comprehensive quantum-mechanical treatment of the theory of lasers but does present a much more detailed discussion than the rather brief reviews contained in many texts on modern optics. We hope therefore that this text will provide a basis for the study of the more advanced books cited in the references.

Chapter 1 covers the fundamentals of laser physics while Chapter 2 describes the principles of operation of a quite comprehensive selection of the various types of laser. Space does not allow an exhaustive coverage and doubtless we have omitted one or two lasers which will become important in the near future. We believe, however, that an understanding of these two chapters will enable the reader to appreciate the operation of new lasers as they appear.

Chapter 3, which discusses the properties of laser radiation, forms the basis for an understanding of why lasers are so useful and of many of their applications. We hope that it will help the reader to devise new applications in various fields. This chapter also describes some of the ways in which the laser output can be modified to enhance its usefulness.

Because of the special properties of laser radiation most laser beams can be focused to a very small spot, in which there is a very high energy density, and Chapter 5 covers some of the applications of lasers which depend on this. These range from cutting and welding metal sheets to an alternative to the surgeon's scalpel. In this chapter, perhaps more than in any other, we have quoted several useful equations. Space does not permit the derivation of such equations and indeed in many cases this would not help in understanding the application to which they are related. Full references are provided to these derivations for the interested reader. In Chapter 6 we have given a mathematical description of holography and presented some of its applications. After a rather slow start the range and number of these applications is steadily increasing. Although a full discussion is beyond the scope of this text, it is hoped that some readers will be encouraged to delve deeper into this fascinating subject.

Finally in Chapter 7 we discuss the role of lasers in optical communications. Topics covered include laser printers, optical disk systems and, most importantly, fiber-optic communications, in which there has been a dramatic growth in the last few years.

We have interspersed a number of worked examples throughout the text, which we hope will illustrate the use of equations, provide typical values of various parameters and enhance the reader's understanding and enjoyment of the book. There are also end-of-chapter questions with numerical solutions provided in Appendix 1. Appendix 2 provides a list of physical constants.

References have also been provided at the end of each chapter. These include suggestions for further reading as well as specific references to various points in the text.

Finally we would like to thank our colleagues, particularly Dr I. D. Latimer, for their interest and many valuable discussions and suggestions, Mrs Pat Weddell for typing the manuscript and our families for their encouragement and forbearance.

Glossary of Symbols

Wherever possible we have endeavored to use the commonly accepted symbols for the various physical parameters needed. Inevitably many symbols have duplicate meanings, and if in any doubt the reader should note carefully both the context and the dimensions. The following list of symbols does not include all the varieties formed by adding suffices, nor does it include all the (fairly frequent) cases where a symbol is used as a measure of physical dimensions.

A	area, spontaneous transition rate (A_{21})
a	fiber radius
B	Einstein coefficient (B_{12}, B_{21}), bit rate
C	capacitance, specific heat capacity
c	velocity of light
D	Diameter, optical density
d	distance
$\mathscr{E}$	electric field amplitude
E	energy, bandgap (E_g)
e	electron charge
F	lens F number
f	modulation frequency, focal length
G	gain
g	lineshape function ($g(\nu)$)
H	heat flow per unit area
h	Planck's constant
$\hbar$	$= h/2\pi$
I	irradiance
i, i	current, $\sqrt{(-1)}$
$\mathscr{J}$	molecular rotational quantum number
J	total momentum
$\mathscr{K}$	diffraction factor
K	thermal conductivity, film development parameter
$k, \mathbf{k}$	unit vector, small signal gain coefficient, threshold gain coefficient (k_{th}) Boltzmann's constant, wave vector.
L	cavity length, angular momentum, coherence length (L_c), heat diffusion length (L_p), Latent heats of fusion (L_f) and vaporization (L_v)
l	mode number

M	mass
m	mass, mode number
$\mathcal{N}$	photon density
N	number of modes, number density
NA	numerical aperture
n	electron concentration, intrinsic carrier concentration (n_i) refractive index
P	power, electrical polarization, pressure
p	axial mode number, hole concentration
Q	'quality' factor
q	transverse mode number, spectrum order
R	electrical resistance, reflectance, ratio of spontaneous to stimulated emission rates
R_H	the Rydberg constant
r	radius of curvature, transverse mode number
S	spin momentum
s	fringe separation
T	transmittance, temperature
t	time, coherence time (t_c), amplitude transmittance
U	electric field amplitude (complex)
V	contact, potential (V_0), voltage, fiber 'V' parameter
v	velocity, group velocity (v_g), molecular vibration quantum number
W	power
w	laser beam width parameter
α	absorption coefficient, angle
β	phase factor
γ	loss coefficient, mutual coherence function (γ_{12}), fiber refractive index profile parameter, ratio of electron energy to rest energy, photographic film density parameter.
Δ	relative fiber refractive index parameter
δ	phase angle
ε_0	electric permittivity of free space
θ	angle, Brewster angle (θ_B)
$\varkappa$	thermal diffusivity
λ	light wavelength
μ_0	magnetic permeability of free space
ν	lightwave frequency
ρ	material density, radiation energy density
τ	lifetime, time
ϕ	phase angle, work function, lens aperture
χ	electric susceptibility
ψ	phase factor
Ω	angular velocity
ω	angular frequency

1

Laser Fundamentals

1.1 THE NATURE OF LIGHT

The term *Laser* is an acronym formed from *l*ight *a*mplification by *s*timulated *e*mission of *r*adiation. Thus to understand the operation of lasers, the special properties of their radiation and their application, we must familiarize ourselves with the present ideas concerning the nature of light.

The Greeks were almost certainly the first to try and explain the nature of light and how vision takes place. Then the advent of experimental science brought about two rival theories. These were the corpuscular theory of Newton, who suggested that light consisted of streams of particles which obeyed his dynamical laws of motion and the wave theories of Hooke and Huygens, who assumed that light had a wave-like nature.

For any theory of light to be accepted it must be able to explain observed phenomena such as reflection, refraction, diffraction and interference. Diffraction is the name given to the ability of light to 'bend round corners' to a certain extent, so that shadows of an object cast on a distant screen are not perfectly sharp even when a point source of light is used. We would expect sharp shadows to be formed if light travelled in straight lines, that is, if it showed rectilinear propagation. Interference is a related phenomenon resulting when light from two or more coherent (refer to Section 3.4) sources combines to form regions of alternating darkness and brightness; these regions are called fringes. (For a more complete description of these optical phenomena see Ref. 1.1.)

Both theories were able to account for some of the phenomena mentioned above, but interference, first demonstrated by Young in 1801, could be explained only in terms of light waves. Young's experiment is shown schematically in Fig. 1.1. Light from a point source falls onto a screen containing two pinholes which in turn act as point sources. Consequently the light from the pinholes has the form of two overlapping spherical wavefronts (see below). It the light is allowed to fall onto a second screen a system of interference fringes forms. The bright fringes form when two or more waves combine together *in phase* so as to reinforce one another; dark fringes form when the waves are out of phase and cancel each other

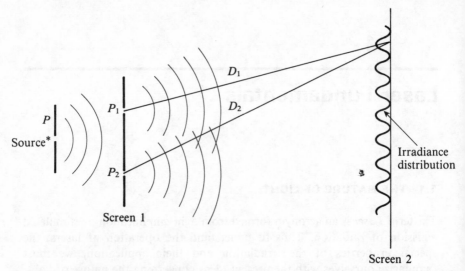

Fig. 1.1 Schematic arrangement for Young's experiment to demonstrate
interference. P, P_1 and P_2 are pinholes which act as point sources of
light.

(Fig. 1.2). Young called these situations constructive and destructive interference respectively.

Clearly as we move across the screen the relative distance $(D_1 \sim D_2)$ of
points on the screen to the two pinholes P_1 and P_2 varies so that the relative
phases of the waves arriving at these points changes. There is, therefore, a
gradual variation from an exactly in-phase to an exactly out-of-phase situation, with a consequent gradual change from bright fringe to dark to bright
and so on. It is convenient to measure the path difference from each point
on the screen to the pinholes in terms of λ, the wavelength of the light. Thus
for example if the path difference is a whole number of wavelengths then
a bright fringe is formed.

Diffraction phenomena can easily be explained in terms of Huygens'
principle of secondary wavelets. Huygens assumed, in order to explain the
propagation of light through apertures and past obstacles, that each point
on a wavefront acts as a secondary source of light and that wavelets spread
out from these points. Then, after a short time, the new wavefront is the
surface which is a tangent to all the wavelets. This is much easier to show in
a diagram than it is to explain in words and Fig. 1.3 is almost self evident.
By a wavefront we mean all points where the light waves have exactly the
same phase, thus for example, the wavefront from a point source is the
surface of a sphere (providing the medium surrounding the source is
optically uniform). The spreading of light through an aperture is easily
accounted for in terms of Fig. 1.4, which also indicates, with a little

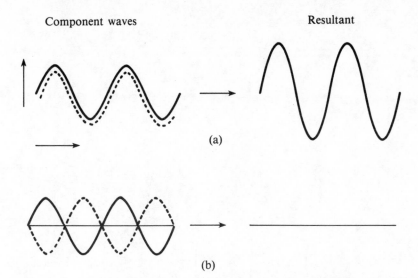

Component waves   Resultant

(a)

(b)

Fig. 1.2   In (a) waves from the two sources arrive at screen 2 in Fig. 1.1 exactly in phase and combine together (or interfere constructively) to give a bright fringe. In (b) two waves arrive at the screen exactly out of phase and cancel each other (or interfere destructively) to give a dark fringe.

thought, that the smaller the aperture the greater will be the diffraction, that is, the amount of spreading of the emergent wavefront.

We see then that a wave theory can easily account for interference and diffraction phenomena while a corpuscular theory cannot. Young was able to explain other phenomena such as the formation of colors in soap films or thin films of oil on wet surfaces in terms of a wave theory by associating different colors of light with different wavelengths. He also suggested that polarization of light can come about only because light has a *transverse* wave nature. By this we mean that the vibrations of the light waves are perpendicular to the direction of travel, unlike the situation with sound traveling through fluids, where the waves are *longitudinal* with the vibrations along the direction of travel.

In a plane polarized beam of light all of the waves have their vibrations coplanar as opposed to the random orientation of the planes of vibration of unpolarized light – the situation is illustrated in Fig. 1.5.

Additional evidence in favor of a wave theory was provided by Fresnel's quantitative explanation of diffraction in terms of light waves, while a major advance in understanding the nature of light was made by Maxwell in 1864. Maxwell combined the experimental work of Faraday, Oersted and Henry on electricity and magnetism into a set of equations from which he deduced the existence of a transverse wave whose speed c in

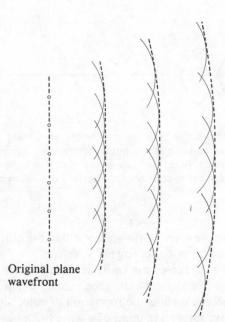

Original plane
wavefront

Fig. 1.3 An illustration of the application of Huygens' principle to the propagation of a plane wavefront (dashed lines). The small circles represent 'point sources' on the original wavefront which emit secondary
wavelets. The new wavefront at a later time is the resultant of these
secondary wavelets. The diagram shows (in an exaggerated way)
that an initially plane wavefront will diverge as it propagates.

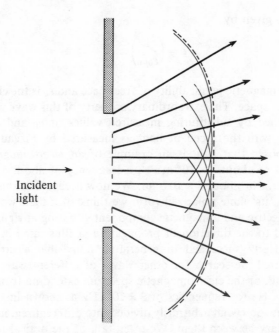

Fig. 1.4 The diffraction of light through an aperture in terms of Huygens' principle. As in Fig. 1.3, the dashed lines represent successive positions of the wavefronts. The arrows, which are normal to the wavefront, indicate the directions of propagation of the light after it passes through the aperture.

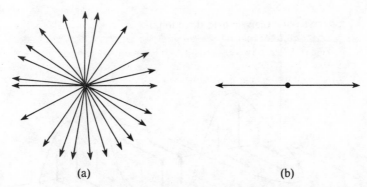

| (a) | (b) |

Fig. 1.5 (a) shows the random orientations of the electric fields of the waves comprising an unpolarized beam of light traveling normal to the plane of the paper. (b) shows the electric field directions of a horizontally plane-polarized beam of light.

free space was given by

$$c = \left(\frac{1}{\varepsilon_0 \mu_0}\right)^{1/2}$$

where μ_0 is the magnetic permeability of free space and ε_0 is the electric per-mittivity of free space. The extraordinary property of this wave was that its speed c, obtained by substituting measured values of μ_0 and ε_0, agreed almost exactly with the speed of light as measured by Fizeau. Maxwell therefore proposed that light is an example of an *electromagnetic* wave having a speed of about $3 \times 10^8 \, \text{m s}^{-1}$, a frequency of about 5×10^{14} Hz and a wavelength of about 5×10^{-7} m. We now accept that this is indeed the case and in its plane polarized form we think of a light wave as con-sisting of an electric and a magnetic component vibrating at right angles to each other and to the direction of propagation as illustrated in Fig. 1.6.

In 1887 Hertz succeeded in generating nonvisible electromagnetic waves and started the search for other waves of different wavelengths so that we now talk of the electromagnetic spectrum extending from frequen-cies of 3×10^{10} Hz to frequencies of 3×10^{20} Hz as shown in Figure 1.7. The spectrum is somewhat arbitrarily divided into different regions, with no definite boundary between them. We often talk of the optical region (not shown in Fig. 1.7) which includes the visible together with the near I.R. and U.V. regions, say from frequencies of 3×10^{13} to 3×10^{16} Hz; it is within the optical region that we generally find laser wavelengths.

All of the waves in the spectrum have a simple relationship between fre-quency ν and wavelength λ, namely

$$c = \nu\lambda = 2.9979 \times 10^8 \, \text{m s}^{-1} \qquad \textit{in vacuo.}$$

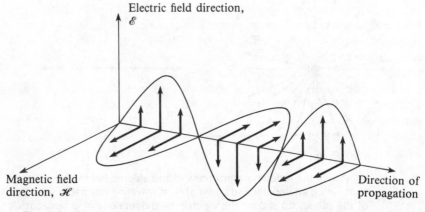

Fig. 1.6   Electric and magnetic fields in a plane electromagnetic wave.

Type of radiation	Wavelength	Frequency (Hz)	Quantum energy (eV)
Radio waves	100 km	3×10^3	1.2×10^{-11}
	300 mm	10^9	4×10^{-6}
Microwaves			
	0.3 mm	10^{12}	4×10^{-3}
Infrared			
	0.7 μm	4.3×10^{14}	1.8
Visible			
	0.4 μm	7.5×10^{14}	3.1
Ultraviolet			
	0.03 μm	10^{16}	40
X rays			
	0.1 nm	3×10^{18}	1.2×10^4
γ rays			
	1.0 pm	3×10^{20}	1.2×10^6

(*Note.* The divisions into the various regions are for illustration only; there is no firm dividing line between one region and the next. The numerical values are only approximate; the upper and lower limits are somewhat arbitrary.)

Fig. 1.7 The electromagnetic spectrum.

In other media the speed c is modified to c', given by

$$\frac{c}{c'} = \frac{\lambda}{\lambda'} = n,$$

where n is the refractive index. λ' is the wavelength in the medium; it is this change in wavelength at the interface between two media which causes refraction.

At this juncture it might be thought that the problem concerning the nature of light had been incontrovertibly resolved in favor of a wave theory. A wave theory, however, still leaves us with some unsolved problems. It fails, for example, to explain the emission and absorption of light and phenomena such as the photoelectric effect.

In the photoelectric effect radiation incident on metal surfaces releases electrons. It was noted that the release of electrons from a given surface occurs only if the incident light is of a high enough frequency. Thus, for example, while very intense red light may be completely ineffective in producing photoelectrons, low-intensity blue light may produce photoelectrons having a marked amount of kinetic energy.

Einstein (1905) explained this effect very simply in terms of the incident light consisting of small bundles of energy or particles which he called photons. He said that the energy of a photon was proportional to its frequency†, that is, $E = h\nu$, where h is the Planck constant. An incident photon can then impart its energy to a single electron giving it a sufficient amount of energy, ϕ, the work function, to overcome the forces holding it to the surface of the metal and to impart to it a certain amount of kinetic energy. That is,

$$E = h\nu = \phi + \tfrac{1}{2}mv^2, \tag{1.1}$$

where m is the mass of the electron and v its velocity.

Example 1.1   The kinetic energy of photoelectrons

Light of wavelength $\lambda = 488$ nm from an argon ion laser falls onto a metal surface which has a work function of 2.2 eV. Let us calculate the maximum kinetic energy of the photoelectrons emitted.

The energy of the incident photons is

$$\frac{hc}{\lambda} = \frac{6.626 \times 10^{-34} \times 2.998 \times 10^{8}}{488 \times 10^{-9}}$$

$$= 4.07 \times 10^{-19}\,\text{J}.$$

The work function is

$$\phi = 2.2\ \text{eV}$$

$$= 2.2 \times 1.6 \times 10^{-19} = 3.52 \times 10^{-19}\,\text{J}.$$

Therefore, maximum kinetic energy of the photoelectrons is

$$(4.07 - 3.52) \times 10^{-19} = 0.55 \times 10^{-19}\,\text{J} = 0.34\ \text{eV}.$$

Note that very few of the photoelectrons are actually emitted with this energy because the majority are released from below the surface, so that energy in addition to the work function ϕ is required.

A wave theory is unable to explain several features of the photoelectric effect. For example it cannot explain the ineffectiveness of high-intensity red light in producing photoelectrons, nor can it explain the instantaneous emission of electrons when a suitable light source is switched on. On the basis of a wave theory a delay would be expected before electrons are emitted because the energy of the light would be spread uniformly across the incident wavefront, so that a certain time would need to elapse before an electron received sufficient energy to enable it to escape.

Therefore it seems that we still have two rival theories of light. We

---

† As the photon is a particle it does not have a frequency and, perhaps, we should more correctly refer to the frequency *associated* with the photon.

must, however, accept both theories and should regard them as being complementary rather than conflicting. When light interacts with light as in interference we use a wave theory, while when light interacts with matter as in the photoelectric effect we use a particle theory. This situation gives rise to what we call the dual nature of radiation.

1.2 EMISSION AND ABSORPTION OF LIGHT

Einstein based his explanation of the photoelectric effect on previous work by Planck who had introduced the idea of light quanta when trying to explain the emission of radiation by black bodies (perfect radiators).

Planck attributed the emission of electromagnetic waves to oscillators producing oscillating electric fields, the important proviso being that the oscillators were allowed to have only certain energy values, which were multiples of $h\nu$. The work of Planck introduced what we now call quantum theory. The important aspect of quantum theory, for our purposes, is that atomic systems have discrete energy levels or energy states.

An explanation of why the light emitted by atoms in gaseous form consists of well-defined wavelengths or spectral lines may also be given on this basis [1.2]. Even though it had been shown by 1823 that each atomic element produces a characteristic and identifiable line spectrum, an explanation of this was not given until 1913, by Bohr. Bohr developed a theory which enabled him to predict the wavelengths of the lines in the simplest of these spectra, namely that of hydrogen. He used an atomic model developed by Rutherford, who had shown that atoms consist of a heavy, positively charged nucleus surrounded by a number of negative electrons; each element has atoms containing a specific number of electrons. To explain why the electrons did not collapse into the positive nucleus it was supposed that the electrons orbited the nucleus much as the planets orbit the sun.

The centripetal force required to maintain the electron in its circular orbit is provided by the Coulombic attraction of the positive nucleus on the negative electron. This can be expressed as

$$\frac{mv^2}{r} = \frac{e^2}{4\pi\varepsilon_0 r^2} \tag{1.2}$$

where m, e and v are the electron mass, charge and velocity respectively, r is the radius of the orbit and ε_0 is the permittivity of free space. Bohr assumed that the single electron of hydrogen was allowed to occupy only certain orbits and that when the electron was in one of these allowed orbits a stable or stationary state ensued in which no energy was emitted by the atom. Each of these allowed orbits corresponded to a definite discrete energy state or level. To explain the line spectrum of hydrogen Bohr then assumed that if the electron, and hence the atom, lost energy by moving from an orbit of high energy (far from the nucleus) to an orbit of lower energy (nearer to the nucleus) then the energy lost would be in the form of a photon of energy $h\nu$, that is, $E_i - E_f = h\nu$, where E_i and E_f are the electron energies before and after the transition. There are many such discrete orbits and therefore many different transitions are possible so that the hydrogen atom emits many different frequencies (or wavelengths) given by the appropriate energy difference divided by h. The situation is illustrated in Fig. 1.8. In general each atom tends to the lowest energy level or ground state, so to produce the hydrogen spectrum we must first of all excite the electron to higher energy levels by heat, by collisions in an electrical discharge tube or by exposure to radiation of appropriate wavelengths. Any wavelengths which an excited atom may emit may also be absorbed by the atom when in lower energy states, though the energy of the incident photons must correspond very closely to the energy difference between the two

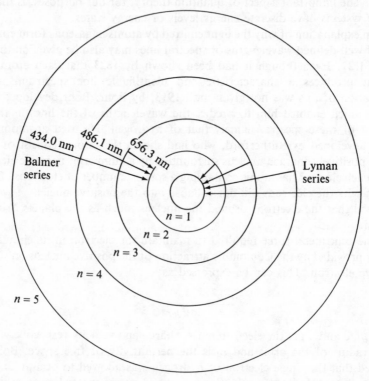

Fig. 1.8   A schematic diagram (not to scale) showing some allowed electron orbits in the Bohr model of the hydrogen atom. The electron transitions giving rise to some of the wavelengths in the line spectrum of hydrogen are also shown.

atomic energy levels involved. This is called *resonant absorption*. We shall return to these excitation and absorption processes in due course.

By analogy Bohr was able to explain the line spectra of other multi-electron atoms, where more complex spectra are produced. While Bohr's theory gives a good description of the situation it is essentially based on classical physics and the modern precise description is based wholly on quantum physics. Quantum physics introduces a description of each electron in an atom in terms of a set of four *quantum numbers*. These may be thought of as coordinates which precisely determine the energy of the electron just as geometrical coordinates are used to determine the location of a point in space. A specification of the allowed values of these quantum numbers determines the energies of the electrons in each atom and predicts the wavelengths of the spectral lines emitted.

While the concept of electron orbits should not be taken too literally it does give a simple pictorial model of the atom and, very important for our purposes, it gives a qualitative description of the origin of the discrete energy levels of atoms. It is worth emphasizing again that because photons are produced when an electron undergoes a downward transition between two well-defined energy levels, the energy of the photon is also well defined. Consequently the frequency and wavelength associated with the photon are well defined; we say that the radiation is monochromatic. For complex atoms having many electron energy levels a large number of combinations are possible so that many different wavelengths may be emitted or absorbed, depending on whether the electrons are initially in high-energy (excited) states or in low-energy states.

1.3   INTERACTION OF RADIATION AND MATTER

For the sake of simplicity let us consider an atom having only two energy levels, an upper level E_2 and a lower level E_1, as shown in Fig. 1.9. Under normal circumstances the atom will be in the lower level as physical systems tend to the lowest possible energy state. Suppose that the atom in the lower level is exposed to radiation of frequency ν_{21}, where

$$\nu_{21} = \frac{E_2 - E_1}{h}.$$ (1.3)

There is then a high probability that it will absorb a photon and be excited to the upper level E_2. This process is referred to as *stimulated absorption* as the incident light energy is necessary for the process to occur; it is illustrated in Figure 1.9(b).

Very soon (usually within a few nanoseconds) after being excited to the higher energy level the atom will emit a photon of energy $h\nu_{21} = E_2 - E_1$ and

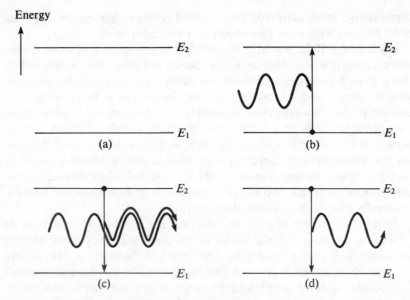

Fig. 1.9   Energy-level diagram illustrating (a) a two-level energy system, (b) stimulated absorption, (c) stimulated emission and (d) spontaneous emission. The black dot indicates the energy state of the atom before the absorption or emission event.

return to the lower level. In 1917 Einstein showed that the emission process can occur in two quite distinct ways. As with the absorption process the emission process can be *stimulated* or it can occur entirely *spontaneously* as illustrated in Figures 1.9(c) and (d).

There are two very important points concerning stimulated emission upon which the properties of laser light depend. Firstly the photon produced by stimulated emission has the same energy as the stimulating photon and hence the associated light waves must have the same frequency [see Section 1.9]. Secondly the light waves associated with the two photons are in phase and have the same state of polarization. This means that if an atom is stimulated to emit light energy the wave representing the stimulated photon adds to the incident wave on a constructive basis, thereby increasing its amplitude. We then have the possibility of *light amplification by stimulated emission of radiation*.

Stimulated radiation is coherent, that is, all of the waves making up a beam of such radiation are in phase (see Section 3.4). The situation might be compared to a long column of soldiers all of whom are marching in step. This is in contrast to spontaneous emission in which the atoms emit in an entirely random way such that there is no phase relationship between the associated waves. Such radiation is said to be incoherent and we might compare it to the (apparently) random movements of the people on a city street.

It must be emphasized at this stage that under normal conditions of thermal equilibrium spontaneous emission in the visible part of the spectrum from an assembly of atoms is much more probable than stimulated emission (by a factor of about $10^{33} : 1$) and therefore the radiation from most optical sources is incoherent. We shall see below that laser action is possible only if we depart from thermal equilibrium.

1.4   THE EINSTEIN RELATIONS

Einstein showed that the three processes of stimulated absorption, stimulated emission and spontaneous emission are related mathematically through the requirement that for a system of atoms in thermal equilibrium with its own radiation the rate of upward transitions (from E_1 to E_2) must equal the rate of downward transitions (from E_2 to E_1).

If there are N_1 atoms in the assembly with energy E_1, then the upward transition rate is proportional to both N_1 and to the number of photons present with the appropriate frequency, ν. The energy density ρ_ν of such photons is simply $\rho_\nu = \mathcal{N} h \nu$, where $\mathcal{N}$ is the number of photons per unit volume. The upward transition rate can then be written as

$$\text{stimulated absorption rate} = N_1 \rho_\nu B_{12},$$

where B_{12} is a constant for a given pair of energy levels (the '12' indicates the energy levels involved).

Similarly if there are N_2 atoms per unit volume in the assembly with energy E_2, then we have

$$\text{stimulated emission rate} = N_2 \rho_\nu B_{21},$$

where again B_{21} is a constant for the pair of energy levels involved.

The spontaneous transition rate depends on the average *lifetime, τ_{21}*, of the atoms in the excited state. The probability that a particular atom will undergo a spontaneous transition in a time dt is dt/τ_{21}, which equals $A_{21} \, dt$, where A_{21} is a constant. Thus as there are N_2 atoms in the upper level, then

$$\text{spontaneous emission rate} = N_2 A_{21}.$$

The constants A_{21}, B_{12} and B_{21} are called the Einstein coefficients and the relationships between them can be established by considering the condition for the assembly of atoms to be in thermal equilibrium: we must have

$$N_1 \rho_\nu B_{12} = N_2 \rho_\nu B_{21} + N_2 A_{21}.$$

From this equation we may write

$$\rho_\nu = \frac{A_{21}/B_{21}}{(B_{12}N_1/B_{21}N_2) - 1}. \tag{1.4}$$

Now the number N_j of atoms in the jth level (or populations) of the various energy levels E_i of a system in thermal equilibrium is given by Boltzmann statistics to be [1.3]:

$$N_j = N_0 \frac{\exp(-E_j/kT)}{\sum_i \exp(-E_i/kT)} \tag{1.5}$$

where N_0 is the total number of atoms and E_j is the energy of the jth level.†
From this equation it can be seen that the ratio of the populations N_1 and N_2 in the levels E_1 and E_2 is

$$\frac{N_1}{N_2} = \exp((E_2 - E_1)/kT) \tag{1.6}$$

and therefore substituting Eq. (1.6) into Eq. (1.4) and using Eq. (1.3) we have

$$\rho_\nu = \frac{A_{21}/B_{21}}{B_{12}/B_{21} \exp(h\nu/kT) - 1} \tag{1.7}$$

Also, because the system is in equilibrium, the radiation within the assembly of atoms must be identical to blackbody radiation which can be described by [1.4]:

$$\rho_\nu = \frac{8\pi h\nu^3}{c^3} \left(\frac{1}{\exp(h\nu/kT) - 1}\right) \tag{1.8}$$

Comparing Eqs. (1.7) and (1.8) for ρ_ν we see that

$$B_{12} = B_{21} \tag{1.9}$$

and

$$A_{21} = B_{21} \frac{8\pi h\nu^3}{c^3} \tag{1.10}$$

These equations are known as the Einstein relations. Equation (1.9) enables

---

† Eq. (1.5) as written assumes that all the available states or energy levels have the same probability of being occupied. In general this is not so, the states have a probability g_i of occupation (g is often called the degeneracy). Equations (1.6)–(1.10) should be modified by including the degeneracies g_1 and g_2. These parameters usually appear in the equations as the ratio g_2/g_1, which is often of the order of unity and we have therefore omitted them for simplicity.

us to evaluate the ratio of the rates of spontaneous and stimulated emission for a given pair of energy levels in thermal equilibrium with the radiation. We see that this ratio, R, is

$$R = \frac{N_2 A_{21}}{N_2 B_{21}\rho_\nu} = \frac{8\pi h\nu^3}{\rho_\nu c^3}. \tag{1.11}$$

Substituting for ρ_ν from Eq. (1.6) then gives

$$R = \exp\left(\frac{h\nu}{kT}\right) - 1. \tag{1.12}$$

Example 1.2. Ratio of spontaneous to stimulated emission rate

Let us now calculate R for the light emitted by an electrical discharge in a gas such as neon in the helium–neon (HeNe) laser. The discharge temperature may be taken as 370 K and for the red line produced by this laser, which has a frequency of $\nu = 4.74 \times 10^{14}$ Hz, we find that

$$R \simeq e^{61.5} \simeq 5 \times 10^{26}.$$

The above calculation confirms that under conditions of thermal equilibrium stimulated emission is most unlikely. We also note that the higher the frequency the less likely is this process. Furthermore the process of stimulated emission also competes with the process of (stimulated) absorption. Clearly, then, if we wish to amplify a beam of light by stimulated emission we must increase the rate of this process relative to the other two. Consideration of the expression for stimulated emission given above indicates that to achieve this for a given pair of energy levels both the population density of the upper level and the radiation density should be increased. Indeed, because of the Einstein relation $B_{12} = B_{21}$ we must ensure that $N_2 > N_1$ (even though $E_2 > E_1$), that is, we must create a *population inversion* (Section 1.6).

So far our discussions have been in terms of transitions between a pair of energy levels E_2 and E_1. Real atoms and atomic systems are characterized by a large number of different energy levels and the various transition processes may occur, though with different probabilities, between any pair of these levels. There are appropriate Einstein coefficients A_{ij}, B_{ij} and B_{ji} (and Einstein relations) for each pair of levels. In considering laser action in a given medium the transition rates between all such pairs of levels should be taken into account, but in practice we can usually reduce the total number of relevant energy levels to three or four (page 19).

1.5 THE GAIN COEFFICIENT

Let us consider a collimated beam of monochromatic radiation passing through an absorbing medium as illustrated in Fig. 1.10, and let us assume that the absorption is due to only one electron transition, namely between levels E_1 and E_2. Then the change in the irradiance (that is, the power flowing across unit area) of the beam as it propagates is given by

$$\Delta I(x) = I(x + \Delta x) - I(x).$$

If the medium is homogeneous ΔI is proportional to the distance travelled Δx and to the irradiance $I(x)$; thus we may write

$$\Delta I(x) = -\alpha I(x)\, \Delta x,$$

where α, the constant of proportionality, is the *absorption coefficient*. The negative sign in this equation indicates a reduction in beam irradiance with distance as, in general, α is a positive quantity; we can write this as a differential equation in the form

$$\frac{\mathrm{d}I(x)}{\mathrm{d}x} = -\alpha I(x), \tag{1.13}$$

which on integration gives

$$I(x) = I_0\, e^{-\alpha x} \tag{1.14}$$

where I_0 is the irradiance of the incident beam.

The amount of absorption (that is, the magnitude of α) depends on how many atoms N_1 there are with electrons in the lower energy state E_1 and how many atoms N_2 there are in the upper state E_2. If N_2 were zero, then the absorption would be a maximum; on the other hand if N_1 were zero the absorption would be zero and the probability of stimulated emission

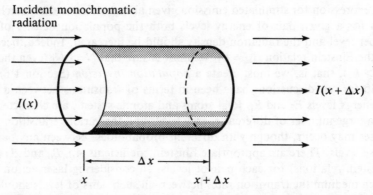

Fig. 1.10 Radiation passing through a volume element of length Δx and unit cross-sectional area of an absorbing medium.

would be greater. In practice we find that the absorption coefficient is proportional to the difference of N_1 and N_2. In thermal equilibrium, as we have seen, $N_1 \gg N_2$ and therefore the irradiance of the beam will decrease exponentially with distance as it propagates through the medium. If, however, N_2 is made greater than N_1 (i.e. a population inversion is created) then α will be negative and the quantity $-\alpha x$ in Eq. (1.14) becomes positive so that the irradiance of the beam will *grow* exponentially in accordance with the equation

$$I(x) = I_0\, e^{kx} \tag{1.15}$$

where k is called the small-signal gain coefficient. We can now derive an expression for k in terms of the population inversion and other parameters of the laser medium. From the discussion in Section 1.3 on stimulated emission and absorption we may write the net rate of loss of photons from the beam, as it travels through the volume element of thickness Δx and unit cross-sectional area (Fig. 1.10), as:

$$\frac{-\mathrm{d}\mathcal{N}}{\mathrm{d}t} = N_1\rho_\nu B_{12} - N_2\rho_\nu B_{21}$$

or, substituting from Eq. (1.9),

$$\frac{-\mathrm{d}\mathcal{N}}{\mathrm{d}t} = (N_1 - N_2)\rho_\nu B_{21} \tag{1.16}$$

where $\mathcal{N}$ is the number of photons per unit volume.

As the irradiance of the beam is the energy crossing unit area per second, it is therefore given by the energy density multiplied by the speed of light in the medium, that is for frequency ν,

$$I = \frac{\rho_\nu c}{n} = \frac{\mathcal{N}h\nu c}{n}.$$

Thus the change in photon density within the beam between the boundaries x and $x + \Delta x$ is

$$-\mathrm{d}\mathcal{N}(x) = (I(x) - I(x + \Delta x))\frac{n}{h\nu c}$$

which, for small values of Δx, may be written as

$$-\mathrm{d}\mathcal{N}(x) = -\left(\frac{\mathrm{d}I(x)}{\mathrm{d}x}\,\Delta x\right)\left(\frac{n}{h\nu c}\right).$$

Hence in a time interval $\mathrm{d}t = (\Delta x/(c/n))$ the rate of decay of photon density is given by

$$\frac{\mathrm{d}\mathcal{N}(x)}{\mathrm{d}t} = \frac{\mathrm{d}I(x)}{\mathrm{d}x}\frac{1}{h\nu}$$

Substituting for $\dfrac{dI(x)}{dx}$ from Eq. (1.13) then gives

$$\frac{d\mathcal{N}}{dt} = -\alpha I(x)\,\frac{1}{h\nu} = -\left(\frac{\alpha\rho_\nu c}{n}\right)\frac{1}{h\nu}. \tag{1.17}$$

Therefore comparing Eqs. (1.16) and (1.17) we see that for the energy levels E_2 and E_1

$$\alpha\rho_\nu\,\frac{c}{n}\,\frac{1}{h\nu_{21}} = (N_1 - N_2)\rho_\nu B_{21}.$$

As k, the small-signal gain coefficient, equals $-\alpha$ we may thus write

$$k = (N_2 - N_1)\,\frac{nh\nu_{21}B_{21}}{c}. \tag{1.18}$$

1.6   ATTAINMENT OF A POPULATION INVERSION

We saw in Section 1.4 that for there to be a reasonable probability of stimulated emission occurring we must greatly increase the population N_2 of the upper level relative to that of the lower level, that is, we must create a population inversion. We may contrast this with the Boltzmann distribution corresponding to thermal equilibrium in Fig. 1.11. We note that we

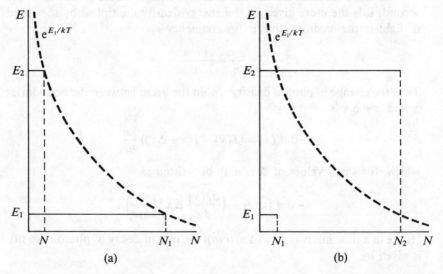

Fig. 1.11   Populations of a two-level energy system (a) in thermal equilibrium, (b) after a population inversion has been produced.

cannot create such a situation whilst maintaining thermal equilibrium merely, for example, by raising the temperature of the system. For as we can see from Eq. (1.6), N_2 can approach, but never exceed N_1 if equilibrium is maintained. To create a population inversion the atoms within the laser medium must be excited or *pumped* into a non-equilibrium distribution through the application of a large amount of energy to the medium from an external source.

There are several ways of pumping a collection of atoms including pumping by optical radiation, collisions within an electrical discharge, passage of a current, electron bombardment and the release of chemical energy. Some of these will be discussed in Chapter 2 when we consider specific lasers. Let us now consider optical pumping in general terms as an example of these techniques as applied in lasers having different energy level schemes.

Clearly if we irradiate an assembly of atoms with very intense radiation of appropriate frequency many atoms will absorb the radiation and be excited from level E_1 to E_2. A little thought, however, will lead us to the conclusion that a population inversion cannot be achieved by optical pumping of the simple two-energy-level system we have considered hitherto. At best, because $B_{12} = B_{21}$, even with very intense irradiation the populations of the upper and lower levels can only be made equal. Optical pumping, and indeed most other pumping methods, requires either a three- or a four-energy-level system.

The three-level system is shown in Fig. 1.12. The laser medium is illuminated by intense radiation from a flash tube and a large number of atoms are pumped into the upper level E_2 from the ground-state level E_0 by absorption of radiation of frequency ν_{02}. From E_2 the atoms decay (usually by some nonradiative decay process) into level E_1 and a population inversion occurs between the levels E_1 and E_0 when N_1 exceeds N_0.

For the inversion to occur with the minimum of pumping, the transition of atoms from E_2 to E_1 should be rapid. This is almost invariably the case in practice as in general the lifetime of atoms in excited states is of the order of 10^{-8} to 10^{-9} seconds. Also the level E_1 preferably should be metastable, that is, have a very long lifetime. Some levels do have long lifetimes which may be as great as a few milliseconds. If these conditions are satisfied atoms can be pumped quickly from E_0 via E_2 into E_1, where they accumulate so that the population N_1 builds up. Eventually when the population inversion is achieved amplification of radiation of frequency $\nu_{10} = (E_1 - E_0)/h$ can take place by stimulated emission.

As the level E_2 is not directly involved in the amplification process it can be broad so that a wide band of wavelengths in the pumping radiation is effective in pumping. This increases the efficiency of the pumping operation. The three-level system requires very high pumping power, however, because the terminal state E_0 of the laser transition is the ground state and

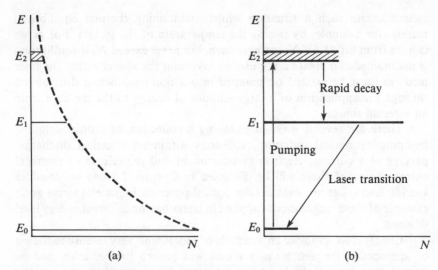

Fig. 1.12   Population of the energy levels by pumping in a three-level system:
(a) Boltzmann distribution before pumping; (b) distribution after
pumping and the transitions involved.

thus rather more than half of the total number of atoms must be pumped
from the ground state into the excited state before a population inversion
can be achieved. The energy required to pump half of the total number of
atoms in the system into E_1 via E_2 is wasted. The three-level system is
therefore inherently inefficient. Nevertheless the first operational laser,
namely the ruby laser, has essentially a three-level arrangement (see Fig.
2.10).

The pumping requirements can be greatly reduced by using the four-
level scheme shown in Figure 1.13. If $(E_1 - E_0)$ is large compared with the
thermal energy, kT, at the temperature of operation, then the populations
of the levels E_1, E_2 and E_3 are all effectively zero before pumping commences. Thus a population inversion can readily be achieved between levels
E_2 and E_1, again the level E_3 may be broad for effective pumping. Typically,
as shown in Fig. 1.13, pumping excites atoms from the ground state into
level E_3, whence they decay rapidly into the metastable level E_2, so that N_2
increases rapidly to give population inversion between E_2 and E_1. If the
lifetime of the transition from level E_1 to level E_0 is short, then the population inversion can be maintained easily with modest pumping. The Nd:YAG
laser has such as energy-level arrangement (see Fig. 2.7) and a measure of
the overall pumping efficiency is the relative ease with which continuous
laser action can be obtained in this material.

In actual laser media many more than three or four energy levels may
in fact be involved. In most cases, however, these can be seen to approximate quite closely to the three- or four-level systems described above.

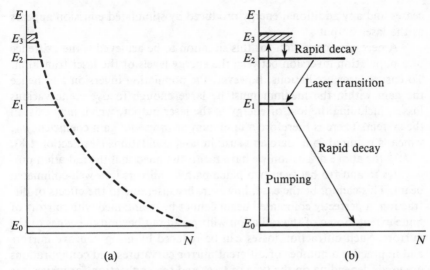

Fig. 1.13 Population of the energy levels in a four-level system: (a) before pumping; (b) after pumping.

1.7 THE OPTICAL RESONATOR

In the vast majority of cases the gain of a pumped or excited medium is quite small (in the region of 10 percent per meter) so that the amplification of an optical beam passing once through the medium is minimal. There are, however, a few situations in which useful amplification can be obtained in this way, for example neodymium doped glass is used to amplify the output of Nd-glass lasers for use in fusion experiments (see Section 5.10.1).

In most situations the overall amplification is increased by placing highly reflecting mirrors (reflectance approaching 100%) at each end of the medium. The optical beam then bounces to and fro through the medium, perhaps as many as one hundred times, thereby increasing the effective length of the medium. The mirrors form an optical cavity or resonator (often called a Fabry–Perot resonator) and together with the active medium constitutes an optical *oscillator* rather than an amplifier.

The mirrors introduce optical feedback to the amplifying medium in an entirely analogous way to positive feedback in an electronic amplifier. Initially spontaneous emission produces a small disturbance at the transition frequency, which passes through the medium within the cavity and undergoes amplification due to stimulated emission. At the end mirror most of the energy is returned into the cavity and passes through the medium, being amplified en route, to the other mirror where the process is repeated. The amplitude of the disturbance grows until a steady-state level of oscillation is reached. At this stage, growth of the wave amplitude within the cavity ceases and any additional energy produced by stimulated emission appears as the laser output.

A necessary condition for this situation to be achieved is the existence of a population inversion between the energy levels of the laser transition. To ensure laser oscillations, however, the population inversion and hence the gain within the medium must be large enough to overcome various losses, including the loss of energy in the laser output, which may exist in the system. There is therefore a minimum or *threshold* gain coefficient k_{th}, which is required to initiate and sustain laser oscillations (see Section 1.8).

In the above discussion we have tacitly assumed that the radiation propagates to and fro between two plane-parallel mirrors in a well-collimated beam. This cannot be the case, however, because, due to the effects of diffraction, a perfectly collimated beam cannot be maintained with mirrors of finite extent. Some of the radiation will spread out beyond the edges of the mirrors. Such diffraction losses can be reduced by using concave mirrors and in practice a number of different mirror curvatures and configurations are used, depending on the type of laser and the application for which it is being used.

Although a detailed analysis of the different systems is rather difficult we may anticipate the results of such an analysis by using simple ray-tracing techniques. Let us consider a ray of light in the optical cavity which is initially traveling at a small angle of inclination to the axis of the system. Then only those mirror configurations which retain the ray within the cavity after several traversals can give rise to stable oscillations. Such cavities are called stable cavities.

Some of the commonly used mirror configurations for stable cavities are shown in Fig. 1.14; they all have various advantages and disadvantages. The plane-parallel system, for example, is very difficult to align, for if the mirrors are not strictly parallel (to within about one second of arc) the optical beam will 'walk off' the mirrors after a few reflections. On the other hand the radiation beam makes maximum use of the laser medium (we say that it has a large mode volume) as there is no focusing of the beam within the cavity. In contrast the confocal system is relatively easy to align (an accuracy of 1.5 minutes of arc is sufficient) but the use of the active medium is restricted (the mode volume is small). By mode volume we mean that fraction of the excited laser medium, that is the gain medium, with which the light being reflected to and fro between the cavity mirrors actually interacts. Consideration of Figs. 1.14 and 3.6 reveals that this fraction depends on the mirror configuration and the modes (see Sections 1.10 and 3.1) which are actually oscillating.

Sometimes we use mirror configurations which give rise to unstable cavities. In these a ray which is initially traveling at a small angle of incidence to the cavity axis will diverge away from the axis after a number of reflections. Such resonators are characterized by high losses, but even so

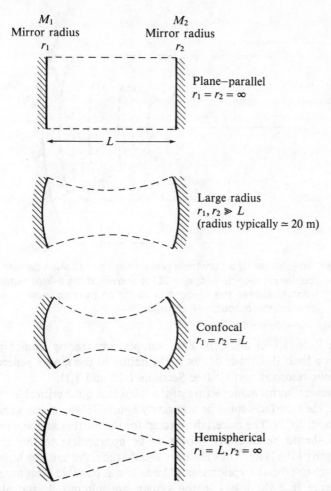

Fig. 1.14   Some commonly-used laser cavity mirror configurations (the dashed
lines show the extent of the mode volume).

they have some useful properties. In particular they can make efficient use
of the mode volume. Another feature is the ease with which the output
coupling of the laser can be adjusted. As Fig. 1.15 shows this can be achieved
simply by altering the mirror separation, thereby changing the amount of
radiation passing around the smaller mirror, which constitutes the output.
The beam will obviously have an annular cross section, but this does not
necessarily limit its usefulness. As unstable resonators have large losses they
can be used effectively only with high-gain media such as carbon dioxide.

It should be noted that while ray-tracing techniques can indicate the
stability of a particular resonator they must be replaced by a more rigorous
analysis based on diffraction theory if more details are required (see for

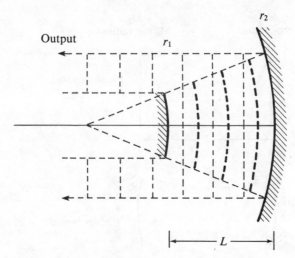

Fig. 1.15   An example of an unstable resonator. The radiation pattern for this confocal cavity ($r_1 = L$, $r_2 = 3L$) is shown. If the mirror separation is slightly altered the amount of radiation passing around mirror r_1, that is, the output, will change.

example Refs. 1.6(b) and (c)). For example, ray tracing cannot predict, except in a limited number of cases, the nature of the modes generated by the various resonant cavities (see Sections 1.10 and 3.1).

In general terms manufacture of the mirrors is quite critical in that, for example, their surfaces must be accurately figured (plane mirrors should be flat to about $\lambda/20$). The materials selected for the mirrors and any reflective coatings should be carefully chosen to be appropriate to the operating wavelength of the laser. Thus not only should the reflectance be high at this wavelength but the absorption should be as low as possible. This latter point is to ensure that the losses in the system are minimized, and also that absorption by the mirrors of very high-power lasers, and the consequent rise in temperature, does not lead to mirror failure.

1.8   THRESHOLD GAIN COEFFICIENT

We saw above that to sustain laser oscillations the gain coefficient must be at least large enough to overcome the losses in the system. The sources of loss include the following:

(1) Transmission at the mirrors, that is, the useful output (one of the mirrors is usually made as reflective as possible while the other, the output mirror, may have a reflectance of about 90%).

(2)   Absorption and scattering by the mirrors.

(3)   Diffraction around the boundary of the mirrors.

(4)   Absorption in the laser medium due to transitions other than the desired one. (Most media have many energy levels and a pair of levels, not directly involved in the laser action, may have the same energy separation as those involved in the laser transition.)

(5)   Scattering at optical inhomogeneities in the laser medium.

To simplify matters let us include those losses, other than the useful output and mirror losses, in a single effective volume loss coefficient γ, which reduces the effective gain coefficient to $(k - \gamma)$.

We can determine the threshold gain coefficient required from the condition that the round trip gain, G, in the irradiance of the beam must be at least unity. If G were less than this the oscillations would die out, whereas if G were greater than unity the oscillations would grow. Let us assume that the laser medium fills the whole of the space of length L between the mirrors M_1 and M_2, which have reflectances R_1 and R_2. Then in traveling from M_1 to M_2 the beam irradiance increases from I_0, say, to I_1, where $I_1 = I_0 \, e^{(k-\gamma)L}$.

After reflection at M_2 the beam irradiance will be $I_0 R_2 e^{(k-\gamma)L}$ and after a complete round trip the irradiance will be $I_0 R_1 R_2 e^{2(k-\gamma)L}$, so that the round trip gain is

$$G = \frac{\text{final irradiance}}{\text{initial irradiance}} = R_1 R_2 e^{2(k-\gamma)L}.$$

Thus the *threshold condition* for laser oscillations is

$$R_1 R_2 e^{2(k_{th}-\gamma)L} = 1, \tag{1.19}$$

where k_{th}, the threshold gain coefficient, is given by

$$k_{th} = \gamma + \frac{1}{2L} \ln\left(\frac{1}{R_1 R_2}\right). \tag{1.20}$$

The first term in Eq. (1.20) represents the volume losses while the second is the loss in the form of the useful output; thus the condition for steady-state laser operation is that the gain equals the sum of the losses. In lasers designed for continuous output (CW) the gain becomes constant at the threshold value. This is because if the round trip gain were less than or greater than unity the cavity energy would correspondingly increase or decrease. It is only when G has been equal to unity for a while that the cavity energy (and hence the laser output) settles down to a steady-state value. This phenomenon is referred to as gain saturation.

The actual value of the gain depends on the population inversion and on the physical properties of the medium (Eq. (1.18)). If k is high then it is relatively easy to achieve laser action and mirror alignment and cleanliness are not too critical. With low gain media, however, the mirrors must be accurately aligned, have high reflectances and be scrupulously clean. It should be noted that lasers with high gain media will not necessarily have high efficiencies. The efficiency, expressed as the ratio of laser light output power to input pumping power, depends on how effectively the pump power is converted into a population inversion, on the probabilities of the different kinds of transitions from the upper energy level and on the losses in the system.

1.9 THE LINESHAPE FUNCTION

Hitherto we have assumed that the atoms in either the upper or lower levels of the laser medium would interact with a perfectly monochromatic beam. This is, in fact, not the case as all spectral lines have a finite wavelength or frequency spread, that is, they have a fluorescent or spectral linewidth. This can be seen in both emission and absorption and if, for example, we were to measure the emission of a typical spectral source as a function of frequency, we would obtain the bell-shaped curve illustrated in Fig. 1.16. The precise shape of the curve is given by the lineshape function $g(\nu)$, which represents the frequency distribution of the radiation in a given spectral line. The precise form of $g(\nu)$, which is normalized so that the area under the curve is unity, depends on the particular mechanisms causing the spectral broadening. The most important mechanisms are collision (or pressure) broadening, natural damping and Doppler broadening. The latter, for example, results from the differences in frequency measured for the radia-

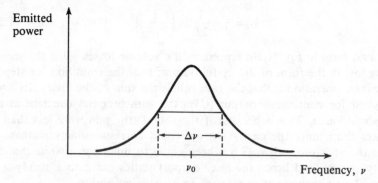

Fig. 1.16 Frequency distribution of the radiation emitted from a group of atoms following transitions from energy levels E_2 to E_1. The precise shape of this distribution, that is the lineshape function $g(\nu)$, depends on the dominant spectral broadening mechanisms.

tion emitted from atoms as they travel away from or towards an observer. The observed frequencies will be in the range

$$\nu^1 = \nu\left(1 \pm \frac{v}{c}\right),$$ (1.21)

where v is the component of the velocity of the atom along the direction of observation and c is the speed of light. The spectral halfwidth $\Delta\nu$ is thus given approximately by

$$\Delta\nu = \frac{2\nu v}{c}.$$ (1.22)

This, and the other broadening mechanisms, are described in Ref. 1.5.

Example 1.3   Spectral broadening due to the Doppler Effect

Let us calculate the spectral broadening due to the Doppler effect in the carbon dioxide laser ($\lambda = 10.6$ m) assuming that the temperature of the pumping discharge is 400 K. The relative atomic masses of carbon and oxygen are 12 and 16.

We may assume that the average thermal velocity of the carbon dioxide molecules along the laser axis is given by

$$\tfrac{1}{2}Mv^2 = \tfrac{1}{2}kT,$$

that is $v = (kT/M)^{1/2}$, where M is the mass of a carbon dioxide molecule and k is Boltzmann's constant.

The spectral broadening is given by

$$\Delta\nu = \frac{2\nu v}{c} = \frac{2v}{\lambda}$$

$$\text{or } \Delta\nu = \frac{2}{\lambda}\left(\frac{kT}{M}\right)^{1/2}$$

From the Avogadro constant

$$M = \frac{44}{6.022 \times 10^{26}} = 7.31 \times 10^{-26} \text{ kg}.$$

$\therefore \quad \Delta v = 51.9$ MHz.

Consequently when we consider the interaction of a monochromatic beam of radiation with a group of excited atoms which emit with a given lineshape $g(\nu)$ and halfwidth $\Delta\nu$ we must recognize that a photon of energy $h\nu$ will not necessarily stimulate another photon of energy $h\nu$. In fact, $g(\nu)$ gives us the probability that the stimulated photon will have an energy in the range $h\nu$ to $h(\nu + d\nu)$. It may be shown that the small signal-gain coefficient, and hence other parameters such as the pumping power, is proportional to

$g(\nu)$ [1.6]. (In calculations we often use the approximation $g(\nu_0) = 1/\Delta\nu$, where ν_0 is the center frequency.) If we take into account the lineshape function, then Eq. (1.18) for the gain coefficient must be modified to

$$k = (N_2 - N_1) \frac{nh\nu_{21}B_{21}}{c} g(\nu) \qquad (1.23)$$

or at the line center,

$$k = (N_2 - N_1) \frac{nh\nu_{21}B_{21}}{c\Delta\nu}. \qquad (1.23a)$$

Thus we note that, other things being equal, the greater $\Delta\nu$ is, the more difficult it is to achieve laser action. For some applications, however, such as mode locking (see Section 3.8), a laser medium with a wide fluorescent transition curve can be an advantage.

1.10 LASER MODES

If the output of a laser is examined with a spectrometer of very high resolving power, such as a Fabry–Perot interferometer, it will be seen that it consists of a number of very closely spaced, discrete frequency components (that is *very* narrow spectral lines) covering a moderately broad spectral range. The discrete components are called *laser modes* and the spectral range they occupy is approximately the fluorescent linewidth of the atomic transition giving rise to the laser output (see also section 3.1). It is obvious that the laser medium will only exhibit gain over the range of frequencies of the fluorescent line. The precise frequencies within this range that are amplified by stimulated emission depends on the nature of the mirrors and their separation, the losses in the system and the broadening mechanism.

1.10.1 Axial modes

For laser oscillations to occur a wave within the cavity must replicate itself after two reflections so that the electric fields add in phase. In other words the mirrors form a resonant cavity and standing-wave patterns are set up in exactly the same way as standing waves develop on a string or within an organ pipe. If we ignore any phase changes which might occur on reflection at the mirrors the phase change experienced by a wave in a round trip is

$$d\phi = \frac{2\pi}{\lambda} (2L) \qquad (1.24)$$

where L is the mirror separation. (We have assumed that the refractive index of the medium is unity.) Hence for laser oscillations we must have

$$\frac{2\pi}{\lambda}(2L) = 2p\pi$$

or $$L = p\lambda/2 \qquad\qquad (1.25)$$

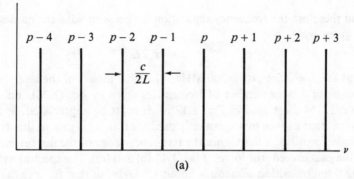

(a)

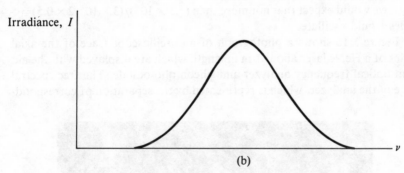

(b)

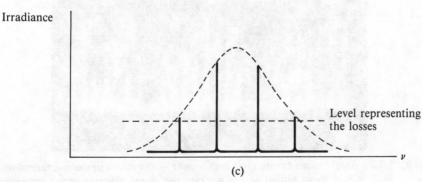

(c)

Fig. 1.17 (a) Cavity modes; (b) the broadened laser transition line; (c) axial modes in the laser output.

where p is an integer. The value of p may be very large because of the small value of the wavelength λ. For example for $L = 0.5$ m and $\lambda = 500$ nm, p is about 2×10^6. Thus many values of p are possible for only a small change in wavelength. Each value of p which satisfies Eq. (1.25) defines an *axial* (or longitudinal) *mode* of the cavity.

As $\nu = c/\lambda$, Eq. (1.25) can be written as

$$\nu = \frac{pc}{2L} \qquad (1.26)$$

and therefore the frequency separation $\Delta\nu$ between adjacent modes ($\Delta p = 1$) is given by

$$\Delta\nu = c/2L, \qquad (1.27)$$

thus for $L = 0.5$ m, $d\nu = 300$ MHz. The axial modes of the laser cavity thus consist of a large number of frequencies given by Eq. (1.26) and separated by $c/2L$ as illustrated in Fig. 1.17(a). It must be appreciated, as indicated above, that a given mode can only oscillate if there is gain at that frequency, in other words if it lies within the frequency range of the fluorescent line and if the gain exceeds the losses (Figs. 1.17 (b) and (c)). The spectral width of the 632.8 nm transition of neon is about 1.5 GHz, so that for a cavity 0.5 m in length we would expect that not more than $(1.5 \times 10^9)/(3 \times 10^8/2 \times 0.5) = 5$ modes would oscillate.

Figure 1.18 shows a photograph of an oscilloscope trace of the axial modes of a HeNe laser about 1 m in length which are displayed with the aid of an optical frequency analyzer and silicon photodiode. The free spectral range of the analyzer, which is represented by the separation of correspond-

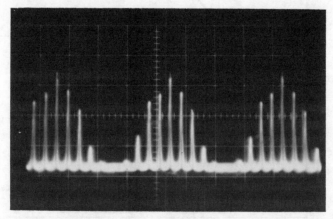

Fig. 1.18 Axial modes formed in a HeNe laser — the mode pattern is repeated (here three times) as the optical frequency analyzer scans through the gain curve of the laser (Photograph courtesy Dr. I. D. Latimer, School of Physics, Newcastle upon Tyne Polytechnic)

ing features in the three spectra shown, is 1.5 GHz, thus the intermodal separation $(c/2L)$ is about 148 MHz. Nine modes are just visible; the apparent frequency spread of the modes is an instrumental effect. The photograph also illustrates the shape of the gain curve.

1.10.2   Transverse modes

The axial modes all contribute to a single 'spot' of light in the laser output, whereas in general if the laser beam is shone onto a screen we observe a pattern of spots. These are due to the transverse modes of the cavity. The axial modes are formed by plane waves traveling exactly along the laser axis joining the centers of the mirrors. In most cases, however, there will be other waves which are traveling just off-axis but which, nevertheless, are able to replicate themselves after covering a more complex closed path such as that shown in Fig. 1.19a. Such modes are referred to as *transverse electromagnetic* or TEM modes. They are characterized by two integers q and r (see Section 3.1) so that as Fig. 1.19b shows, we have TEM_{00}, TEM_{01}, TEM_{11} etc. modes (q gives the number of minima (or phase reversals) as the beam is scanned horizontally and r the number of minima as it is scanned vertically). The higher-order TEM_{qr} modes are formed by waves traveling off-axis and can easily be eliminated by the use of apertures to narrow the cavity width.

The TEM_{00} mode is often called the uniphase mode as all parts of the propagating wavefront are in phase, consequently a laser operating only in this mode has the greatest spectral purity and degree of coherence. In general, however, we see that the laser output might consist of a number of discrete frequency (or wavelength) components being a complex combination of longitudinal and transverse modes, which in addition to determining the coherence also determines the amount of divergence of the laser output. These characteristics are usually important in relation to the potential uses of the laser.

In this chapter we have given a rather qualitative description of laser theory with the aims of enabling the reader to appreciate the nature of laser radiation and to understand the modes of operation of the various lasers described in Chapter 2. A truly quantitative approach to meeting these aims would have required a quantum-mechanical description which is beyond the scope of this text; the interested reader should consult the more advanced books given in Ref. 1.6.

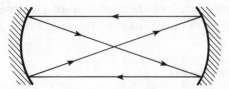

Fig. 1.19a An example of a non-axial self-replicating ray which gives rise to transverse modes.

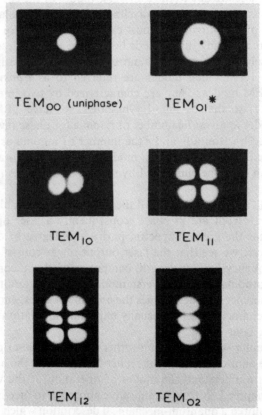

Fig. 1.19b Some low-order transverse mode patterns of a laser. The modes are designated TEM_{qr} where q and r are integers referring to the numbers of minima as the laser beam is scanned horizontally and vertically. The TEM_{01}^{*} mode is a combination of TEM_{01} and TEM_{10} modes. (From M. J. Beesley, *Lasers and their Applications* (1972), courtesy of Taylor and Francis Ltd.)

PROBLEMS

1.1 Show that for Young's experiment the separation of neighboring bright fringes is approximately $\lambda D/d$, where λ is the wavelength of the light used, D the distance from screen 1 to screen 2 and d is the separation of the sources P_1 and P_2 (Fig. 1.1). Given that the sources are 2 mm apart and the screens are 0.85 m apart, find the fringe spacing for the red line of a HeNe laser ($\lambda = 632.8$ nm).

1.2 If the two pinholes in Young's experiments are such that the amplitudes of the wave emitted by one is twice that emitted by the other, determine the fringe visibility (Section 3.4) and compare this with the case where both amplitudes are the same.

1.3 Given that the wavelength of the green line of the HeNe laser is 543.5 nm, calculate the maximum value of the work function of a photocathode which could be used in a photomultiplier to detect this light.

1.4 Write down the potential energy of an electron distance r from a charge of $+e$ and hence with the aid of Bohr's quantum condition $mvr = nh/2\pi$ and Eq. (1.2) show that the radii of the Bohr orbits are given by

$$r_n = \frac{n^2 h^2 \varepsilon_0}{\pi m e^2}.$$

Show also that as $E_i - E_f = h\nu$, the spectral lines in the hydrogen spectrum, Fig. 1.8, are related by

$$\bar{\nu} = \nu/c = R_H \left(\frac{1}{n_f^2} - \frac{1}{n_i^2} \right)$$

where R_H is a constant (the Rydberg constant). Evaluate the radius of the first Bohr orbit of the hydrogen atom and the energy required to ionize the atom.

1.5 For a system in thermal equilibrium calculate the temperature at which the rates of spontaneous and stimulated emission are equal for a wavelength of 10 μm, and the wavelength at which these rates are equal at a temperature of 4000 K.

1.6 If 0.5% of the light incident onto a medium is absorbed in 1 mm, what fraction is transmitted by the medium if it is 0.1 m long? Calculate the absorption coefficient of the medium.

1.7 If the irradiance of a beam of light increases by 25% after a round trip through a gain medium which is 0.3 m long, calculate the small-signal gain coefficient k assuming no losses.

1.8 Given that the lifetime of the upper level of the 632.8 nm transition in the HeNe laser is 1×10^{-7} s, calculate the degree of population inversion required to give a gain coefficient of 0.07 m^{-1} ignoring line-broadening effects.

1.9 Calculate the Doppler broadened line width in the argon ion laser for $\lambda = 488$ nm transition, given that the temperature of the discharge is 6000 K and the relative atomic mass of argon is 38.95. Repeat the calculation for the 632.8 nm line of the HeNe laser, where the temperature of the discharge is about 400 K. The relative atomic mass of neon is 20.2.

1.10 Using the result of Problem 1.9, estimate the threshold gain coefficient for the

632.8 nm line of the HeNe laser, given that the threshold population inversion is $1 \times 10^{15}\,\mathrm{m}^{-3}$ and the spontaneous lifetime of the upper laser level is $1 \times 10^{-7}\,\mathrm{s}$.

1.11 In a ruby laser ($\lambda = 694.3$ nm) the ruby crystal is 0.1 m long and the mirror reflectances are 0.95 and 0.9. Given that the losses are 10% per round trip, that the spontaneous lifetime of the upper laser level is 3×10^{-3} s, that the linewidth is 1.5×10^{11} Hz and that the refractive index is 1.78, calculate the threshold gain coefficient and population inversion.

1.12 Calculate the mode number nearest the line center of a carbon dioxide laser ($\lambda = 10.6\ \mu$m) which is 2 m long. Calculate the frequency separation of modes and estimate how many modes lie within the spectral linewidth (see example 1.3).

REFERENCES

1.1   See, for example,
   (a)   R. S. Longhurst, *Geometrical and Physical Optics*, (3rd edn), Longman, London, 1973.
   (b)   D. Falk, *Seeing the Light,* Harper & Row, 1986.
   (c)   R. W. Ditchburn, *Light* (2nd edn), Blackie, 1962.
1.2   M. N. Rudden & J. Wilson, *Elements of Solid State Physics,* Wiley, Chichester, 1980, Chapter 1.
1.3   M. Alonso and E. J. Finn '*Fundamental University Physics,* Vol. III (Quantum and Statistical Physics), Addison Wesley, Reading, Mass., 1968, Chapters 10 & 13.
1.4   Ref. 1.1c, Section 17.32.
1.5   (a)   Ref. 1.1c, Chapter 4.
   (b)   See also Ref. 1.6(b), Chapter 5 or 1.6(c), Chapter 7.
1.6   (a)   J. Wilson and J. F. B. Hawkes, *Optoelectronics: An Introduction*, Prentice-Hall, London, 1983.
   (b)   A. Yariv, *Optical Electronics,* (3rd edn), Holt-Saunders, 1985.
   (c)   J. T. Verdeyen, *Laser Electronics*, Prentice-Hall, Englewood Cliffs, N.J., 1981.
   (d)   D. C. O'Shea, W. R. Callen and W. T. Rhodes, *Introduction to Lasers and Their Applications*, Addison-Wesley, Reading, Mass., 1977.
   (e)   M. J. Beesley, *Lasers and Their Applications,* Taylor-Francis, London, 1972.

2

Operation of Practical Lasers

As we have seen in the previous chapter, at the heart of every laser is an active medium which exhibits optical gain over a narrow range of wavelengths, and in fact the name given to a laser is invariably that of the active medium employed. In this chapter we survey of the many different types of laser that are commonly available, paying particular attention to the energy-level structure of the active medium and the pumping method employed to achieve the necessary population inversion.

Since the first practical laser was built in 1960 using a crystal of pink ruby [2.1] the number and variety of materials used for the active medium has increased enormously. So much so that one is tempted to think that almost any material will suffice if subject to appropriate pumping. Even though this is an exaggeration it is nevertheless true that a vast choice exists, although when it comes to *commercial* lasers the range is more limited.

It is convenient to divide lasers into four main types depending on the physical nature of the active medium employed. Thus we have doped insulating lasers, semiconductor lasers, gas lasers and dye lasers. Within these main groupings the lasers often have a number of features in common such as general energy-level schemes and pumping mechanisms.

2.1 DOPED INSULATOR LASERS

Here the active medium consists of impurity ions embedded within a solid host lattice. Usually the impurities occupy positions normally occupied by host ions. The energy levels involved in the laser transitions are those of the impurity ions. This is not to say that the host lattice is unimportant, since such physical properties as thermal conductivity and thermal expansivity are important in determining the power levels at which the laser can be operated. In addition the host lattice modifies the impurity ion energy levels so that when the same ion is used in different hosts somewhat different lasing wavelengths are obtained.

Because of the importance of the energy-level structure in determining laser action we turn now to a general discussion of energy levels of impurity ions in solids. Some familiarity with elementary atomic structure is assumed; those without such knowledge may omit the next section but will have to take the resulting energy-level diagrams on trust. Only a very brief treatment can be attempted, those seeking further enlightenment (in what is a rather difficult topic!) may consult the texts of Ref. 2.2.

2.1.1 Impurity ion energy levels in solids

From our point of view the two most important types of ion are the so-called *transition metal* ion and the *rare earth* ion. In the former the low-lying energy levels of interest result from the presence of electrons in the unfilled 3d subshells. A typical example is Cr^{3+}, which has the electron configuration

$$1s^2 2s^2 2p^6 3s^2 3p^6 3d^3.$$

We see that all electrons are in filled subshells except for the three which are in the 3d subshell. (The 3d subshell can accommodate up to 10 electrons.) Rare earth ions, on the other hand, are characterized by the presence of electrons in the unfilled 4f subshell. Thus Nd^{3+} has the electron configuration

$$1s^2 2s^2 2p^6 3s^2 3p^6 3d^{10} 4s^2 4p^6 4d^{10} 4f^3 5s^2 5p^6.$$

Here there are 3 electrons in the 4f subshell (which has a maximum capacity of 14).

When the ion is situated in the lattice it is surrounded by charged host ions with which it will interact. One obvious source of interaction is the Coulomb force between the host ionic charges and the electrons in the unfilled subshells (this is by no means the whole story, but from our point of view it will suffice). Because of its origin it is referred to as the *crystal field* interaction.

The effect of the crystal field on a given ion depends markedly on how well shielded the electrons in the unfilled subshells are. In the rare earths, for example, the 4f subshell is physically fairly well shielded by other electrons in full subshells situated further out from the nucleus (i.e. those in the 5s and 5p subshells) whilst by contrast the 3d subshells in transition-metal ions are not at all well shielded. The importance of these remarks will become evident in due course.

The low-lying energy levels of the ion are determined by the forces acting on and between the electrons in unfilled shells. (The electrons in filled shells can be regarded as inert.) These forces are many and varied and to consider the effect of their operating simultaneously would give little insight into the resulting energy levels. Fortunately the forces vary widely in magnitude and it is usually possible to arrange them in order of importance. The procedure is then to deal with the effects of these forces one at a time, starting with the most important and working through to the least important. From our point of view there are three main interactions to be considered, namely (1) the Coulomb forces acting between the electrons in unfilled shells, (2) the crystal field interaction, and (3) a coupling between electron spin and orbital angular momentum known as *spin–orbit* coupling. The latter may be thought of as arising from the interaction of the magnetic field produced by the orbiting electron with its own magnetic moment. The first of these interactions is usually much the largest and we deal with its effects first.

The inter-electron Coulomb interaction has the effect of splitting the single-electron configuration into a number of levels each described by a particular pair of values of L and S, where L and S are obtained by adding together vectorially the angular and spin momenta of the separate electrons. In this way the three 3d electrons in Cr^{3+} form the eight so-called *terms* ^2S, ^2P, ^2D, ^2F, ^2G, ^2H, ^4P and ^4F. Here the capital letters denote the L values where the usual spectroscopic convention is followed (i.e. S, P, D, F, G, ... corresponding to $L = 0, 1, 2, 3, 4, ...$). The suffices denote the value of $2S + 1$ or the *spin multiplicity*. Thus the term ^4P is one where $S = \frac{3}{2}$ and $L = 1$. In general each term has a different energy.

There now remain the crystal field and the spin–orbit interactions; unfortunately these have differing relative importance in transition and rare earth ions. In the former, where the crystal field interactions are expected to be large (remember the 3d electrons are unshielded), the spin–orbit is the smaller of the two. In the rare earth ions this position is reversed. Hence in transition metal ions the second force to be considered is that due to the crystal field. This splits the term energy levels into further levels which are labeled with a letter related to the symmetry of the crystal field (and *not* to the angular momentum). The value of the spin multiplicity is still quoted, however. In theory we should now proceed to a consideration of the effects of spin–orbit coupling, but this is often unnecessary. This is because the strength of the crystal field tends to vary slightly throughout the material due to slight inhomogeneities. The result is a spread in the exact position of the energy levels, which is often large enough to mask any spin–orbit effects. The successive splitting of the energy levels as further interactions are introduced is illustrated for the case of Cr^{3+} in Al_2O_3 (ruby) in Fig. 2.1.

In rare earth ions, on the other hand, we must consider the spin–orbit interaction before the effects of the crystal field. The former splits up the term energy levels into 'multiplets' by causing the energy of a state to be dependent on the total momentum quantum number J, where **J** is the vector sum of **L** and **S**. Thus a ^4F term ($S = \frac{3}{2}$, $L = 3$) is split into four multiplets with $J = \frac{9}{2}, \frac{7}{2}, \frac{5}{2}$ and $\frac{3}{2}$. These are written as $^{2S+1}L_J$. For example, $^4F_{9/2}$ indicates a multiplet where $J = \frac{9}{2}$, which is derived from the term $L = 3$, $S = \frac{3}{2}$.

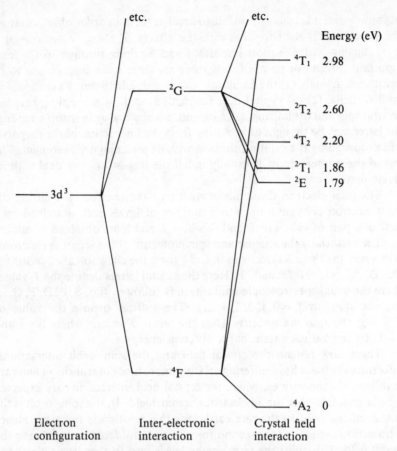

Fig. 2.1 The origins of the low-lying electronic energy levels in Cr^{3+}. Successive interactions split the original $3d^3$ electron configuration into an increasing number of energy levels.

Figure 2.2 illustrates the situation for Nd^{3+} in yttrium aluminum garnet $(Y_3Al_5O_{12})$ or YAG.

The crystal field acts to give a further splitting of the multiplets. For an ion with an odd number of electrons in an unfilled shell the crystal field will split a given multiplet into at most $J + \frac{1}{2}$ crystal field levels. (The maximum splitting is obtained only when the crystal field has a low symmetry.) Thus a $^4F_{9/2}$ multiplet will split into at most five crystal field levels.

We should now be in a position to appreciate the significance and origin of the energy-level diagrams of transition metal and rare earth ions in insulating solids. Indeed we have deliberately used as examples two important laser materials as we shall see later in the chapter. Having

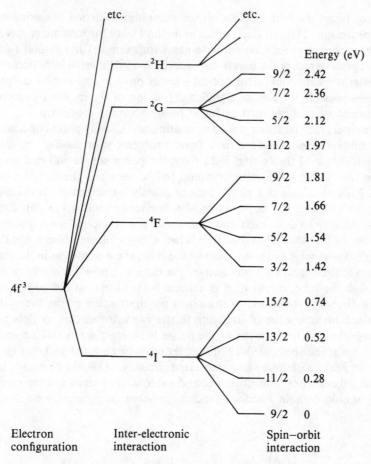

	Energy (eV)

Fig. 2.2 The origins of the low-lying electronic energy levels of Nd^{3+}.

considered the energy-level structures involved, we now turn to a general discussion of the pumping methods used to obtain population inversion.

2.1.2 Pumping methods

As we saw in Chapter 1, to initiate laser action we need to excite electrons from the ground state of the system into a higher energy level. The electrons then make their way back to the ground state by making transitions between intermediate levels, one of which is the actual laser transition. For doped insulator lasers the initial excitation (or pumping) is carried out using optical absorption. This is a fairly efficient method since the ions are relatively densely packed in space (compared to gases for example) and exhibit fairly broad optical absorption bands (or closely spaced lines) which occur at wavelengths where convenient optical sources provide appreciable output. It is then possible for a quite significant fraction of the incident pumping radiation to be usefully used as far as lasing action is concerned.

Pumping may be either pulsed or continuous. Usually pulsed operation is the simpler since there are then fewer problems with cooling the laser material. (Most of the 'waste' light from the pump source will end up as heat in the system.) The most common pulsed source is the low-pressure xenon flashtube. This is a glass or more usually a quartz tube containing xenon (or krypton) gas at pressures of a few torr (1 torr = 133 Pa). Electrodes are provided at each end and these are connected to a charged capacitor of 50–2000 μF at 1–4 kV. When a high-voltage pulse is applied to a coil of wire wrapped round part of the tube, some of the gas in the tube becomes ionized and hence conductive. The capacitor now discharges rapidly through the tube, resulting in an intense burst of optical radiation. Too rapid a discharge, however, can result in the destruction of the tube, and it is usual to have a small inductor in the capacitor circuit to slow the discharge down. The duration of the pulses is typically a few milliseconds. The flashtube may be cooled if required by providing a water jacket. Figure 2.3 illustrates the flashtube and associated circuitry. It should be noted that the charged capacitors constitute a considerable safety hazard and the power supply should contain interlock mechanisms that automatically discharge

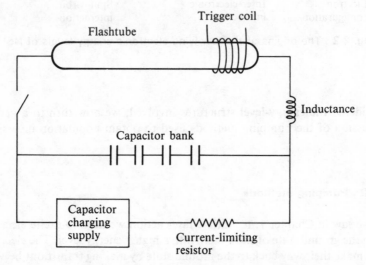

Fig. 2.3 Flashtube drive circuitry.

the capacitor if there is any chance of the terminals being accidentally touched.

Sources for continuous pumping include tungsten halogen lamps and high-pressure mercury discharge lamps. The power supplies may be somewhat bulky since lamp input powers of a kilowatt or more are usually required.

Whatever pumping source is used there still remains the problem of coupling as much pumping radiation as possible into the lasing medium. Usually the latter is in the form of a rod a few millimeters in diameter and a few tens of millimeters long, and both flashtube and rod are placed within a cavity with highly reflective walls. There are several possible geometries that can be used, and these are illustrated in Fig. 2.4. The earliest designs used a helical flashtube surrounding the laser rod, both being enclosed within a cylindrical reflecting cavity (Fig. 2.4(a)). Although this arrangement gives good uniformity of irradiation within the rod the optical coupling is not very good. A much simpler technique is to have a linear flashtube

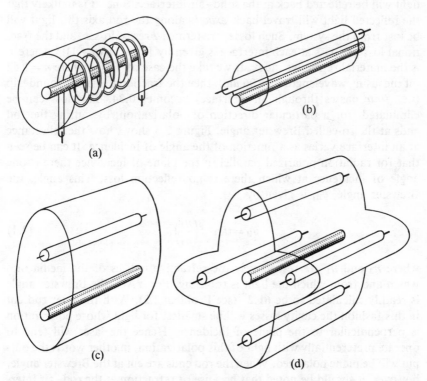

Fig. 2.4   Some of the more common flashtube geometries used for optical pumping: (a) a helical flashtube round the laser rod; (b) close coupling between flashtube and rod; (c) flashtube and rod along the two foci of an elliptical cavity and (d) a multi-elliptical cavity.

alongside the rod with a reflecting surface round both (a sheet of metal foil wrapped round the two can be quite effective!). Although this so called *close-coupling* arrangement gives good coupling efficiency, the uniformity of irradiation is poor.

Another popular arrangement is to have the linear flashtube and rod lying along the two focal lines of an elliptical reflector (Fig. 2.4(c)). Any light leaving one focus of the ellipse is then reflected to pass through the other focus. As might be expected the radiation tends to be highly concentrated close to the center of the rod and a more uniform energy distribution can be obtained with multiple lamps and multiple elliptical focusing arrangements (Fig. 2.4(d)).

2.1.3 Fresnel losses

If the laser rod ends are cut perpendicularly to the rod axis, then some laser light will be reflected back at the solid–air interface. Since it is unlikely that the reflected light will travel back *exactly* along the rod axis this light will be lost from the system. Such losses are termed *Fresnel* losses, and the fractional loss per pass at each interface is given by $[(n-1)/(n+1)]^2$ where n is the material refractive index. If we take the case of YAG, where $n = 1.82$ (at the lasing wavelength of 1.06 μm), then the fractional loss per round trip (i.e. *four* passes through an interface) becomes 0.34. This loss can be eliminated, for a particular direction of polarization, by cutting the rod ends at the so-called Brewster angle. Figure 2.5 shows how the reflectance at an interface varies as a function of the angle of incidence. It can be seen that for radiation polarized parallel to the plane of incidence there is one angle of incidence at which there is no reflection loss. This angle, the Brewster angle, θ_B, is given by

$$\theta_B = \tan^{-1}\left(\frac{n_2}{n_1}\right), \tag{2.1}$$

where n_2 and n_1 are respectively the refractive indices of the media into which and from which the light is traveling. For YAG, the Brewster angle is readily calculated to be $61.2°$ (see Problem 2.2). With the laser rod cut in this fashion the cavity losses will be smallest for light whose polarization is perpendicular to the plane of incidence. Hence the laser will tend to operate preferentially with light of this polarization, in other words the output will be plane polarized. When the rod ends are cut at the Brewster angle, however, it should be noted that because of refraction at the rod–air interface the cavity end mirrors will have to be angled as shown in Fig. 2.6. Fresnel losses can also be reduced by forming antireflection coatings on the end of the laser rod, in which case the ends usually have a very small wedge

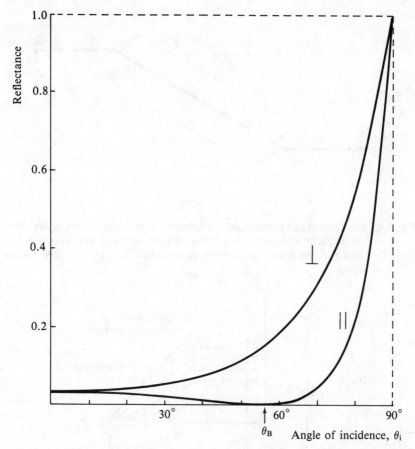

Fig. 2.5   Reflectance as a function of the angle of incidence for light polarized parallel (∥) and perpendicular (⊥) to the plane of incidence.

angle ($\sim 6°$). This is done to ensure that any reflection that does take place is not along the laser axis.

After this rather lengthy preamble, we now turn to a discussion of the different types of doped insulator laser available.

2.1.4   The Nd:YAG laser

The origin of the energy level structure of the Nd^{3+} ion in YAG was discussed in Section 2.1.1. The Nd^{3+} ions replace yttrium ions in the lattice, with a maximum possible doping level of about 1.5%. Figure 2.7 shows the levels involved in the laser action. We see that we have essentially a four-level system (Section 1.6.1) with the lasing transition taking place between

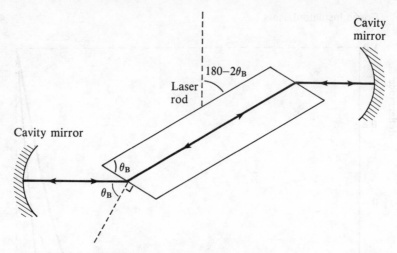

Fig. 2.6 Laser cavity alignment using a laser rod with ends cut at the Brewster angle. With this arrangement the internal angle of the laser rod is θ_B and the rod itself is inclined at an angle of $180° - 2\theta_B$ to the vertical.

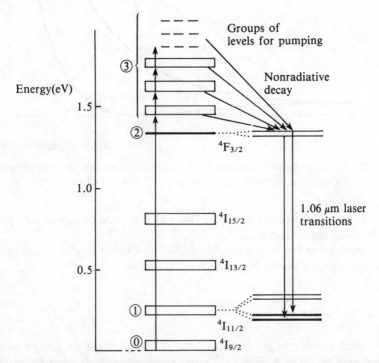

Fig. 2.7 Simplified energy-level diagram for the neodymium ion in YAG showing the principal laser transitions. Laser emission also results from transitions between the $^4F_{3/2}$ levels and the $^4I_{15/2}$ and $^4I_{13/2}$ levels but at only one tenth of the intensity of the transitions shown.

the $^4F_{3/2}$ and $^4I_{11/2}$ states. The terminal state ($^4I_{11/2}$) is sufficiently far above the ground state to be practically empty at room temperature. The initial and final states are split into 2 and 6 crystal field levels respectively, so that several lasing wavelengths are possible. The most powerful of these occurs at 1.064 μm and this is usually the one used.

Since it is a four-level system the pumping requirements are modest and for pulsed operation can be met with a fairly simple flashlamp and reflecting cavity. To avoid overheating and subsequent damage of the laser rod cooling air may be blown through the cavity. As we have mentioned in Section 2.1.2, the optical pulse from the flashtube lasts for a few milliseconds. It usually takes about 0.5 ms for population inversion to be achieved. Once stimulated emission has started it rapidly depopulates the upper lasing level, much faster in fact than the pumping can re-excite the electrons, so that laser action is expected to momentarily stop until a sufficient population inversion can be built up again. We would expect therefore a regular pulsation in the output. Rapid fluctuations in the output (called 'spikes') are indeed observed (with durations of a few microseconds). Unfortunately the spikes occur at irregular time intervals and with random amplitudes, as illustrated in Fig. 2.8. The theory of laser spiking is not fully understood, but it is believed that it involves a phenomenon known as 'mode hopping'. Thus when lasing takes place several modes may be operating at once, but between one laser spike and the next the modes which are oscillating may change (mode hopping). Spatial and temporal interference between the different modes then causes the laser output to vary in an irregular manner.

The total energy output during a single flashtube pulse can range from

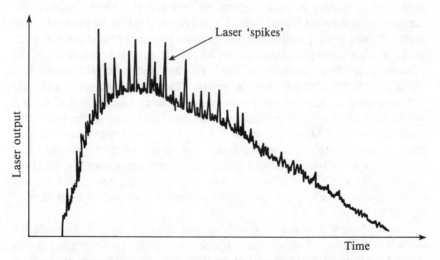

Fig. 2.8 Typical output from a flashtube pumped Nd: YAG laser, showing laser 'spiking'.

0.01 J to 100 J with pulse repetition frequencies up to 300 Hz. The average power during a pulse can be quite large, thus a 10 J pulse lasting for some 0.5 ms implies an average power of some 2×10^4 W. During the individual spikes of course the power level will be higher still. Indeed it is possible, as we shall see in Chapter 3, to compress the total pulse energy into a single spike by a technique known as Q-switching; powers of up to 10^8 W may then be achieved.

Continuous wave (CW) operation is also possible; the most popular pumping source being the quartz–halogen lamp. The most effective pumping bands lie between 700 nm and 900 nm in wavelength, which are reasonably close to the peak output of the lamps which occurs at about 1 μm. Even so only a few percent of the total radiation emitted is usefully absorbed in the laser material. Consequently the overall power efficiency (and this comment also applies to pulsed lasers) is fairly low, typically in the range 0.1–2%. CW outputs of up to several hundred watts are possible, which implies that large amounts of waste heat will be evolved, necessitating water cooling of the laser rod.

2.1.5   Nd : Glass lasers

Glass has several advantages as a host material compared to YAG. It is isotropic, cheaply and easily fabricated and will accept larger doping concentrations of Nd (up to 6%). On the other hand it has a lower thermal conductivity which prohibits CW operation and indeed limits the pulse repetition frequency in pulsed operation to a few Hz. Overall power efficiencies are somewhat higher than in YAG (up to 5%) partly because of the higher doping levels possible but also because the absorption lines are much broader. This latter phenomenon may be readily understood in terms of the inherent amorphous structure of glass. The Nd^{3+} ions find themselves in a variety of slightly different environments. Thus each experiences a slightly different crystal field and has its own set of energy levels. Looked at as a whole each absorption line becomes broadened and most of the fine detail observed when YAG is the host is lost. This line broadening has two obvious consequences, firstly it makes for more efficient pumping and secondly it raises the threshold pumping requirements (see Eq. (1.23a)). However, in addition, the broad emission profile (and hence gain profile) is an advantage when the technique of 'mode locking' is used (this is described in Section 3.8).

It is possible to make laser rods up to 1 m in length with diameters of up to several tens of millimeters, which are capable of generating pulses some 3 ms long with energies of up to 5000 J. In very high-powered pulsed

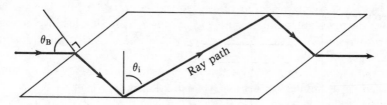

Fig. 2.9   Ray path in a slab laser structure. Total internal reflection at the slab edges keeps the ray within the slab.

systems Nd : glass disks can be used to amplify a laser beam (see Section 5.10.1).

One of the factors limiting peak power levels in rod laser structures arises from the nonuniform heating of the rod both by the pump and by the beam as it travels through the rod. Temperature differences within the rod lead to refractive index differences, which in turn lead to beam distortion. It has been suggested that this situation can be improved by using a slab structure such as illustrated in Fig. 2.9. Here the laser beam follows a zig-zag path undergoing total internal reflection (see Section 7.1.2) at both top and bottom. The thermal gradients set up within the slab are found to distort the beam to a much lesser degree than in a rod and so higher powers should be possible.

2.1.6   The ruby laser ($Cr^{3+} : Al_2O_3$)

The ruby laser is of historical interest since it was the first successful laser; however, although still manufactured, it is not widely used at present. The active medium is aluminum oxide (Al_2O_3) with about 0.05% by weight of chromium as an impurity. The active ions are chromium, Cr^{3+}, which replace aluminum ions in the lattice. We have already discussed the origin of the energy levels in Section 2.1.1 (see Fig. 2.2). Figure 2.10 shows the levels which are of importance in the lasing action. The lasing transition (at 694 nm) is between the ^2E and $^4A_2$ levels and terminates on the ground state; ruby is thus a three-level laser system. Consequently rather more than half of the total number of ions have to be pumped into the ^2E state to create a population inversion. Pumping takes place via the two broad bands $^4T_1$ and $^4T_2$. As with the Nd : YAG laser, pulsed operation can be obtained by pumping with a flashtube. CW operation is more difficult because of the higher pumping requirements. A high-pressure mercury arc lamp is often used, whose output matches the ruby absorption bands quite well.

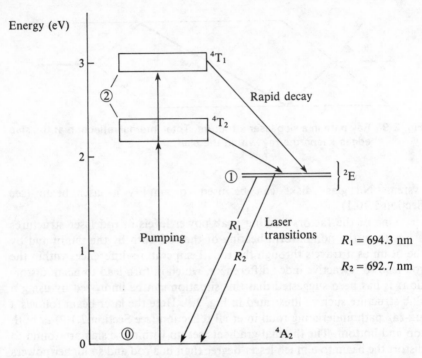

Fig. 2.10 The three-level system of the ruby laser. Pumping is due to the Cr^{3+} ions absorbing blue (excitation to $^4T_1$ levels) and green (excitation to $^4T_2$ levels) light. The wavelengths of the R_1 and R_2 laser lines are temperature dependent; the values given are typical.

2.1.7 The alexandrite laser (Cr^{3+} : $BeAl_2O_4$)

Alexandrite, which has a spectroscopy closely resembling that of ruby, was first made to lase as a three-level system in 1973 at a wavelength of 680 nm. Some years later, however, emission at longer wavelengths was obtained with the pumping characteristics of a four-level system. Moreover it was found that the lasing wavelength could be varied over the range 700–820 nm. This is our first example of a *tunable* laser. A model energy level scheme which has been proposed to explain this behavior is shown in Fig. 2.11. Electrons in the ^2E level (the 'storage level') are thermally excited into the $^4T_2$ level and the lasing transition is then between this and a group of so-called 'vibronic levels'. As their name implies, these arise from the presence of lattice vibrations, and we may imagine them to be associated with a nonequilibrium distribution of the lattice ions surrounding the Cr^{3+} ions. When they relax back to their equilibrium positions the impurity ion returns to its 'true' ground state. Although the vibronic levels in fact form

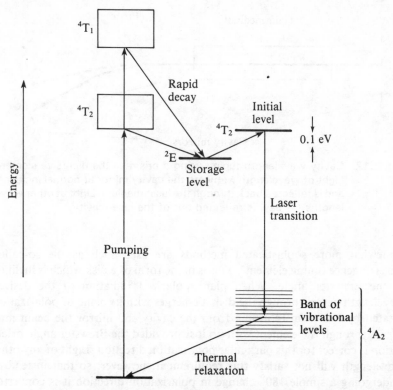

Fig. 2.11 Schematic energy-level diagram for active levels in the Alexandrite laser. The laser is effectively a four-level system. The laser transition terminates on one of a band of closely-spaced vibronic levels associated with the ground state thus allowing the laser to be tuned over the range 700–815 nm. Note that the 'initial level' is in fact the bottom of the $^4T_2$ band, the two have been drawn as if they were separate for pictorial convenience.

a discrete set they are sufficiently close together for us to regard them as forming a continuum.

By itself the laser will only operate at one particular wavelength (that for which the system offers greatest small-signal gain), and to take advantage of the tuning possibilities we must introduce additional components into the optical system. What we require is a variable very narrow bandwidth filter which introduces only a little loss at the chosen wavelength but exhibits a high loss at all other wavelengths. There are several ways of realizing this: one of the most readily understood is to insert a dispersing element such as a prism into the cavity as shown in Fig. 2.12. Depending on the angle of the prism only one wavelength will strike the end mirror at normal incidence and thus be reflected back and amplified. In practice

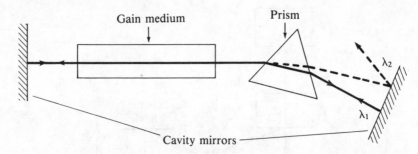

Fig. 2.12 Cavity wavelength tuning using a prism as the dipersive element. Light of wavelength λ_1 meets the cavity mirror at normal incidence and is reflected back through the laser medium. Light at other wavelengths (λ_2 say) is reflected out of the laser cavity.

somewhat more sophisticated methods are used such as the so-called 'birefringence tuning element'. This is in the form of a disk which is inclined at the Brewster angle. When plane polarized radiation of the desired wavelength passes through the disk it emerges with its plane of polarization rotated by $180°$. On returning from the cavity end mirror the beam may repass through the element with no loss provided the Brewster angle orientation is correct for this particular polarization direction. Light of any other wavelength will not satisfy this requirement, however, so that instead of undergoing a simple $180°$ change in polarization direction it is converted into elliptically polarized radiation. (This may be thought of as two plane-polarized beams of unequal intensity which are out of phase and whose polarization directions differ by $90°$.) When this beam attempts to repass through the element some Fresnel loss will now be experienced, which may be sufficient to prevent lasing. The 'no-loss' wavelength may be varied by rotating the disk about the normal to its face.

2.1.8 Color or F center lasers

When alkali halides are exposed to high energy radiation, such as X-rays or electron beams, point defects are formed which introduce new electron energy levels within the material. Optical absorption between these levels can cause a normally transparent host material to become colored – hence the name *color* center. There are several different types of defect centers, the simplest of which is the F center (the use of the letter F derives from the German word for color, *F*arben). The F center is formed when a cation vacancy is created leaving a region of net positive charge. An electron can then orbit this region much as an electron orbits round the proton in the hydrogen atom (see Section 1.2); indeed there are certain similarities

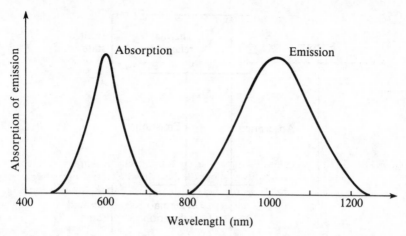

Fig. 2.13   The absorption and emission spectra of F color centers in KCl. The separation between the peaks is an example of the Stokes shift.

between the resulting energy-level structures. Two big differences, however, are that the energy levels are broadened into bands and that absorption and emission of radiation between the same two bands often takes place over different wavelength regions. For example, Fig. 2.13 shows the absorption and emission spectra of F color centers in KCl.

The broadening of the electronic energy levels can be explained by considering the effects of the lattice vibrations. As in the alexandrite laser (Section 2.1.7) this results in our having a group of closely spaced vibronic levels instead of a single level. In the present instance, however, both ground and excited states are broadened. Now the equilibrium position of the lattice when the electron is in the ground state does not correspond to the equilibrium position (i.e. the lowest electron energy) when the electron is in the excited state. Furthermore the electron transition takes place so rapidly that the lattice is unable to adjust its position. Consequently during absorption, transitions occur between a group of levels close to the bottom of the ground-state band to a group of levels close to the top of the excited-state band. Shortly after absorption has taken place the surrounding ions relax to the equilibrium position corresponding to the excited state and the electron then moves to the lowest levels within the band. Emission involves transitions between these levels and a group near the top of the ground-state band. Figure 2.14 illustrates these processes. We can see quite clearly from this diagram why absorption can occur at shorter wavelengths than emission. (Such a shift between absorption and emission is called the Stokes shift.)

The color center laser is optically pumped, usually with another laser whose output lies within the colour center absorption band. Population

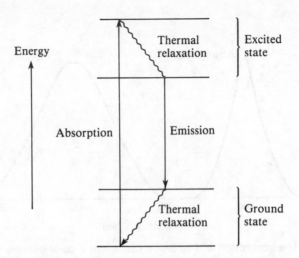

Fig. 2.14 An illustration of how the Stokes shift comes about. Absorption
takes place at higher energy (that is longer wavelength) than does
emission.

inversion takes place between states at the bottom of the excited-state band
and states at the top of the ground-state band. The laser can be 'tuned' to
operate over the wavelength range covered approximately by the emission
band. Thus color centers formed in thallium-doped KBr, for example, when
pumped with 1.06 μm radiation from a Nd : YAG laser can be used to
generate laser radiation covering the range 1.4–1.6 μm with efficiencies of
some 20%. One difficulty is that the color centers themselves can become
unstable when the laser is operated at room temperature, and usually
cooling to liquid nitrogen temperatures is necessary.

2.2 SEMICONDUCTOR LASERS

Although made from 'solid' materials semiconductor lasers differ considerably, both in respect of the energy-level structures and pumping
mechanisms, from the doped insulator types we have just been considering.
In contrast to the single energy levels observed in isolated atoms (albeit
sometimes broadened by lattice vibrations) electrons in semiconductors
occupy broad bands of energy levels. Each band consists of a very large
number of closely packed energy levels. These levels cannot be associated
with individual atoms but with the material as a whole, their origin, in
rather qualitative terms, is not too hard to visualize. We may imagine
that a solid is built up by bringing together a large collection of atoms that

initially are well separated. When they are far apart there will be practically no interactions between the electrons belonging to different atoms and each will behave as an isolated atom. The energy-level structure of the group will thus be a superposition of all the energy levels of each isolated atom. If we start to bring the atoms closer together, however, the electrons will start to interact and each electron must be considered as belonging to the collection of atoms as a whole and not just to a particular atom. Now the Pauli exclusion principle states that in such a situation each electron must be assigned a different set of quantum numbers. These are labels that describe all the 'knowable' physical properties of the electrons, including energy. Thus it is apparent that all the electrons cannot now share the same energy.† Each original energy level splits into a closely packed bunch of levels which we term an *energy band*. We would expect the width of the band to increase as the interatomic distance decreases and the electron–electron interaction increases, as illustrated in Fig. 2.15. There is even the possibility that the bands will overlap at sufficiently small atomic spacing. For typical semiconductors, however, the equilibrium atomic separation results in a sequence of bands with energy 'gaps' in between.

We must remember that in the original atoms not all of the energy levels will be occupied, indeed at fairly low temperatures levels will be fully occupied up to the highest occupied level and empty from then on. This follows through into the band picture with all bands being fully occupied up to a certain one and empty thereafter. From our point of view the most important features are the topmost occupied band, the first empty band and the gap in between, which are termed the *valence band*, the *conduction band* and the *energy gap* respectively (Fig. 2.16).

If the temperature of a semiconductor is raised, then it becomes possible for electrons in the valence band to be thermally excited into the conduction band. This is an important process since it causes the material to become electrically conducting. Surprising as it might seem at first sight, none of the electrons in a completely full band can take part in electrical conduction. We may understand this when we realize that when a current is flowing, the electrons must acquire an extra component of velocity along the applied electric field direction, that is, they must increase their total energy. Electrons in a full band cannot do this since they would have to move up into an otherwise occupied energy state, and this is not allowed by the Pauli exclusion principle.

This situation is changed, however, as soon as we excite just one electron from the valence band to the conduction band. Conduction can now take place, furthermore it can do so via *two* mechanisms. Not only can

---

† It is possible for electrons with different quantum numbers to have the same energy; such a situation is called *degeneracy*. However, the extent of degeneracy encountered in practice does not alter the conclusions reached here.

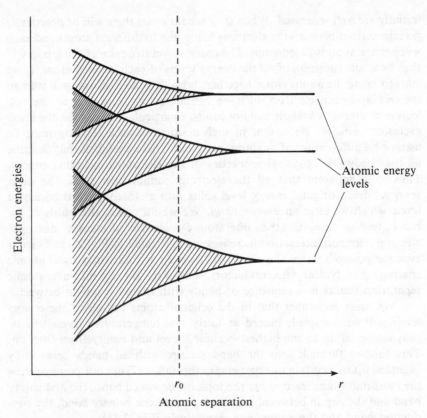

Fig. 2.15   A schematic illustration of the origin of energy bands in solids. The value r_0 represents a typical equilibrium value for the atomic separation.

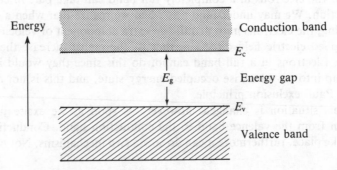

Fig. 2.16   The energy band structure at the top of the occupied energy levels at OK. An energy gap (E_g) separates the valence band (full) from the conduction band (empty).

the electron promoted to the otherwise empty conduction band help in conducting electricity but so can the electrons remaining in the valence band. Since in the latter case rather a large number of electrons are involved the problem looks at first sight somewhat intractable. However, it is not too difficult to show that the motion of all the electrons in a band from which one has been removed is equivalent (in mathematical terms) to a situation where we have a band containing a single particle. This fictitious particle (called a *hole*) has to be given certain physical properties to ensure its correct behavior, the main one of interest to us being that it must have a *positive charge*. When we picture holes on an electron energy diagram we must remember that, because of the opposite charges, increasing hole energies are in the direction of decreasing electron energies. Put more succinctly, what is 'up' for an electron is 'down' for a hole.

In a pure semiconductor material (or *intrinsic* material) the number of electrons and holes must be always equal (this follows from the definition of a hole) and this number can be changed by changing the temperature. There is, however, another way of changing the electron and hole populations and that is by doping the semiconductor with atoms whose valences (i.e. electron bonding requirements) differ from that of the host material. For example suppose we dope silicon (tetravalent) with phosphorus (pentavalent). Each phosphorus atom replaces one of the silicon atoms and four of its five valence electrons are used to satisfy the bonding requirements of its four neighbors (Fig. 2.17). This leaves one electron which is redundant to bonding requirements and consequently it is only weakly bound to the phosphorus atom. It is readily detached and promoted into the conduction band, where it behaves exactly like any other conduction electron. This process, of course, does not produce an extra hole; indeed the number of holes must decline since it may be shown that for any semiconductor

$$np = n_i^2, \qquad (2.2)$$

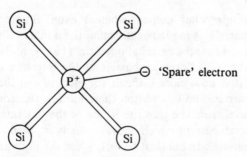

Fig. 2.17 Bonding of phosphorus in silicon. Because of the differing valencies, there is a 'spare' electron associated with the phosphorus ion which is surplus to its bonding requirements.

where n and p are the electron and hole densities respectively and n_i is the electron (or hole) concentration that would be present in intrinsic material. Thus doubling the electron concentration by doping causes the hole population to be halved.

Such dopants as we have been discussing are known as *donors* (they *donate* electrons to the conduction band) and the material is known as *n-type*. Doping that will increase the hole population is also possible by using impurity atoms which have a valence of one less than the host, for example boron in silicon. Such dopants are called *acceptors* and the resulting material is called *p-type*. The carrier with the largest concentration is known as the *majority* carrier, whilst the other is called the *minority* carrier.

One of the most fundamental of electronic devices involves forming a junction between p and n materials. Such a device acts as a diode, i.e. a device that will pass current in one direction but not in the other. Even more interesting from our point of view is that when a current is flowing through the junction it may, under certain circumstances, emit radiation. (This is the basis for the light emitting diode or LED.).

Suppose we imagine making a junction by simply placing pieces of n and p material in physical contact. Because there are more electrons in the conduction band of the n material than there are in the conduction band of the p material, electrons tend to flow from the n to the p conduction band. Similarly holes flow from the p to the n valence band. (Such flows, which are determined by concentration gradients, are termed *diffusion*.) Because the electrons and holes carry charge, this flow causes the two sides of the junction to become electrically charged. The n side becomes positively charged, the p side negatively charged. The resulting charge separation produces an electric field which opposes the diffusive flow and eventually an equilibrium situation is reached when there is no net charge flow. The charge build-up causes an energy level 'barrier' of height eV_0 to appear at the interface as shown in Fig. 2.18, where V_0 is known as the *contact* or *diffusion* potential.

We now consider what happens when an external potential is applied. Suppose the p material is made negative and the n material positive (called *reverse* bias); in this case the external potential (V, say) adds to the internal potential, and the total potential barrier at the interface becomes larger ($= e(V_0 + V)$). It is now more difficult for electrons in the n material to surmount this barrier, and in addition there are few electrons about in the p material to travel from the p to the n side of the junction (Fig. 2.19(a)). The result is a small current which conventionally is taken as flowing from the n to the p material. In contrast to this, when the polarities are reversed (in *forward* bias) the internal barrier height is reduced ($= e(V_0 - V)$) making it easier for carriers to surmount the barrier, and the result is a relatively large conventional current flow from the p to the n material

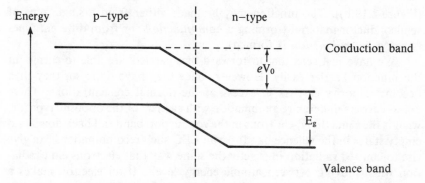

Fig. 2.18 Energy-level barrier (height eV_0) created when a p–n junction is formed. The top of the conduction band and the bottom of the valence band have been omitted for convenience.

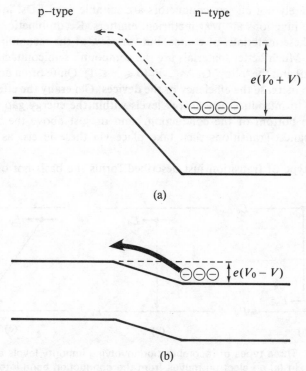

(a)

(b)

Fig. 2.19 The barrier height at a p–n junction when (a) reverse bias and (b) forward bias of magnitude V is applied. In the former case, very few electrons can surmount the barrier, whilst in the latter a much larger number can do so.

(Figure 2.19(b)). The junction may be made either from a single type of semiconductor material (forming a *homojunction*) or from different types (when a *heterojunction* is formed).

We have just seen that in forward bias carriers are able to surmount the junction barrier easily. However, once they have done so, they then become minority carriers in excess of the normal concentrations. These excess carriers undergo recombination with carriers of the opposite type (or, what is the same thing, electrons in the conduction band fall back down into empty states in the valence band). In an LED such recombinations can give rise to emitted radiation in exactly the same way that electrons emit radiation when moving between atomic energy levels. If an electron makes a radiative transition from the bottom of the conduction band (energy E_c) to the top of the valence band (energy E_v) then the wavelength of light emitted is given by

$$\frac{hc}{\lambda} = E_c - E_v = E_g. \tag{2.3}$$

Unfortunately not all semiconductors are suitable for LEDs, in particular Si and Ge junctions are *very* inefficient emitters. Recombination still takes place in these materials, of course, but very few of the recombinations are radiative. Much better materials are the compound semiconductors GaAs, doped GaP and the 'alloy' $GaAs_{1-x}P_x$ ($0 \leqslant x \leqslant 1$). Quite often doping must be used to increase the efficiency of the devices. Generally the effect of such doping is to introduce new energy levels within the energy gap either just below the bottom of the conduction band or just above the top of the valence band. Transitions then take place via these levels, as shown in Fig. 2.20.

The type of transition just described forms the basis not only of the

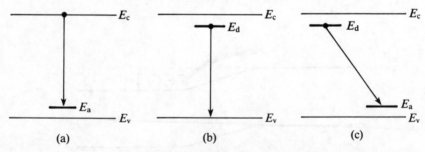

Fig. 2.20 Three types of recombination involving impurity levels are shown. In (a) an electron moves from the conduction band into an empty acceptor level. In (b) an electron in a donor level recombines with a hole in the valence band. In (c) an electron in a donor level falls into an empty acceptor level. This latter process requires that the donor and acceptor are physically close together.

LED but also the semiconductor laser. How then are the requirements for population inversion and optical feedback to be met? Population inversion is rather tricky to define in the present context but we may take it that we require the simultaneous presence of high densities of electrons and holes. Such densities may be obtained for short distances ($\sim 1 \, \mu$m) on either side of a forward biased p–n junction. A schematic structure for a GaAs homo-junction laser is shown in Fig. 2.21. Laser action can only be sustained within the narrow region shown (called the *active* region). Optical feedback is usually obtained by using the reflections from carefully cleaved end faces of the semiconductor. Although the amount of reflection is relatively small it is often sufficient for lasing to take place. Fabrication of more elaborate mirrors is much more costly and, except in special cases, does not justify the trouble involved.

We may readily calculate the reflectance (R) of a semiconductor–air in-terface by using the formula (see Section 2.1.3)

$$R = \left(\frac{n-1}{n+1}\right)^2 \tag{2.4}$$

where n is the semiconductor refractive index. For GaAs, for example, $n = 3.6$, whence $R = 0.32$.

The amount of population inversion, and hence gain, is determined by the current flowing. At low current any population inversion achieved is

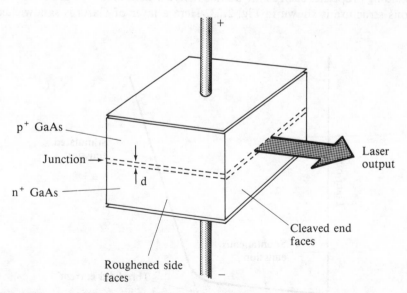

Fig. 2.21 Schematic construction of a GaAs homojunction semiconductor diode laser (side lengths about 200–400 μm). The emission is con-fined within the narrow junction region of width d.

offset by the losses present and lasing does not occur. Any radiation generated is due to spontaneous emission (as in an LED) which increases linearly with drive current. Beyond a critical current (the *threshold* current), however, lasing commences and radiative output then increases very rapidly with increasing current, as shown in Fig. 2.22.

One feature of semiconductor lasers which distinguishes them from almost all others is their very wide beam divergence. We tend to think of lasers as producing parallel or very slightly diverging beams but this is not so for semiconductor lasers. Essentially this stems from the very small dimensions of the cross section of the active region. These dimensions are of the same order as the wavelength of the light and so we get appreciable diffraction effects. Even though the junction widths may be relatively quite wide, lasing often takes place nonuniformly across the end face of the active region, after being confined to areas with linear dimensions of a micron or so. The beam spread is generally smaller in the plane of the junction than at right angles to it, where typically the angle of divergence is $40°$.

A major difficulty with homojunction lasers is that there is little to stop the radiation from spreading out sideways from the gain region and suffering loss instead of gain. For this reason homojunction lasers can usually only be operated in pulsed mode and with current densities of the order of $400 \, A \, mm^{-2}$ or higher. A dramatic reduction in the threshold current density can be achieved using more complicated structures with light-guiding properties such as the *double heterostructure*. A typical device with this structure is shown in Fig. 2.23. Here a layer of GaAs is sandwiched

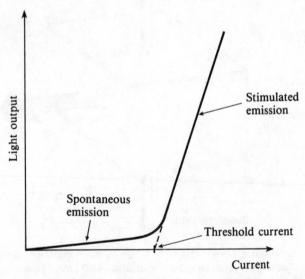

Fig. 2.22 Light output-current characteristic of an ideal semiconductor laser.

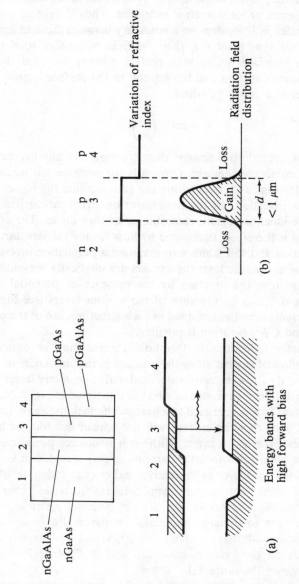

Variation of refractive index

Radiation field distribution

Loss

n   p p   p
2   3 4

Loss — Gain — Loss

d — < 1 μm

(b) is how the structure aids the confinement of both carriers and optical radiation within the gain region.

pGaAs

pGaAlAs

1 2 3 4

nGaAlAs

nGaAs

Energy bands with high forward bias

1 2 3 4

(a)

Fig. 2.23 Structure of a double heterostructure laser (a). Also shown (b) is how the structure aids the confinement of both carriers and optical radiation within the gain region.

between two layers of the ternary compound $Al_xGa_{1-x}As$, which has a larger energy gap than GaAs and also a smaller refractive index. The active region is within the GaAs layer, the refractive index differences between this and the surrounding layers cause light to be confined to the active layer due to the phenomenon of total internal reflection. Thus if light in a medium of refractive index n_1 is incident on a boundary between this and a medium of refractive index n_2 ($n_2 < n_1$), then the light will suffer total internal reflection (the interface acting as a perfect mirror) provided the angle between the beam direction and the normal to the surface is greater than the so-called *critical angle* θ_c, where

$$\theta_c = \sin^{-1}\left(\frac{n_2}{n_1}\right). \tag{2.5}$$

In addition to optical confinement this structure has another beneficial effect, that of carrier confinement. Obviously the more densely we can pack together the electrons and holes within the gain medium the higher will be the population inversion. In the homojunction structure carriers diffuse away from the junction region, recombining as they do so. The extent of the gain region is therefore determined by how far the carriers move away from the junction and still manage to maintain a population inversion. In the double heterostructure laser the carriers are physically prevented from diffusing away from the junction by the presence of potential barriers created by the differing energy gaps of the various layers (see Fig. 2.23). Threshold currents densities obtained in such structures are of the order of $10 \, A \, mm^{-2}$ and CW operation is possible.

Even greater reductions in threshold current may be obtained by restricting the flow of current along the junction plane into a narrow 'stripe' which may be only a few microns wide. Such stripe geometry lasers may be made in many different ways, one of which is illustrated in Fig. 2.24. In this device the current flow is restricted to a narrow channel just above the active region. It is hoped that the current will not spread out too far laterally before it reaches the active layer. With such structures power output of 10 mW can be obtained with drive currents of less than 500 mA.

Lasers based on GaAs as the active region emit radiation of about 0.9 μm wavelength. For certain applications (such as fiber-optical communications, see Chapter 7) this may not be ideal. Recently attention has been paid both to ternary compounds, based on $In_xGa_{1-x}As$ and to quaternary compounds based on $Ga_xIn_{1-x}P_yAs_{1-y}$. The emission wavelength depends on the exact composition and in $Ga_xIn_{1-x}P_yAs_{1-y}$, for example, can cover the range 1.1–1.7 μm.

Even longer lasing wavelengths can be obtained from the so-called *lead salt* lasers. These are used in infra red spectrometers since it is possible to vary their bandgap (and hence output wavelength) by changing the temperature. Typical compounds used are $Pb_{1-x}Cd_xS$, $PbS_{1-x}Se_x$ and

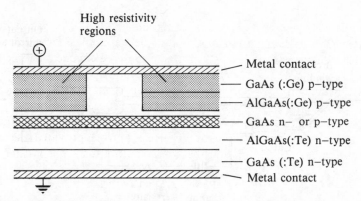

Fig. 2.24 Schematic cross section (end view) of one type of stripe geometry laser diode. The stripe is defined by proton bombardment to form high-resistivity material.

$Pb_{1-x}Sn_xSe$. With these the wavelength range from 3 to 30 μm can be covered, though it should be emphasized that each individual laser covers a *very* much more restricted range. By varying the temperature from 15 K to 100 K a typical tuning range of some 10^{-2} eV can be covered (at 10 μm, for example this corresponds to a wavelength range of 1 μm). Although coarse tuning of the laser is carried out by changing the temperature of the surroundings, fine tuning is often achieved by varying the current flowing through it. This also changes the temperature of the diode, of course, but has the disadvantage of affecting the power output as well.

One big difference between semiconductor lasers and most other types is their exceedingly small size. This severely limits the total power output, since at high powers the optical flux can cause mechanical damage to the facets and bring about failure of the laser. If high powers are required, then arrays of single lasers are used, which may be physically separate or fabricated on the same substrate.

2.3 GAS LASERS

As laser gain media, gases offer an interesting contrast to solids. Because of the difference in densities the population inversions that can be achieved in gases are much less than in solids. (A Nd:YAG rod contains some 6×10^{25} Nd atoms m^{-3}, whereas an HeNe laser only has 10^{21} Ne atoms m^{-3}). In consequence we would expect high-power gas lasers to be relatively large. On the other hand gases are much more homogeneous than solids and may be readily circulated for cooling and replenishment purposes.

Since the atoms in gases exhibit very narrow absorption lines it is impractical in most cases to use optical pumping. Instead atoms are almost

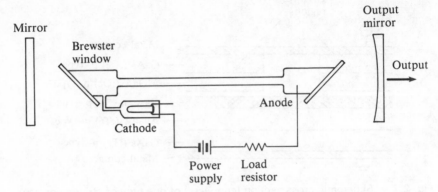

Fig. 2.25 Schematic construction of a low-power gas laser such as the helium–neon laser. The load resistor serves to limit the current once the discharge has been initiated.

always excited within a gas discharge. A schematic gas laser is shown in Fig. 2.25. The gas, at fairly low pressure, is contained within a glass discharge tube with anode and cathode at either end. If the cavity mirrors are outside the tube, then Brewster windows may be used at the ends of the tube to minimize reflection losses (this, of course, will result in a plane polarized output (see Section 2.1.3)). Voltages of a few kilovolts applied across the tube then initiate a gas discharge. The gas may need to be pre-ionized, as in the flashtube, by the application of a high-voltage pulse either to one of the electrodes or to a short length of wire wrapped round the tube. In such a discharge both free electrons and ions will be present as well as neutral atoms. The free electrons in the discharge are accelerated by the electric field as they travel towards the anode, and if they collide with a neutral atom or ion they may give up some or all of their energy to it, thus 'pumping' the atom or ion to an excited state.

For convenience we divide gas lasers into three main categories: atomic, ionic and molecular, depending on whether the lasing transitions take place between the energy levels of atoms, ions or molecules.

2.3.1 Atomic lasers

2.3.1.1 The HeNe laser

By far the commonest atomic laser (indeed one of the commonest of all types of laser) is the HeNe laser. The active medium is a mixture of helium and neon in the ratio of about ten parts of helium to one part of neon. The mixture is contained in a narrow bore tube a few millimeters in diameter and from 0.1 to 1 m long at a pressure of about 10 torr. A discharge is induced as outlined above but a point to note is that because the tube resistance falls to low values once a discharge has started a resistor must be placed in series with the power supply to limit the current.

The lasing transitions take place between the energy levels of Ne. Several different transitions are possible starting from the two groups of levels designated 3s and 2s, as shown in Fig. 2.26. Unfortunately direct electron excitation to these levels is rather inefficient and an 'intermediary' must be used. Somewhat fortuitously helium has energy levels ($2\,^1S$ and $2\,^3S$) which are quite close in energy to the 3s and 2s neon levels, and furthermore they are readily excited in the discharge. When an excited helium atom subsequently encounters an unexcited neon atom it may give up its energy to the neon, thus causing excitation of the required neon levels. The helium and neon levels are not *exactly* coincident but the difference is small and easily taken up by the kinetic energies of the atoms after energy exchange.

We may represent the excitation process by the equations:

$$e_1 + He = He^* + e_2 \quad \text{and} \quad He^* + Ne = Ne^* + He \qquad (2.6)$$

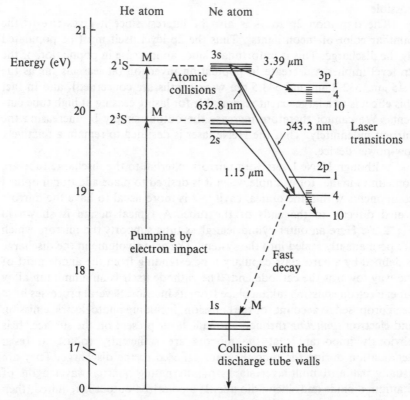

Fig. 2.26 Energy levels relevant to the operation of the HeNe laser. M indicates a metastable state (see p. 19).

where e_1 and e_2 are the electron energies before and after the collision, and the asterisk indicates that the atom is in an excited state.

Each of the four main laser transitions (at 3.39 μm, 1.15 μm, 632.8 nm and 543.5 nm) shares with one of the others either a common starting or terminating level. Thus the transitions are always competing with each other and precautions must be taken to prevent the two unwanted wavelengths from lasing. Usually all that is required is for the mirrors forming the laser cavity to be highly reflective at only the wanted wavelength.

The HeNe laser is another example of a four-level system and as such we require that the population of the lasing transition terminal level be kept as low as possible. This implies that electrons in the terminal level should decay as rapidly as possible back to the ground state. In neon this is a two-step process; the first, 2p to 1s, is a rapid transition, but the second, 1s to the ground state, is not so rapid. The latter transition rate is, however, enhanced by collisions with the walls of the discharge tube, and indeed the gain of the laser is found to be inversely proportional to the tube radius. For this reason the discharge tube diameter should be kept as narrow as possible.

The transition 2p to 1s is also of interest since it gives rise to the familiar color of 'neon lights'. Thus the 2p level itself must be populated by the discharge. This is unfortunate since an increase in population of the 2p level implies a decrease in population inversion (at least as far as the 1.15 μm, 632.8 nm and 543.5 nm wavelengths are concerned), and in fact this effect is to a large extent responsible for lasing ceasing at high tube currents. We cannot therefore increase the output simply by increasing the current indefinitely. Thus the HeNe laser is destined to remain a relatively low-power device.

Although HeNe lasers with mirrors external to the discharge tube are sometimes made, for example when it is desired to place additional optical components within the optical cavity, it is more usual to have the mirrors sealed directly to the ends of the tube. A typical design is shown in Fig. 2.27. Here an outer cylindrical glass tube supports the mirrors which are permanently sealed into the system. The active volume in the discharge is defined by a hard glass capillary tube extending from the anode most of the way towards the cathode end. The cathode itself is an aluminum alloy tube; electron emission taking place from its interior. Several processes have been proposed to account for the emission, including photoelectric emission and electron *tunneling* through an oxide layer present on the surface. It is obviously important that the mirrors are sufficiently robust to resist degradation during the time they are exposed to the discharge. They are usually made of multilayer stacks of alternating quarter wavelengths of titanium dioxide and silicon dioxide. If a polarized output is required, then a window orientated at the Brewster angle may be incorporated.

Although the HeNe laser gives a low power output, typically ranging

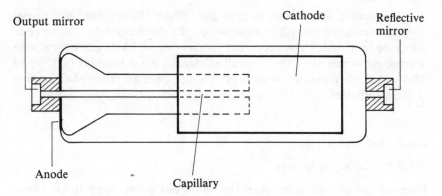

Output mirror · Cathode · Reflective mirror · Anode · Capillary

Fig. 2.27 Typical structure of a sealed mirror HeNe laser.

from 0.5 to 10 mW, it has other compensating virtues such as an exceptionally narrow lasing linewidth combined with excellent beam 'quality' (see Sections 3.3 and 3.4). It is also small and light enough to be readily portable.

2.3.1.2 The copper vapor laser

The copper vapor laser has been known for some time but it has become important only quite recently when various improvements in the associated technology have enabled high powers and reasonable lifetimes to be achieved. As the name implies the active medium is copper vapor, and to maintain a high enough concentration of copper in the discharge the tube has to be kept at fairly high temperatures. To attain these temperatures a discharge is initiated in an alumina tube, which is between 10 and 80 mm in diameter. The tube contains neon at 25–50 torr pressure and also a reservoir of solid copper. The waste heat from the discharge raises the temperature of the tube to between 1400°C and 1500°C when the copper has a vapor pressure of about 0.1 torr. During use copper vapor tends to diffuse toward the ends of the tube (where the temperature is lowest) and deposit itself there. After some several hundred hours of operation therefore fresh supplies of copper have to be added.

Lasing can be obtained at two wavelengths, 578 nm and 510 nm. Unfortunately both these transitions end on metastable levels and lasing can only take place for a short time before population inversion is destroyed. Subsequent deactivation of the terminal level takes some 25 μs, after which time lasing can recommence. Of necessity, therefore, the laser is operated in a pulsed fashion. The pumping current pulses are, of course, additional to the heating current and they require rather special power supplies. Rapid risetimes of some 20 A/ns are necessary together with peak currents of about 1 kA.

The copper vapor exhibits high gain (some 1% per mm) and consequently even uncoated plane windows on the discharge tube can serve as
adequate 'mirrors'. Pulse repetition frequencies of 5 kHz are typical with
average powers of 10–40 W. Overall efficiencies are reasonably high (up to
2%) so that when only a few watts of average power are required air cooling
is often sufficient.

2.3.2   Ion lasers

2.3.2.1   The argon ion laser

Here we turn to a gas laser where the transitions are between the electronic
energy levels of an ion. As usual the excitation takes place within a gas
discharge. Firstly the neutral argon atom is ionized, which requires an
energy of 15.75 eV. Then the ion is further excited to a group of levels
19.68 eV above its ground state. The relatively large excitation energies and
the fact that a two-stage process is involved would lead us to expect a rather
low overall power efficiency for this laser, and indeed typical values are only
a few hundredths of a percent!

Figure 2.28 shows the energy level diagram for the argon ion laser.
Transitions take place between the 4p and 4s levels, resulting in a group of
lines lying between 454 and 529 nm with the most intense at 488 and
514.5 nm. Because of the large pumping energies required the discharge
itself must be very intense, requiring current densities of up to 10 A mm^{-2}.
Even in a relatively low-powered device about a kilowatt or so of power
may need to be dissipated. Considerable engineering skill is required to
achieve operational reliability in the face of these harsh operating conditions. A typical tube design is shown in Figure 2.29. Brewster windows and
the use of external cavity mirrors serve to eliminate damage to the mirror
surfaces. The tube itself must be made from a refractory material such as
graphite or beryllium oxide. The efficiency of the laser is increased if a
magnetic field is applied along the tube axis. The ions spiral along the tube
axis and are kept away from the walls. Metal disks with holes at their
centers are usually placed at intervals along the tube. The holes define the
active region, while the disks themselves serve to conduct heat away from
the discharge to the tube walls. A water jacket surrounding the tube is often
used for additional cooling. Another feature of interest is the provision of
a gas return path. This is necessary because during operation the positive
ions generated tend to collect at the cathode, a return line helps to equalize
the pressure throughout the tube. It may be provided for by drilling off axis
holes in the cooling disks.

By using mirrors that are sufficiently reflective over a wide wavelength
range output can be obtained at a number of wavelengths simultaneously;
the highest-power argon ion lasers are operated in this way. Single line

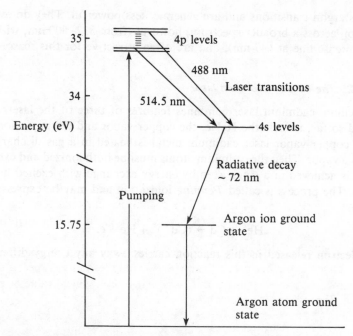

Fig. 2.28 Simplified energy level diagram for the argon laser. Ten or more laser lines are produced but the two shown are by far the most intense.

operation may be achieved by introducing a tuning element, such as a prism, into the cavity in the usual way.

In addition to argon other noble gases can be made to lase, the most important being krypton. Krypton laser transitions do not show as much

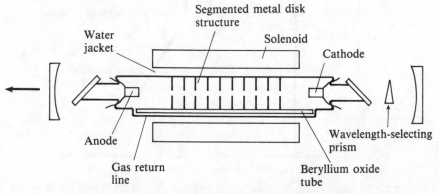

Fig. 2.29 Construction of a typical argon ion laser.

gain as argon transitions and are generally less powerful. They do exhibit emission across a broader spectrum, however (from 337–800 nm, with the most intense line at 647 nm), and are often attractive for this reason.

2.3.2.2 The helium–cadmium laser

The helium–cadmium laser combines features of three of the lasers considered so far, namely the HeNe, the copper vapor and the argon ion. As in the copper vapor laser cadmium metal is heated in a gas discharge to obtain a vapor. Then the cadmium atoms must be both ionized and excited, which is achieved in a single step by energy exchange with excited helium atoms. The process is called *Penning* ionization and may be expressed as follows:

$$\text{He}^* + \text{Cd} \rightarrow (\text{Cd}^+)^* + \text{He} + \text{e}. \tag{2.7}$$

The electron released in this reaction carries away any energy difference

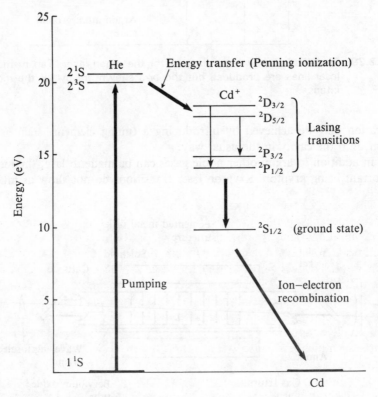

Fig. 2.30 Energy level diagram illustrating the transitions taking place in the HeCd laser.

between the two excited states. Lasing can then take place (at 325 nm and 442 nm) between the initial Cd^+ excited states and some states nearer the Cd^+ ground state. These in turn return to the Cd ground state with an ion–electron recombination at the tube walls (Fig. 2.30).

Tube voltages and currents are very similar to the HeNe laser, although the He pressure is somewhat higher (at around 6 torr). Output powers range from 5 to 50 mW, with the higher outputs at 442 nm. The cadmium is contained in a reservoir near the anode and may have to be replenished from time to time since it tends to diffuse toward the cooler (cathode) end of the tube. For this reason the cathode needs protecting from cadmium contamination and this is usually done by incorporating some form of cold trap just before it.

Cold traps may also be needed to protect the Brewster windows or end mirrors. Additionally the helium itself can be lost by a number of processes including burial under condensing cadmium and cathode sputtering, and again some means of replenishment is necessary. The efficiency of the cadmium laser is much higher, however, than the Ar ion laser (with which it is a competitor in certain applications) and normally air cooling of the laser tube is sufficient.

2.3.3 Molecular lasers

2.3.3.1 The carbon dioxide laser

The carbon dioxide laser is by far the most important laser of its class and in terms of technological applications it is arguably one of the most important of all. It exhibits both high efficiency (up to 30%) and high power output; CW powers of several tens of kilowatts are available. Thus applications such as welding and cutting of steel, pattern cutting, weaponry and laser fusion become possible.

The lasing transitions involved are different from all those considered hitherto since they involve the energy levels resulting from the quantization of the vibrational and rotational energy of the CO_2 molecule. As far as vibrations are concerned there are basically three different types or modes, which we designate symmetric, bending and asymmetric, and which are illustrated in Fig. 2.31. Each of these vibrations is quantized. That is to say the energy of the molecule, when it is in one of these modes, is an integral multiple of some fundamental value. We can refer to the particular state of the molecule by specifying this quantum number. In general we need a set of three such numbers (since we have three different modes). The numbers are quoted in the order referred to above: thus (0, 3, 0) refers to a state which is vibrating in a bending mode with three units of vibrational energy. As well as vibrating, the whole molecule can rotate about its center of mass. The fundamental rotational energy quanta are, however, much smaller than

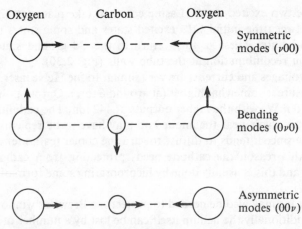

Fig. 2.31 The vibrational modes of the CO_2 molecule.

the vibrational quanta and as a result the vibrational energy levels are split into a number of closely spaced rotational sublevels which are labeled with the rotational quantum number $\mathscr{J}$. Figure 2.32 shows the energy-level diagram of CO_2.

As in the He–Ne laser, excitation is a two-step process, this time with

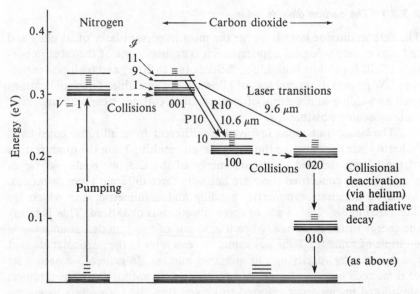

Fig. 2.32 Simplified energy level diagram for the carbon dioxide laser. Each vibrational level has many rotational levels associated with it. $\mathscr{J} = 1, 2$, etc. The letters P and R represent transitions where $\mathscr{J}$ changes by $+1$ and -1 respectively.

nitrogen involved as the intermediary. The first vibrational levels of N_2 are close to the (001) vibrational levels of CO_2. The latter form the initial levels of a large number of laser transitions between 9.2 and 10.8 μm (Fig. 2.32), with the strongest at 10.6 μm. A number of factors make this excitation process very efficient, one of which is evident from the scale of Fig. 2.32. The first excited state of nitrogen lies a mere 0.3 eV above the ground state, which contrasts markedly with the 20 eV or so required for the excitation of He in the HeNe laser. There are many more electrons in the discharge with 0.5 eV than there are with 20 eV of energy[†]. In addition the first excited state of nitrogen is metastable so that once excited the nitrogen is highly likely to exchange its energy with a carbon dioxide molecule before it de-excites by spontaneous emission. The addition of a third gas, helium, helps to increase the efficiency still further. Helium acts in several ways, for example by transporting waste heat to the tube walls and by assisting in the deactivation of the lower laser levels. The relative amounts of the gases used depends markedly on the type of system but in general the nitrogen and carbon dioxide concentrations are comparable, the helium concentration being larger than either. Low overall pressures (i.e. about 10 torr) are generally used for CW operation but short, high-energy pulse lasers operate at higher pressures.

A wide range of internal structures may be used depending on the power levels and beam quality required, and we now consider a number of these.

SEALED-TUBE LASERS

By a sealed-tube laser we mean one like the HeNe where the discharge gases are completely sealed within the discharge tube. The problem with this arrangement, as far as the CO_2 laser is concerned, is that during discharge conditions the CO_2 tends to break down into CO. This reaction is sufficiently rapid that, if no precautions were taken, lasing would cease after a few minutes. One solution is to add hydrogen or water vapor to the gas mixture, to react with the CO and regenerate CO_2. Gas cooling is another difficulty and generally the total power output is limited to less than 100 W. Sealed tube designs are not very common but are used in conjunction with the so-called waveguide design. Here the inner dimensions of the tube are small (the order of millimeters) and form a dielectric waveguide. Excellent beam quality is obtained together with a relatively large output in view of the small tube diameters. Excitation is obtained by means of either an electrical discharge or an intense radio-frequency field that can penetrate the waveguide material. The latter method has the advantage that no metal structures are required inside the waveguide.

[†]In fact the excitation requires something like 2 eV due to the complicated nature of the excitation process, but the remark is still valid.

GAS-FLOW LASERS

Both degradation and cooling problems may be alleviated by allowing the gas to flow through the laser tube. In the simpler designs both the gas flow and the electrical discharge take place along the tube axis. If no attempt is made to recycle the gas, then a fresh mixture must be supplied continuously. Since, however, gas pressures are relatively low, the demands are not excessive. Vacuum pumps are used to remove the waste gases from the tube, either for recycling purposes or merely to discharge them into the atmosphere. The power output of these lasers increases linearly with tube length at a rate of some 60 W per meter. For power outputs of greater than a few kilowatts, however, the tube lengths required become impracticably large.

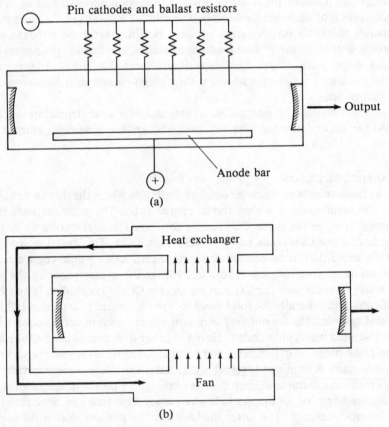

Fig. 2.33 Schematic diagram of a TEA CO_2 laser; the discharge is perpendicular to the axis of the laser cavity ('side' view (a)). A high gas flow is required whch can also take place perpendicular to the axis ('top' view (b)).

A much more rapid gas flow and a corresponding increase in maximum power output is possible if the flow takes place transversely to the lasing axis. The electrical discharge can also be usefully applied transversely (and normally to the gas flow) as illustrated in Fig. 2.33. These designs are capable of CW power levels of some tens of kilowatts. Larger outputs are possible but the sheer size and power requirements begin to preclude common industrial use. Such lasers are definitely one-off designs although they may be important for certain specialized applications.

TRANSVERSELY EXCITED ATMOSPHERIC (TEA) LASERS

So far in our discussion raising the power output in CO_2 lasers has involved increasing the length and/or the gas flow rate. There is, however, another option, namely that of raising the gas pressure. Unfortunately this carries with it the penalty of an increase in the voltage needed to excite the discharge, and at relatively high pressures the requirements may become embarrassingly large. For example at atmospheric pressure the breakdown voltage is $1.2 \, \text{kV mm}^{-1}$. Obviously at this pressure it would be difficult to contemplate a longitudinal discharge in a tube several meters long. On the other hand a transverse discharge over a length of some 10 mm or so would be much more acceptable. CW operation also causes problems because of discharge instabilities which occur at pressures above 100 torr. Thus high-pressure lasers are of necessity pulsed and are pumped using a transverse discharge. Such lasers are termed transversely excited atmospheric (TEA) even though the gas pressures may cover quite a wide range about atmospheric (Fig 2.33). Very high-power pulses may be achieved having durations down to 50 ns and with energies of up to 100 J.

At very high pressures (above 10 atmospheres) molecular collisions cause the individual lines to broaden into a continuum and a more or less continuous tuning of the laser output becomes possible. Line broadening is also useful when the technique of mode locking is used to generate nanosecond duration pulses (see Section 3.8).

GASDYNAMIC LASERS

With gasdynamic lasers we reach, from a laser point of view, the possibility of the quite staggering power levels of some hundreds of kilowatts. Population inversion is created through thermodynamic means rather than in a gas discharge. A nitrogen–carbon dioxide mixture is heated and compressed and then allowed to expand rapidly through a nozzle into a low-pressure chamber. In the high-temperature regime most of the energy is stored in the vibrational modes of the nitrogen molecule. After expansion and cooling most of the rotational and translational energy of the nitrogen molecule is rapidly lost by collisions with other molecules whilst the vibrational energy is stored for rather longer. Resonant collision processes can then populate the (001) levels of the carbon dioxide molecule and hence create a population inversion between these and the (100) levels. Gasdynamic lasers, however, are not commercially available and in any case there are few, if any, real uses for such high powers especially in view of the size and complexity of the laser structure (they resemble rocket motors in several respects!).

OPTICS

One of the difficulties with having an output at around 10 μm is that 'normal' optical materials, such as glass or quartz, are quite useless for components such as Brewster windows, since they exhibit very high absorption at this wavelength. There are a number of materials which are transparent but many of them suffer from having rather poor mechanical properties. Germanium, gallium arsenide, zinc sulfide, zinc selenide and various alkali halides have all been used. The latter show the lowest absorption of all but are fairly soft and hygroscopic (that is they absorb water from the atmosphere). Metal mirrors can be used for the 100% reflecting mirror. In high-power designs even a small amount of absorption can lead to appreciable heating up of the optical component, and then some form of forced cooling may be necessary.

2.3.3.2   *The nitrogen laser*

In contrast to the CO_2 laser the transitions in the nitrogen laser are between electronic energy levels of the nitrogen molecule and give rise to an output in the ultra violet at 337 nm. Interestingly the levels between which lasing action takes place would appear to have entirely the wrong relative lifetimes. Remember in an ideal situation the lifetime of the upper level should be long whilst that of the lower level should be short. In nitrogen the reverse is true! Obviously we cannot hope for CW operation in these circumstances, although pulsed operation is possible. The pulse widths are, however, very narrow since as soon as lasing begins the population of the terminal state increases rapidly and after a few nanoseconds population inversion is reduced to a level where lasing cannot be supported. Such a laser is termed *self-terminating*. Pumping is not trivial since it has to take place in a time which is less than the pulse width.

Usually a configuration similar to the TEA CO_2 laser is adopted. A capacitor is rapidly discharged between electrodes placed transversely to the laser axis and the gas may be cooled by flowing it through a heat exchanger laser. Interestingly very high gains are possible, so much so that only one mirror need be used. Such high gain operation is termed *superradiant*. Pulse energies are up to a few millijoules and, because of their very short duration, the peak powers can be in the region of megawatts.

2.3.3.3 *The excimer laser*

The word 'excimer' is a contraction of *exci*ted di*mer*, by which is meant a diatomic molecule which, whilst being stable in its excited state, is not so in its ground state. Typical of such materials are the rare gas halides such as ArF, KrF and XeCl. If we draw a diagram of energy versus atomic separation for the ground state of a 'normal' molecule, we obtain a curve with an energy minimum occurring at the equilibrium separation of the molecule. Similar curves may be drawn for the excited states. For dimers, however, although the excited states may have such minima the ground states do not. This situation is illustrated in Fig. 2.34.

Obviously in equilibrium there are very few dimer molecules present in the ground state, since it is inherently unstable. We cannot therefore get excitation directly from the ground state. Several possibilities exist using indirect excitation within the discharge. For example in ArF the following processes can take place. First we get *electron attachment*, as represented

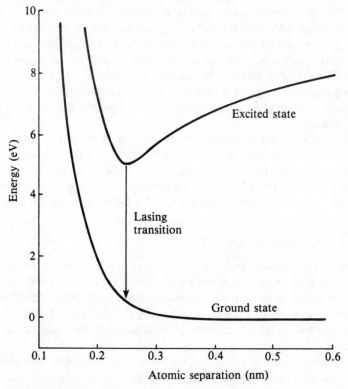

Fig. 2.34 Potential-energy curves for the KrF excimer laser.

by the equation:

$$e + F_2 \rightarrow F^- + F. \tag{2.8a}$$

The negative ions thus formed can then combine with positive ions that are present to give an excited molecule:

$$Ar^+ + F^- \rightarrow (ArF)^*. \tag{2.8b}$$

In spite of this seemingly roundabout route such reactions can be very efficient in producing excited dimer molecules.

Because of the low population in the ground state, population inversion is easily achieved. Furthermore even when lasing commences the ground state population remains low because the ground state is inherently unstable. Once a molecule is in that state the atoms move rapidly apart and the molecule dissociates.

Gaseous discharges, electron beams and even photon beams have all been used for pumping, although commercial lasers rely on conventional gaseous discharge techniques. Vigorous pumping is needed to initate the above reactions and this invariably leads to the adoption of pulsed operation. The requirements are similar in several respects to those of the nitrogen laser, although for different reasons. Sometimes the gas in the discharge is pre-ionized using ultra-violet or X-ray excitation which helps to speed up the discharge. Quite often provision is made for changing the type of gas fill and thus altering the lasing wavelength. In any case regular replenishment of the gases is necessary to avoid degradation of the output. It is worth bearing in mind that some of these (particularly fluorine) can be quite hazardous.

A comparatively large number of excimer lasers has been developed covering the wavelength range 120–500 nm. Some of these, especially XeF and KrF, are quite efficient (up to 10–15%). Peak powers of up to 1 J with average powers of some 200 W can be obtained. Such high-power pulses are particularly useful as pump sources for dye lasers (see Section 2.4).

2.3.3.4 The chemical laser

Although the energy outputs of high-powered laser systems sound impressive from an optical power point of view they are rather insignificant when compared to the energy released in common chemical reactions. For example a kilogram of high explosive will yield about 8 MJ. The chemical laser uses this energy to produce population inversion and hence lasing action.

A popular reaction for such purposes is that which can take place between hydrogen and fluorine. If both are present only in their molecular form then no reaction takes place; however, if by some means single atoms of either species can be generated, then the following two reactions initiate a 'chain reaction' during which all the hydrogen and fluorine can recombine

$$F + H_2 \rightarrow HF + H \ (+ energy)$$
$$H + F_2 \rightarrow HF + F \ (+ energy). \tag{2.9}$$

The HF molecules thus formed are in vibrationally excited states and population inversion may be obtained between these states and the ground state. Lasing action at a variety of wavelengths from 2.5 to 3.4 μm has been observed. Not all chemical lasers involve molecular vibrational/rotational levels and excitation into upper electronic energy levels has been observed.

Some of the most powerful laser pulses ever produced have been from chemical lasers, for example, hydrogen fluoride lasers have yielded pulses of up to several hundred joules. Other features which make such lasers interesting are the fact that little or no electrical power is needed and that high output to volume and weight ratios are possible. Not surprisingly the constructional technology is fairly similar to that of the gas dynamic laser; they are not yet available commercially.

2.3.3.5 *Far infra-red lasers*

Finally in this section on molecular lasers we come to a group of materials where lasing transitions occur between nearby rotational levels (that is

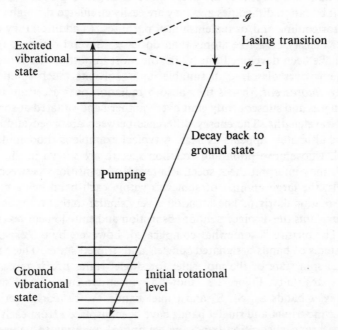

Fig. 2.35 Schematic diagram of the transitions involved in a typical far infra-red laser.

belonging to the same vibrational state). Such lasers are still mainly at the research and development stage. As might be expected, because of the relatively close energy spacing of rotational levels, the output wavelengths are in the far infra-red ranges, in fact they cover a range of about 30–2000 μm (or 2 mm!). A large number of molecules have been investigated although so far most of these have been fairly simple hydrocarbons (e.g. methane, formic acid etc.). In almost all cases a CO_2 laser is used to pump the lasing material from its ground state into some rotational level of an excited vibrational state. Population inversion is then established between adjacent levels in the excited state (Fig. 2.35).

So far, however, such lasers are probably of more interest for the insight they give into the energy-level structure of the molecules involved than anything else. It is possible to convert them into tunable devices for spectroscopic and photochemical applications (see Section 4.6) but otherwise potential applications seem rather sparse.

2.4 LIQUID DYE LASERS

Liquids have several advantages over both solids and gases for use as laser gain media. Like gases they are much more homogeneous than solids, there are no fabrication difficulties and they are easily circulated through the laser cavity for cooling and/or replenishment purposes. In addition they contain a larger density of active atoms than do gases. Several different types of liquid have been developed but by far the most important are those based on organic dyes dissolved in suitable liquid solvents. Such solutions are strongly *fluorescent*; that is they absorb radiation over a certain band of wavelengths and subsequently emit over another band situated at somewhat longer wavelengths. The energy difference between absorbed and emitted photons ultimately appears as heat. A typical example is rhodamine 6G in ethanol, whose absorption and emission spectra are shown in Fig. 2.36.

We may interpret these spectra in terms of transitions between bands of levels, the large number of sublevels within each band being of vibrational/rotational origin. The situation is very similar to that in color centers which explains the displacement of absorption and emission curves (see Fig. 2.14). The picture is somewhat complicated, however, by the existence of two systems of bands designated 'singlet' and 'triplet' states. These refer to the total spin state of the molecule; for singlet states this is zero and for triplet states unity. Figure 2.37 shows a typical dye energy level structure with singlet bands S_0, S_1, S_2 and triplet bands T_1, T_2 (for pictorial convenience the triplet and singlet bands have been displaced from each other).

The broad absorption bands enable optical pumping to be used. The dye molecule is thereby excited from its ground state S_0 to states near the

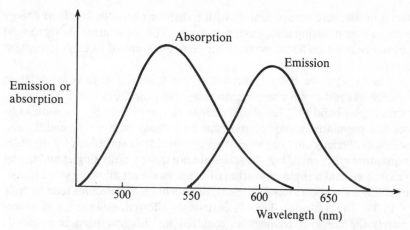

Fig. 2.36 Absorption and emission curves for rhodamine 6G.

top of the excited state band, S_1 and the molecule then rapidly relaxes to states at the bottom of this band. Lasing action can then take place between these states and those near the top of S_0. The latter are sufficiently far above the bottom of the band for them to be almost empty at room temperature, thus the dye laser is a four level system and threshold is reached at a very small population inversion. Unfortunately the $S_1 \rightarrow S_0$ transition is often very rapid (~ 10 ns), necessitating intense pumping to achieve population

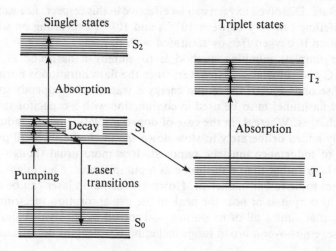

Fig. 2.37 Energy-level scheme for a dye molecule. The laser transitions terminate above the lowest energy in the S_0 singlet state so the laser is a four-level system. $S_1 \rightarrow T_1$ transitions lead to strong absorption at the laser wavelengths, thereby quenching laser action. $S_1 \rightarrow S_2$ transitions may also quench laser action in some dyes.

inversion. Because we are dealing with transitions between bands of energy levels, a range of lasing transitions is possible. The consequent ability to tune the laser over a significant range of wavelengths is one of its most important features.

Up to now we have ignored the triplet levels; unfortunately their presence has rather adverse consequences. We note from Fig. 2.37 that the lowest triplet band (T_1) lies slightly lower in energy than S_1. As soon as S_1 becomes populated some spontaneous transitions between S_1 and T_1 can take place. Strictly this singlet $\rightarrow$ triplet transition is forbidden by the rules of quantum mechanics, but the states are not quite wholly singlet and triplet in character, and a slight relaxation of the rules occurs allowing some transitions. Since the transition $T_1 \rightarrow S_0$ is also forbidden molecules tend to 'pile up' in T_1. The transition $T_1 \rightarrow T_2$ is strongly allowed, however, and unfortunately the range of frequencies required for this transition corresponds almost exactly to that involved in the lasing transitions. Thus, once a significant number of molecules have found their way into T_1, the absorption arising from the $T_1 \rightarrow T_2$ transition reduces the gain and may stop laser action altogether. The result is that, unless special techniques are used, the laser will only operate in a pulsed mode; the pulse duration being of the order of a microsecond (this being the time taken for the population of T_1 to build up to significant concentrations). Between pulses sufficient time must be given for the transition $T_1 \rightarrow S_0$ to take place and empty the T_1 levels. It is possible to improve this situation in some instances by the use of *triplet quenchers*. These are substances which increase the transition rate from T_1 back to the ground state. Dissolved oxygen can be effective in this respect. For example, the T_1 lifetime can vary between 10^{-3} s and 10^{-7} s depending on whether the solution is oxygen free or saturated with oxygen.

The simplest pumping method is to employ a flashtube as in the Nd : YAG and ruby lasers. However, since the flash duration is normally a few milliseconds a lot of the output energy is wasted. Consequently specially designed flashtubes must be used in conjunction with a capacitor suited to fast discharges. Whereas, in the case of doped insulating lasers, inductance is usually added deliberately to slow down the discharge, here all possible sources of inductance must be removed. It is more usual though to use another laser rather than a flashtube as a pump source. This might at first sight seem to be rather inefficient. However, the pump laser can be chosen to have its output at or near the peak in the dye absorption spectrum, thus ensuring that almost all of its output is absorbed by the dye. A flashtube, of course, emits over a broad range including wavelengths not absorbed by the dye.

An obvious way to contain the dye is within a glass tube fitted with Brewster windows and external mirrors. This has the advantage that some form of wavelength tuning mechanism may be placed in the cavity. The dye cell can be quite small since the medium exhibits a large gain. Care must be taken, however, since such small quantities of liquid can easily overheat and the dye itself decompose. Usually the dye is rapidly circulated through the cell, and this not only prevents overheating but also ensures that the concentration of molecules which are in the triplet states is kept low. An ingenious extension of the fast flow idea enables the glass container for the dye to be dispensed with altogether. If the dye solution is forced through a suitably shaped nozzle a smooth stable laminar sheet about one millimeter thick can be obtained. After flowing through the air for a short distance the dye may be caught and returned to a reservoir for recirculation. The gain of the dye medium is such that even this small thickness is sufficient to give laser action. The pumping laser beam is focused onto a small spot on the jet so that dye passes through the gain region in a very short time. If this time is shorter than that taken for the triplet state population to become excessive, then CW operation becomes possible. Typically the pumping beam is focused down to a spot some $10\ \mu m$ in diameter; dye flowing at $10\ m^{-1}\ s$ will then traverse the gain region in about $10^{-6}\ s$, which is sufficiently short to allow CW operation.

A possible optical layout is shown in Fig. 2.38. The cavity axis is 'folded' which enables the laser output to be parallel to the pump beam, and in addition it also effectively increases the cavity length. To help reduce cavity losses the dye jet stream is orientated at the Brewster angle with respect to the cavity axis, with the pump beam incident at just less than this angle. The best choice of pump laser depends on a number of factors including the dyes to be used (and hence the position of their absorption bands), the output power required, whether pulsed or CW operation is needed and not least, of course, cost (including capital and running costs).

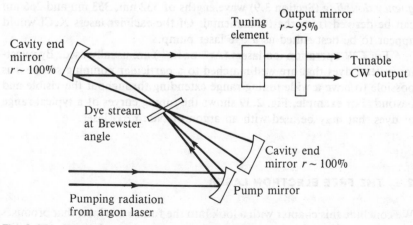

Fig. 2.38 Schematic diagram of a tunable, CW, laminar-flow dye laser. The dye stream is perpendicular to the page.

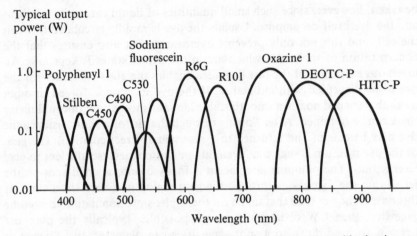

Fig. 2.39 Relative outputs of some common laser dyes pumped by ion lasers. Rhodamine 6G (R6G), for example, is pumped by 5 W of power from all the argon lines. The coumarin dyes are labeled C, C490 is pumped by 2.3 W at 488 nm.

When optimally pumped, dyes can convert up to 25% of the pump power into laser outputs. However, if only one pump laser is available, then not all dyes are optimally pumped. Care must be taken when using ultra violet pump sources since the shorter wavelengths can cause dissociation of the dye molecules. For pulsed outputs, nitrogen, excimer, Nd : YAG and copper vapor lasers have all been used as pump sources. Obviously since Nd : YAG lasers normally operate at 1.06 μm their output cannot be used directly; however, by using the technique of *harmonic generation* or *frequency doubling* (Section 3.9) wavelengths of 532 nm, 353 nm and 266 nm can be derived from the fundamental. Of the excimer lasers XeCl would appear to be best suited as a dye laser pump.

For CW operation ion lasers (Ar^+ or Kr^+) are usually used. By selecting several dyes that are well matched to a particular pumping source it is possible to have a wide tuning range extending throughout the visible and beyond. For example, Fig. 2.39 shows the tuning curves of a typical range of dyes that may be used with an argon or Nd : YAG laser.

2.5 THE FREE ELECTRON LASER

We conclude this chapter with a look into the future at a laser that promises the sort of characteristics laser users have long dreamed about: tunability over a wide range (from the extreme ultra violet to millimeter wavelength!)

with high-power, high-efficiency and potentially low cost. So far, however, the device is very much at the research and development stage: the general operating principles have been verified but efficiencies so far are low and designs have not yet been optimized.

The operating principles of the free electron laser are quite different from any of the lasers considered so far. The basic source of energy is a beam of relativistic electrons (that is electrons traveling at a speed very close to that of light). Under certain circumstances they can be induced to give up some of their energy to a beam of photons traveling in the same direction. The coupling between the two takes place via the Coulomb interaction. However, since the electric field of the light beam is at right angles to its direction of travel, the electrons cannot give up any of their energy to the photons unless they too have a component of velocity perpendicular to the direction of travel. Hence the electron beam is made to travel through a so-called 'wiggler' magnet. This generates a spatially periodic magnetic field which alternates its sign periodically along the direction of propagation of the electron beam. As the electrons pass through the wiggler field they undergo transverse oscillations as shown in Fig. 2.40. As a result of these oscillations the electrons spontaneously emit radiation peaked in the forward direction at a wavelength λ given by

$$\lambda = \frac{\lambda_w}{2\gamma^2} \qquad (2.10)$$

where λ_w is the wiggler (spatial) period and γ is the ratio of the total electron energy to its rest energy (0.511 MeV) [2.3]. Such radiation is termed *magnetic*.

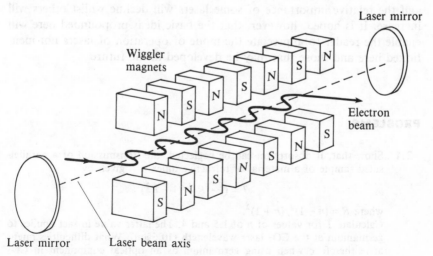

Fig. 2.40 Schematic diagram of the free electron laser.

The bandwidth, $\Delta\lambda$, of the radiation is given by

$$\frac{\Delta\lambda}{\lambda} \simeq \frac{1}{2N} \tag{2.11}$$

where N is the number of wiggler periods.

To induce the electron beam to lose large amounts of energy to the optical beam is not as easy as might at first appear. If the electron beam is 'tuned' to emit at exactly the wavelength of the light beam (as given by Eq. (2.10)), then in fact the energy exchanges between the two beams are equal and opposite.

One way around this is to inject the electrons at an energy slightly higher than the 'resonant energy', the electrons then tend to be pulled back towards the resonant condition. Obviously only a small amount of energy (the difference between the initial and final electron energies) can be extracted by this method. Alternative methods have been proposed, such as changing the wiggle period so that the final 'resonant' electron energy is less than at the start. The electrons then tend to 'home' in to the resonant condition and in so doing give up energy to the light beam − up to 10% energy extraction can probably be achieved in this way. To make the lasers more efficient requires a careful re-use of the electron energy once the beam has traversed the interaction region. There are two basic approaches to this, one is to re-circulate the actual electrons, and the other is to extract the electron energy and then use it for beam generation. So far neither of these possibilities has received serious attention.

In this chapter we have attempted to cover (albeit broadly) most of the different types of laser that have significant applications. Inevitably there are some omissions and doubtless in the coming years new lasers will emerge and the relative importance of some lasers will decline whilst others will increase. It is hoped, however, that the basic ideas propounded here will enable the reader to appreciate the mode of operation of lasers not mentioned here and those that may be developed in the future.

PROBLEMS

2.1 Show that, if absorption can be neglected, the transmission of a parallel-sided sample of a material of refractive index n is given by

$$T = (1 - R)^2/(1 - R^2)$$

where $R = (n - 1)^2/(n + 1)^2$.

Calculate T for values of n of 1.5 and 4. The latter value in fact applies to germanium at the CO_2 laser wavelength (10.6 μm). What difficulties might arise therefore when using germanium as an optical component in CO_2 lasers?

87

From the point of view of lens design, can you think of any advantage in having a medium of high refractive index?

2.2 With reference to Fig. 2.6, show that a laser rod cut at the Brewster angle will have an internal angle of θ_B and will be inclined at the angle $180° - 2\theta_B$ to the vertical. Calculate these angles for the case of an Nd:YAG laser rod where $n = 1.82$.

2.3 Show that the condition for the slab waveguide to operate is that the internal angle of the slab θ_1 satisfies the condition:

$$\theta_1 < 90° + \tan^{-1} n - \sin^{-1}(1/n)$$

Calculate the maximum internal angle that can be used in an Nd:YAG slab laser when $n = 1.82$.

2.4 With reference to Fig. 2.7 estimate the maximum possible efficiency of an Nd:YAG laser. Take the efficiency to be given by the ratio of optical power output to input pumping power.

2.5 A pulsed Nd:YAG flashlamp pumped laser operates using a 100 μF capacitor charged up to 2 kV. The laser emits an approximately triangular pulse (as in Fig. 5.5) of duration 1 ms and peak power 1 kW. Calculate the overall power efficiency of the laser.

2.6 Given that the alexandrite laser can be made to operate as a three-level system (with lasing taking place between the ^2E and $^4T_2$ levels) at a wavelength of 680 nm, redraw Fig. 2.11, providing it with an energy scale. Include the highest and lowest vibronic levels involved, assuming that in a four-level mode of operation the output can be tuned between 700 nm and 815 nm. The peaks of the pumping bands are at 590 nm and 410 nm.

2.7 Calculate the approximate peak wavelengths expected from LEDs made from the following materials:

	GaAs	GaP	CdTe	InP	SiC
E_g(eV)	1.44	2.26	1.50	1.35	3.00

2.8 A pulsed GaAs laser emits square pulses of duration 200 ns with a pulse repetition frequency of 1 kHz. Given that the average power emitted by the laser is 1 mW, calculate the peak optical power flux through the emitting facet (dimensions 100 μm × 2 μm).

2.9 The quantum efficiency of a semiconductor laser is given by the ratio of the rate of emission of photons to the rate of flow of electrons into the diode. Derive an expression for the ratio of the quantum efficiency to the power efficiency. Calculate a value for this ratio for a GaAs laser which operates with a forward voltage of 1.85 V and emits at 850 nm.

2.10 From Fig. 2.34 estimate the lasing wavelength expected from a KrF excimer laser.

2.11 Although in the present volume energy-level diagrams are labeled in terms of electron-volts (eV) another unit sometimes encountered is the cm^{-1}. This quantity is given by the reciprocal of the equivalent wavelength (measured in cm). Show that 1 eV is equivalent to 8065 cm^{-1}.

2.12 Calculate the wiggler magnet spatial period required in a free electron laser if it is to oscillate at 3.3 μm when using a beam of electrons of energy 43 MeV. Given that the cavity length is 10 m estimate the bandwidth of the radiation.

REFERENCES

2.1 T. H. Maiman, 'Stimulated Optical Radiation in Ruby Masers', *Nature*, London, **187**, 493–494, 1960.

2.2 (a) G. K. Woodgate, *Elementary Atomic Structure* (2nd edn), McGraw-Hill, London, 1980.

   (b) D. S. McClure, 'Electronic Spectra of Molecules and Ions in Solids', *Solid State Physics*, **9**, 399–525, 1959.

2.3 C. A. Brau, 'The Free-electron Laser: An Introduction', *Laser Focus*, **17**, 48–56, 1981.

More detailed information on specific lasers can be obtained from the following:

D. C. Brown, *High Power Nd: Glass Laser Systems*, Springer-Verlag, Berlin, 1981.

B. E. Cherrington, *Gaseous Electronics and Gas Lasers*, Pergamon Press, Oxford, 1979.

W. W. Duley, *CO₂ Lasers, Effects and Applications*, Academic Press, New York, 1976.

M. H. Dunn and J. N. Ross, 'The Argon Ion Laser', *Progress in Quantum Electronics*, **4**, 233–269, 1976.

A. F. Gibson and M. H. Key, 'High Power Lasers', *Rep. Prog. Phys.*, **43**, 1–65, 1980.

P. Hammerling, A. B. Budgar and A. Pinto (eds.), *Tunable Solid State Lasers*, Springer-Verlag, Berlin, 1985.

S. A. Loser, *Gasdynamic Lasers*, Springer-Verlag, Berlin, 1981.

S. Martellucci and A. N. Chester (eds.), *Free Electron Lasers*, Plenum, New York, 1983.

A. Mooradian, 'Tunable Infrared Lasers', *Rep. Prog. Phys.*, **42**, 1533–1564, 1979.

C. K. Rhodes (ed.), *Topics in Applied Physics: Volume 30. Excimer Lasers* (2nd edn), Springer-Verlag, New York, 1984.

M. J. Shaw, 'Excimer Lasers' *Progress in Quantum Electronics*, **6**, 3–54, 1981.

M. T. Stich (ed.), *Laser Handbook*, Vol 3, North-Holland Publishing Company, Amsterdam, 1979.

G. B. H. Thompson, *Physics of Semiconductor Laser Devices*, Wiley, Chichester, 1980.

C. S. Willett, *An Introduction to Gas Lasers: Population Inversion Mechanisms*, Pergamon Press, Oxford, 1974.

In addition there is a useful series of introductory articles by J. Hecht in *Lasers and Applications*:

'An Introduction to Carbon-Dioxide Lasers', September 1982, pp. 83–90.

'The Neodymium Laser', November 1983, pp. 57–62.

'Excimer Laser Update', December 1983, pp. 43–49.

'III–V Semiconductor Diode Laser Review', February 1984, pp. 61–67.

'Comparing Types of Dye Laser', July 1984, pp. 53–61.

'Vibronic Solidstate Lasers – Review and Update, September 1984, pp. 77–82.
'Ion Lasers in Review', October 1984, pp. 55–61.
'Diode Laser Report', November 1984, pp. 89–92.
'Basics of the Ruby Laser', May 1985, pp. 121–125.

3

Properties of Laser Radiation

Before we discuss laser applications we need to examine in more detail than was possible in Chapter 1 those properties of laser radiation such as linewidth, brightness, beam divergence and coherence which make lasers so valuable. We also review various techniques used to modify the output of lasers to give them even greater flexibility. In fact an example of such a technique has already been described in the previous chapter, where we saw that by inserting a frequency-selective element into the optical cavity it is possible to tune the operating frequency of certain lasers to any desired value within the gain linewidth. In addition we deal with techniques of mode locking and Q switching, which give rise to very short laser pulses of extremely high power, and frequency doubling, which again extends the operating wavelength range of a laser output, and consider methods used to stabilize the operating frequency of the laser.

3.1 LASER LINEWIDTH

As we explained in Section 1.9 the laser medium will support lasing over a spectral range that is ultimately limited by the natural linewidth of the relevant transition. In practice the spectral range will be somewhat less than this, depending on the cavity losses and the strength of the pumping. The presence of the optical cavity then serves to limit the oscillating frequencies to certain discrete values within this range, each different frequency being associated with a 'cavity mode' (Section 1.10).

It is convenient to divide cavity modes into two types, namely axial (or longitudinal) and transverse. The former are conceptually similar to standing waves on a string and may be designated by an integer p, where the frequencies of oscillation are given by $pc/2L$, where L is the cavity length. For normal cavity lengths the modes have values of p which are quite large ($\approx 10^6$).

As was mentioned in Section 1.10.2, the transverse modes are characterized by two integers q and r and are designated by TEM_{qr}. Again the oscillating frequencies are determined by the values of q and r but so

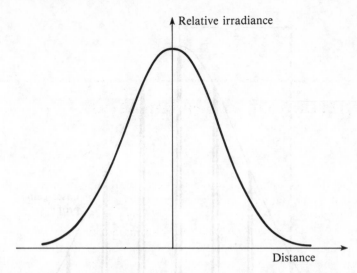

Fig. 3.1 Irradiance distribution across the cross section of a TEM_{00} transverse laser mode.

also is the spatial extent of the mode. Higher values of q and r give rise to more complex and more widely spread out irradiance patterns across the cross section of the beam (see Fig. 1.18). In contrast to p, both q and r normally take on small values (< 10). The simplest transverse mode is the TEM_{00} mode which exhibits the so-called *Gaussian* irradiance profile as illustrated in Fig. 3.1. It should be noted here that the separation of modes into two distinct types is merely for descriptive convenience. In reality modes should be designated as TEM_{qrp} so that each TEM_{qr} 'mode' really gathers together a larger number of separate 'axial' modes under one heading. The frequency dependence of the transverse modes on the values of q and r is quite complicated. For interest, however, we may note [3.1] that the frequency is given by

$$\nu_{qrp} = \frac{c}{2L} \left(p + \frac{1+q+r}{\pi} \cos^{-1}(g_1 g_2)^{1/2} \right) \tag{3.1}$$

where

$$g_1 = 1 - \frac{L}{r_1} \quad \text{and} \quad g_2 = 1 - \frac{L}{r_2}.$$

Here r_1 and r_2 are the mirror radii, being positive for concave mirrors and negative for convex mirrors. For example, taking $r_1 = r_2 = 2L$ (i.e. $g_1 = g_2 = \frac{1}{2}$) yields

$$\nu_{qrp} = \frac{c}{2L} \left(p + \frac{1+q+r}{3} \right).$$

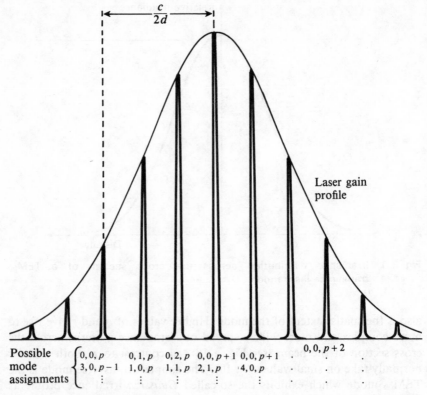

Possible mode assignments	$0,0,p$ $3,0,p-1$ $\vdots$	$0,1,p$ $1,0,p$ $\vdots$	$0,2,p$ $1,1,p$ $\vdots$	$0,0,p+1$ $2,1,p$ $\vdots$	$0,0,p+1$ $4,0,p$	$0,0,p+2$

Fig. 3.2   The mode frequency spectrum for a cavity (where $r_1 = r_2 = 2L$) superimposed on the laser gain profile. Note that many modes have the same frequency (that is they are 'degenerate').

Figure 3.2 shows how the mode frequencies for this situation might fit within the gain profile.

We can readily appreciate that if several modes are operating simultaneously, then the total frequency spread of the laser radiation is of the order of the gain profile. One obvious way to reduce the frequency spread therefore is to reduce the number of modes, so that only one of them is able to oscillate. This may be achieved by inserting a limiting aperture in the cavity, the diameter being chosen so that most of the TEM_{00} mode is able to pass through without significant attenuation. The higher-order transverse modes, however, have larger spatial spreads within the cavity and consequently they will suffer sufficiently high losses to prevent them from operating altogether. However, even if only the TEM_{00} mode is oscillating several axial modes may still be present. We note from Eq.(3.1) that the frequency spacing of these modes is inversely proportional to L, the cavity length. Hence if we now *increase* the frequency spacing by reducing the cavity length we then reduce the number of axial modes operating. When the axial mode separation approaches the width of the gain curve it is possible that only a single mode remains.

The linewidth of the laser output is then equal to that of a single longitudinal mode, and this can be very narrow indeed. It is, in fact, directly related to a quantity called the *quality factor* (Q) of the cavity. The term quality factor should be familiar to electrical engineers who use it in connection with the sharpness of the resonances of tuned circuits. Here we may define Q as

$$Q = \frac{\text{resonant frequency}}{\text{linewidth}} = \frac{\nu}{\Delta \nu}. \tag{3.2}$$

This equation is no help in calculating Q, however, and we must turn to an alternative definition,

$$Q = \frac{2\pi \times \text{energy stored in the resonator at resonance}}{\text{energy dissipated per cycle}}. \tag{3.3}$$

We may now derive an expression for Q by considering a bunch ($\mathcal{N}_p$) of photons traveling backwards and forwards between the cavity mirrors, as illustrated in Fig. 3.3.

After the photons have completed one round trip their numbers will be reduced to $\mathcal{N}_p R_1 R_2$ where R_1 and R_2 are the mirror reflectances and the corresponding energy loss is $\mathcal{N}_p(1 - R_1 R_2)h\nu$ (we assume no absorption losses in the mirrors). This loss occurs over a time of $2L/c$, hence the rate of energy loss is $\mathcal{N}_p(1 - R_1 R_2)h\nu c/2L$. Now the time taken for 1 cycle of the electric field of the corresponding electromagnetic wave is $1/\nu$ or λ/c and in this time the energy lost is $\mathcal{N}_p(1 - R_1 R_2)h\nu\lambda/2L$. The total energy in the cavity is $\mathcal{N}_p h\nu$ and hence the expression for Q can be written

$$Q = \frac{2\pi \mathcal{N}_p h\nu}{\mathcal{N}_p h\nu (1 - R_1 R_2)\lambda/2L} = \frac{4\pi L}{\lambda} \frac{1}{(1 - R_1 R_2)}.$$

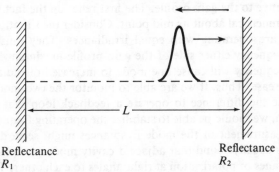

Reflectance
R_1

Reflectance
R_2

Fig. 3.3 A bunch of photons bouncing back and forth between the mirrors in a laser cavity.

Hence
$$\Delta \nu = \frac{\nu}{Q} = \frac{c(1 - R_1 R_2)}{4 \pi L} . \tag{3.4}$$

Example 3.1   Single mode linewidth

We may use Eq. (3.4) to estimate the linewidth of a laser where
$R_1 = R_2 = 0.99$ and $L = 0.5$ m. From equation (3.4) we have

$$\Delta \nu = \frac{3 \times 10^8 (1 - (0.99)^2)}{4 \pi \times 0.5} = 950 \text{ kHz}.$$

Since, in fact, the active medium is actually supplying energy to the oscillating modes, the energy dissipation can in theory be zero and hence Q infinite. In practice there are always losses which prevent this happening, but, even so, linewidths of about 1 Hz have been achieved.

Another problem is that although the linewidth of a single mode may be exceptionally narrow, its center frequency may well change with time. This is bound to happen unless the effective length of the cavity remains highly stable. Thus rigid construction and temperature control are necessary unless some form of compensation can be introduced. Generally it is possible to stabilize the laser operating frequency to something like 1 MHz (to get this in perspective we should realize that this corresponds to 1 part in 10^9!). Two ways of achieving this are described in the next section.

3.2   LASER FREQUENCY STABILIZATION

There are two commonly used methods of frequency stabilization in gas lasers, both of which involve holding the operating frequency at some fixed position relative to the gain profile. The first relies on the fact that the gain profile is symmetrical about its mid point. Consider the situation when only two modes are operating with equal irradiances. They must be equally spaced in frequency either side of the gain profile maximum. Any drift in the mode frequency will cause one mode to increase in irradiance and the other to decrease. Thus, if we are able to monitor the two-mode irradiance and then use the difference to operate a feedback loop that controls the cavity length, we should be able to stabilize the operating frequency. At first sight the measurement of the mode irradiances might seem difficult. Fortunately it is usually found that adjacent cavity modes are plane polarized with their planes of polarization at right angles to each other. Thus we need only split the laser output into two, insert suitably orientated pieces of polaroid into the two beams, and then allow them to fall onto two detectors.

The output of the detectors is then proportional to the irradiance of the model. A simple way of applying the feedback is to let any difference in output of the detectors modulate the current passing through a heating coil wrapped round the laser tube. Any changes in relative mode irradiance will then alter the tube temperature and hence the effective length of the cavity. This in turn will vary the mode frequencies.

The second frequency stabilization method to be considered here depends on a phenomenon known as the *Lamb dip*. To understand this we must look a little more closely into the reasons for the broadening of the gain curve (section 1.9). In gas lasers, the laser transition is known as an 'inhomogeneously broadened transition'. Put simply this means that the different frequencies that go to make up a single emission line result from transitions involving different groups of atoms. The main reason groups of atoms emit at different frequencies is because of their differing relative velocities along the direction of emission. This is in fact an example of the Doppler effect; a rather more familiar example is the apparent change in frequency of the sound from a moving source (e.g. a police siren) as it passes the observer. Suppose a particular atom is moving with velocity v towards a stationary observer. In its own frame of reference it may be emitting at a frequency ν_0, but to the observer its frequency is given by

$$\nu = \nu_0 \left(1 + \frac{v}{c} \right), \tag{3.5}$$

where c is the velocity of light.

We suppose now that the laser cavity length has been adjusted so that only one mode is oscillating at a frequency ν_m. As we have seen, each mode is essentially a standing wave, which can of course be regarded as being made up from two waves of equal irradiance traveling in opposite directions. These two waves, because they have the same frequency but different velocities, will not be able to cause stimulated emission from the same groups of atoms. Thus the wave traveling in one direction along the tube (say along the z axis) will only interact strongly with those atoms whose velocity component along this direction is $+ v_z$, where

$$\nu_m = \nu_0 \left(1 + \frac{v_z}{c} \right).$$

On the other hand the wave traveling in the opposite direction will only interact strongly with those atoms having a velocity component $- v_z$. There are therefore in general two groups of atoms whose stimulated emission contributes to the laser output. Suppose, however, that the oscillating mode frequency is changed so that it is equal to ν_0; then only those atoms with $v_z = 0$ can now interact with either wave. Thus there is a smaller total number of atoms overall able to interact with either beam and the resulting output power must be less than when ν_m is not equal to ν_0. As a function

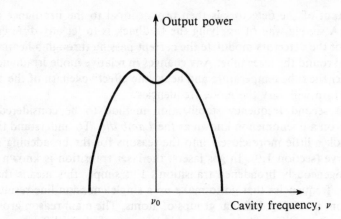

Fig. 3.4 Output power as a function of frequency of a single mode laser. The minimum at the center of the curve ($\nu = \nu_0$) is known as the Lamb dip.

of mode frequency, therefore, the laser output displays a minimum at $\nu_m = \nu_0$. This phenomenon is illustrated in Fig. 3.4. We can now see that if initially the laser is operating near ν_0, then we can stabilize the operating frequency at the value ν_0 by adjusting the cavity length so that the output power is minimized. There are several methods that can be used to vary the cavity length, for example by heating the cavity or by mounting one of the mirrors on a piezoelectric crystal so that its position can be altered by varying the voltage applied across the crystal.

3.3 BEAM DIVERGENCE

One of the striking features of most lasers is that the output is in the form of an almost parallel beam. This is a very useful feature for a number of applications since it means that it is very easy to collect the emitted radiation and focus it onto a small area using a fairly simple lens system. By contrast conventional sources emit radiation nearly isotropically over a solid angle of 4π sr or so, and only a small fraction of it can be collected and focused. However, even a laser beam is not perfectly parallel. This is not because of some fault in the laser design but is due to diffraction caused by the wave nature of light. We shall see that it is possible to reduce the amount of divergence, but only at the expense of an ever increasing beam width.

Consider a monochromatic beam of light of 'infinite' extent which passes through a circular aperture of diameter D. The beam will now diverge by an amount dependent on the size of D (Section 1.1). To visualize the result more easily we may imagine the emergent beam to be focused onto a screen as illustrated in Fig. 3.5(a). The resulting irradiance distribution on the screen is shown in Fig. 3.5(b); it consists of a bright area surrounded by concentric alternate dark and bright rings. The pattern is formed by the interference of the wavefronts coming from different parts of the aperture. Most of the light energy (some 84%) is contained within the central spot, which is known as the Airy disk. A measure of the amount

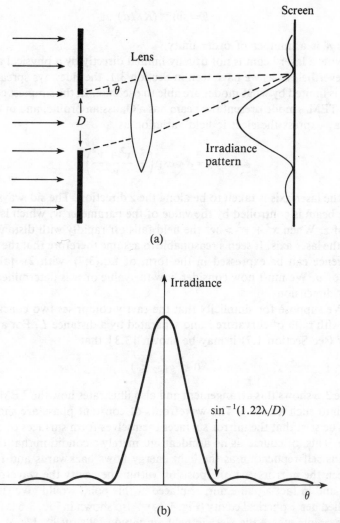

(a)

(b)

Fig. 3.5 Beam divergence from a circular aperture: the angular irradiance distribution is shown in (b); this pattern could be made visible by focusing the light onto a screen as in (a).

of diffraction is given by the angle θ, where 2θ is the angle subtended by the disk diameter. It may be shown that (see for example Ref. 3.2)

$$\sin \theta = 1.22\lambda/D \tag{3.6}$$

where λ is the wavelength of the light. Thus most of the diffracted radiation is contained within a cone of semi angle $\theta = \sin^{-1}(1.22\,\lambda/D)$. Similar results are obtained when differently shaped apertures are used, and in general an aperture of dimension d gives rise to an angular divergence given by

$$\theta = \sin^{-1}(K\lambda/d) \tag{3.7}$$

where K is a number of order unity.

Now a laser beam is not usually limited directly by a physical aperture but nevertheless, as we have seen in Section 3.1, the sideways spread of the beam is limited by what modes are able to oscillate. In the simplest case with just a TEM$_{00}$ mode present the beam has a Gaussian profile, and in this case we may express the electric field variation as

$$\mathscr{E}(x, y) = \mathscr{E}_0 \exp\left(-\frac{x^2 + y^2}{w^2}\right). \tag{3.8}$$

Here the laser axis is taken to be along the z direction. The sideways spread of the beam is controlled by the value of the parameter w, which is a function of z. When $x^2 + y^2 > w^2$ the field falls off rapidly with distance away from the laser axis. It seems reasonable to assume therefore that the angular divergence can be expressed in the form of Eq.(3.7), with $2w$ taking the place of d. We must now consider how the value of w is determined by the cavity dimensions.

We suppose for simplicity that the cavity comprises two concave mirrors, with radii of curvature r and separated by a distance L. For a 'stable' cavity (see Section 1.7) it may be shown [3.3] that

$$0 \leqslant g_1 g_2 \leqslant 1. \tag{3.9}$$

Figure 3.6 shows this arrangement and also illustrates how the TEM$_{00}$ mode 'fits' into such a cavity. The wavefronts of constant phase are shown and it can be seen that the mirror surfaces themselves form surfaces of constant phase. This, of course, is no accident but merely a condition that the mode remains self-replicating as the light energy flows backwards and forwards between the mirrors. At one position within the cavity the wavefronts are plane and in fact plane mirror placed at this point would give rise to the so-called hemispherical cavity (Fig. 1.14). Also shown in Fig. 3.6 is the locus of the points where the electric field amplitude falls off by $1/e$ of its maximum value (that is, where $x^2 + y^2 = w^2$). The smallest value of w is designated as w_0. It is not too difficult to show (see, for example, Ref. 3.4)

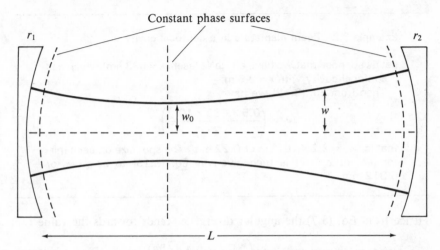

Fig. 3.6 TEM$_{00}$ mode within a laser cavity. The mode 'adjusts' itself so that the mirror surfaces are surfaces of constant phase.

that

$$w_0^2 = \frac{\lambda}{\pi} \left[\frac{L(r_1 - L)(r_2 - L)(r_1 + r_2 - L)}{(r_1 + r_2 - 2L)^2} \right]^{1/2} \qquad (3.10)$$

and also that the variation of w with z is given by

$$w(z) = w_0 \left[1 + \left(\frac{z\lambda}{\pi w_0^2} \right)^2 \right]^{1/2}, \qquad (3.11a)$$

where z is measured from the position of minimum beam diameter. At large values of z Eq. (3.11a) reduces to

$$w(z) \simeq \frac{z\lambda}{\pi w_0}. \qquad (3.11b)$$

In the case of a nearly confocal cavity where $r_1 = r_2 = r \gtrsim L$ Eq. (3.10) reduces to

$$w_0^2 \simeq \frac{\lambda}{2\pi} (L(2r - L))^{1/2} \qquad \text{or} \qquad w_0^2 \simeq \frac{\lambda r}{2\pi}. \qquad (3.12)$$

Substituting this value into Eq. (3.11a) yields

$$w(z) = w_0 \left[1 + \left(\frac{2z}{r} \right)^2 \right]^{1/2} \qquad (3.13)$$

Equation (3.13) shows that the beam will diverge as z increases, and for $z \gg r$ we have

$$w = w_0 \frac{2z}{r}. \qquad (3.14)$$

Example 3.2   Beam diameters in a confocal cavity

Let us suppose that we have an HeNe laser ($\lambda = 633$ nm) which has a confocal cavity with $r = 0.5$ m.
  Then from Eq. (3.12) we have

$$w_0 = \left(\frac{0.5 \times 633 \times 10^{-9}}{2\pi}\right)^{1/2}$$

that is, $w_0 = 2.2 \times 10^{-4}$ m or 0.22 mm. The spot size on each mirror (i.e. at $z = r/2$) is then given by Eq. (3.13) to be $\sqrt{2}w_0$ or 0.312 mm.

Hence from Eq. (3.7) the angular divergence tends towards the value

$$\theta = \sin^{-1}\left(\frac{w}{z}\right) = \sin^{-1}\left(\frac{2w_0}{r}\right). \tag{3.15}$$

From Eq. (3.12) we have $r = 2\pi w_0^2/\lambda$. Substitution for r in Eq. (3.15) then yields

$$\theta_{\text{confocal}} = \sin^{-1}\left(\frac{\lambda}{\pi w_0}\right). \tag{3.16a}$$

Often $\lambda/\pi w_0 \ll 1$ and thus

$$\theta_{\text{confocal}} = \lambda/\pi w_0. \tag{3.16b}$$

We see immediately that this agrees with that expected from the generalized result $\theta = \sin^{-1}(K\lambda/d)$ Eq.(3.7)), where $2w_0$ takes the place of d and the constant K has the value $2/\pi$. In fact it is of interest to note that a Gaussian beam gives the smallest beam divergence that is theoretically possible.

Example 3.3   Laser beam divergence

We may now calculate the beam divergence of the confocal laser cavity described in Example 3.2. There we calculated a value for w_0 of 2.2×10^{-4} m. Assuming that $\lambda = 633$ nm (i.e. the HeNe laser wavelength), then from Eq.(3.16a),

$$\theta = \sin^{-1}\left(\frac{633 \times 10^{-9}}{\pi \times 2.2 \times 10^{-4}}\right)$$
$$= 0.000\,916 \text{ rad}\quad\text{or}\quad 0.052^{\circ}.$$

Although most lasers exhibit low beam divergences there is one notable exception and that is the semiconductor laser. Here the laser cavity is very small and emission takes place from a rectangular area whose dimensions are the order of microns. For fairly wide active regions, beam divergences are in agreement with calculations assuming diffraction from a rectangular aperture, as illustrated in Example 3.4.

Example 3.4   Beam divergences in semiconductor lasers

We consider a GaAs laser ($\lambda = 900$ nm) whose active region has cross-sectional dimensions of 3 μm $\times$ 10 μm. Perpendicular to the plane of the junction we therefore have (using Eq. (3.7) with $K \approx 1$)

$$\theta_\perp \simeq \sin^{-1}\left(\frac{900 \times 10^{-9}}{3 \times 10^{-6}}\right) = 17^\circ,$$

while in the plane of the junction

$$\theta_\parallel \simeq \sin^{-1}\left(\frac{900 \times 10^{-9}}{10 \times 10^{-6}}\right) = 5.2^\circ.$$

In double heterostructure lasers, however, the active regions are very narrow, often having dimensions smaller than the laser wavelength. Obviously the formula $\theta \approx \sin^{-1}(\lambda/d)$ cannot be used when $d < \lambda$; in these circumstances an empirical expression which has been found to agree with experiment is

$$\theta_\perp = 1.1 \times 10^3 x(d/\lambda),$$

where x is the mole fraction of aluminum in the aluminum gallium arsenide side of the junction ($\text{Al}_x\text{Ga}_{1-x}\text{As}$). For example, taking the typical values $d = 0.1$ μm, $x = 0.3$ and $\lambda = 0.9$ μm gives $\theta_\perp \approx 37^\circ$. The occurrence of such relatively large beam divergences is one of the snags associated with using semiconductor lasers.

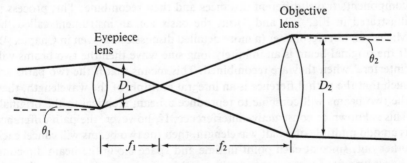

Fig. 3.7 Reduction in beam divergence using a reverse telescope arrangement. With eyepiece and objective lenses having diameters and focal lengths of D_1, f_1 and D_2, f_2 respectively, then the beam width is enlarged by the factor $D_2/D_1 = f_2/f_1$ and the divergence is decreased by the factor f_1/f_2.

Beam divergence may be reduced by passing the beam through a 'reverse telescope' lens arrangement as illustrated in Fig. 3.7. The beam diameter is enlarged by the factor f_2/f_1 and hence the divergence angle is decreased by f_1/f_2.

3.4   BEAM COHERENCE

One of the characteristics of stimulated emission is that the stimulated wave is in phase with the stimulating wave; that is, the spatial and temporal variation of the electric field of the two waves are the same. Thus in a 'perfect' laser we would expect the electric field to vary with time in an identical fashion for every point on the beam cross section. Such a beam would have perfect *spatial coherence*. Another related property is the *temporal coherence*, which refers to the relative phase relationship of the electric field at the same place as a function of time. If the phase changes uniformly with time then the beam is said to show perfect temporal coherence. These ideas are illustrated in Fig. 3.8.

Coherence is often specified in terms of the *mutual coherence function* $\gamma_{12}(\tau)$. This quantity, which is in fact a complex number, is a measure of the correlation between the light wave at two points P_1 and P_2 at different times t and $t + \tau$. It has an absolute value between 0 and 1. When it has the value zero the light is completely incoherent, while a value of unity implies complete coherence. Although these extreme values are never achieved in practice, the light from a gas laser operating in a single transverse mode has a value quite close to unity.

Two useful quantities that are related to temporal coherence are the coherence time and the coherence length. To understand these we consider what happens when we take a beam, split it into two equal parts, let the two components travel different distances and then recombine. This process is illustrated in Fig. 3.9, and forms the basis for an instrument called the Michelson interferometer (a more detailed discussion is given in Chapter 4). If the original beam is an infinitely long sine wave then the two beams will 'interfere' when they are recombined. This means that if the two paths are such that the path difference is an integral multiple of the wavelength, then the two beams will combine to reproduce a beam identical to the original. This is known as constructive interference. If, however, the path difference is an odd multiple of a half wavelength, then the two beams will cancel each other out, since at each point in time and space along the beam direction the electric field components of the two beams are equal and opposite and sum to zero. With a path difference part way between these values we obtain an intermediate resultant amplitude. However, 'real life' light beams cannot be represented by infinitely long sine waves. Disregarding lasers for a moment let us consider a group of atoms undergoing spontaneous emission.

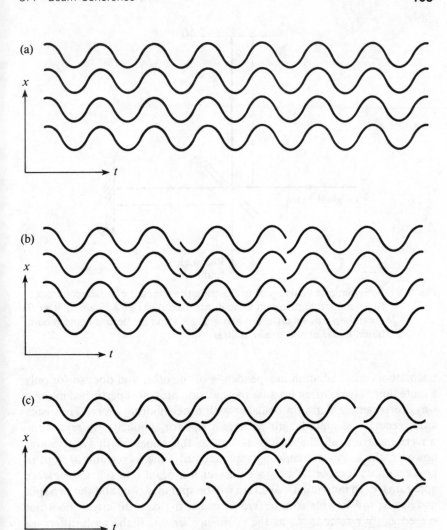

Fig. 3.8 An illustration of coherence. In (a) we show a perfectly coheren beam. All the constituent waves are in phase at all times. In (b) we have a beam which is spatially coherent, but which exhibits onl partial temporal coherence. This is because the waves simultaneousl change their phases by an identical amount every few oscillations. In (c) we show an almost completely incoherent beam where the phases of each wave change randomly at random times. Note however that even in this case some small degree of tempora coherence remains, since over very short time intervals the phase are to some extent predictable.

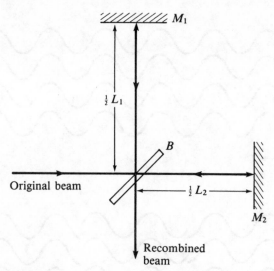

Fig. 3.9 Schematic optical layout to illustrate the concept of beam coherence. An incoming light beam is split into two parts at a beam splitter B, each then travels different distances (L_1 and L_2) before being recombined again at the beam splitter.

Each atom emits radiation independently of the other and does so for only a finite time. This is often because the emission process is perturbed in some way, for example during a collision with a neighboring atom. Thus each atom generates a finite-length wavetrain and for simplicity we regard the wavetrains from all the atoms as having the same length (L_c). Since, however, the atoms are emitting spontaneously, the wavetrains are not in phase with each other. If now we pass such a beam into our interference apparatus, each individual wavetrain will be split into two, and the two split wavetrains will be able to interfere *provided* the path difference does not exceed L_c. We refer to L_c as the *coherence length*. If the path difference does exceed L_c, then the two halves of each wavetrain cannot overlap in time when they are recombined, and hence they cannot interfere. In addition, when the path difference lies between zero and L_c, then only a part of each wavetrain can take part in interference (Fig. 3.10). This implies that as we increase the path difference from zero up to L_c then the irradiance fluctuations corresponding to constructive and destructive interferences will gradually diminish and die out altogether at L_c.

In reality of course, the wavetrains are not all the same length but are distributed in some way about a mean value. The conclusion that the irradiance fluctuations will gradually reduce, however, still remains valid. Similarly the exact definition of coherence length is somewhat more involved, but we may still take it to be the path difference at which the irradiance fluctuations die out.

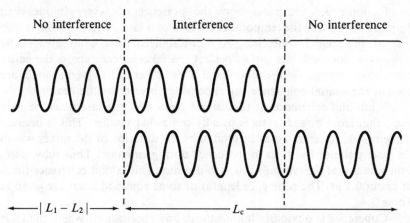

Fig. 3.10 When two identical wavetrains of length L_c which have traveled different distances (L_1 and L_2) are recombined they can only interfere over a length $L_c - |L_1 - L_2|$.

The *coherence time* t_c may then be defined as the time taken for the source to emit a wavetrain of length L_c. Thus:

$$t_c = L_c/c, \qquad (3.17)$$

where c is the velocity of light. In fact it can be shown [3.5] that the coherence time is related to the linewidth of the emission ($\Delta\nu$) via the equation

$$t_c = \frac{1}{\Delta\nu}. \qquad (3.18)$$

Although we started this discussion of coherence by considering spontaneous emission, the ideas of coherence length and coherence time apply equally well to laser radiation.

Example 3.5 Coherence lengths of conventional and laser radiation sources

We consider first of all the light emitted from a low-pressure sodium lamp. A typical linewidth of the sodium D lines (both lines taken together) at $\lambda = 589 \ \mu m$ is 5.1×10^{11} Hz. Equation (3.18) then gives $t_c = 2 \times 10^{-12}$ s and from Eq. (3.17), $L_c = 0.6$ mm. We may contrast these values with those applicable to an HeNe laser. If many modes are operating, then the linewidth is about 1500 MHz giving a coherence length of 0.2 m. However, if the laser is operating in a single mode stabilized to 1 MHz, then the coherence length is some 1500 times greater, i.e. 300 m.

Example 3.5 illustrates how the presence of several modes can dramatically reduce the temporal coherence of a laser, and the same is also true of the spatial coherence. A well-stabilized laser emitting a single transverse mode exhibits almost perfect spatial coherence across the entire beam cross section. On the other hand if a number of transverse modes are present the spatial coherence varies considerably across the beam.

While the coherence of the output from CW gas lasers can be very high, that from pulsed lasers is usually somewhat smaller. This is because the temporal coherence may be limited by the duration of the spikes within the laser pulse or by shifts in frequency during emission. Thus ruby lasers emit spikes that are typically 0.6 μs in duration and exhibit coherence times of about 0.1 μs. The coherence lengths of some common lasers are given in Table 3.1.

Coherence is obviously important in any applications where the laser beam is split into parts that traverse different distances. These include the interferometric measurement of distance and holography, which are dealt with in Section 4.2.1 and Chapter 6.

Table 3.1 Summary of coherence lengths of some common lasers

Laser	Typical coherence length
HeNe single transverse, single longitudinal mode	up to 1000 m
He-Ne multimode	0.1 to 0.2 m
Argon multimode	0.02 m
Nd : YAG	10^{-2} m
Nd : glass	2×10^{-4} m
GaAs	1×10^{-3} m
Ruby: for whole output pulse within a spike forming part of the pulse	10^{-2} m $\leqslant c$ times spike length, i.e. $\leqslant 30$ m

3.5 BRIGHTNESS

Brightness is defined as the power emitted per unit area per unit solid angle (the SI units of brightness are thus W m^{-2} sr^{-1}). Sometimes the term specific brightness is used and this is the brightness per unit wavelength range. We have seen in Section 3.3 that the divergence of laser beams is generally very small when compared to more conventional sources. Thus although similar amounts of optical power may be involved the small solid angle into which the laser beam is emitted ensures a correspondingly high brightness.

Example 3.6 Brightness of an HeNe laser

Consider an HeNe laser with an output of 3 mW and a beam divergence of 3×10^{-3} ° or 5.2×10^{-5} rad. This corresponds to a solid angle of $(\pi \times (5.2 \times 10^{-5})^2) = 8.5 \times 10^{-9}$ sr. We take the radius of the spot on the laser mirror to be 0.3 mm, which gives a spot area of $\pi(0.3 \times 10^{-3})^2$ m². Thus the brightness of the laser beam is given by

$$\frac{3 \times 10^{-3}}{(8.5 \times 10^{-9})(2.8 \times 10^{-7})} = 1.2 \times 10^{12} \, \text{W m}^{-2} \, \text{sr}^{-1}.$$

For comparison purposes the brightness of the sun is a mere 1.3×10^6 W m^{-2} sr^{-1}! Indeed values as high as 10^{21} W m^{-2}sr^{-1} have been achieved using an Nd : glass laser followed by optical amplifiers.

High brightness is essential for the delivery of high power per unit area to a target. In this context the size of the spot to which the beam can be focused is also important and this is dealt with in the next section.

3.6 FOCUSING PROPERTIES OF LASER RADIATION

We have seen that all laser beams possess a degree of divergence, even though in certain cases this may be extremely small. In Fig. 3.6 we showed the spreading of a Gaussian beam, where at comparatively large distances from the narrowest part of the beam (diameter $= 2w_0$) the beam diameter varies linearly with distance (Eq. 3.11b). A suitable focusing lens inserted into the diverging beam 'reverses' the situation, that is it produces a converging beam that is 'focused' at a distance nearly equal to f (the focal length of the lens) from the lens. Thus if w_L is the beam radius at the lens we may write, by analogy with Eq. 3.11b,

$$w_L = \frac{\lambda f}{\pi r_s},$$

in which r_s represents the focused beam radius. Hence

$$r_s = \frac{\lambda f}{\pi w_L}. \tag{3.19a}$$

If we assume that the light exactly fills the aperture of the lens, then $w_L = D/2$, where D is the lens diameter, and thus:

$$r_s = \frac{2}{\pi} \lambda \frac{f}{D} \qquad \text{or} \qquad r_s = \frac{2}{\pi} \lambda F, \tag{3.19b}$$

where $F(=f/D)$ is known as the *F number* of the lens. It is usually impracticable to work with *F* numbers that are much less than unity and so we may say that the minimum value of r_s is approximately equal to the wavelength of the radiation.

Example 3.7 Focused power densities of radiation

We consider a 1 mW HeNe laser (uniphase output) with a lens of F number 1. From Eq.(3.19b) the radius of the focused spot then equals $(2/\pi) \times 6.3 \times 10^{-7}$ m. Hence the power per unit area is equal to

$$\frac{1 \times 10^{-3} (\pi)^2}{\pi (2 \times 6.3 \times 10^{-7})^2} \; \mathrm{W\,m^{-2}} \quad \text{or} \quad 2 \times 10^9 \; \mathrm{W\,m^{-2}}.$$

Although the total power output of a laser is usually increased by allowing it to operate with a number of higher-order modes present, this does not necessarily mean that the focused power density is correspondingly higher. Indeed it is often less; this is because the focused beam pattern is similar to the mode patterns illustrated in Fig. 1.19 and hence cover a larger area than the uniphase mode.

3.7 Q-SWITCHING

Q-switching is a technique for obtaining short, intense bursts of radiation from lasers. It involves deliberately introducing a time-dependent loss into the cavity. With a high loss present the gain due to the population inversion can reach quite large values without laser action occurring. The high loss thus prevents laser action while energy is being pumped into the excited state of the medium. If, when a large population inversion has been achieved, the cavity loss is suddenly reduced, laser oscillations can then begin. The threshold gain is now much less than the actual gain, however, and this ensures a very rapid build-up of laser oscillations. All the available energy in fact is emitted in a single, large pulse. This quickly depopulates the upper lasing level to such an extent that the gain is reduced below threshold and lasing action stops. The time variation of some of the laser parameters during Q-switching is shown schematically in Fig. 3.11. Q-switching dramatically increases the peak power obtainable from lasers.

As we saw in Chapter 2, the output of an insulating crystal laser such as Nd:YAG when operated in the pulsed mode consists of many random 'spikes' of about 1 μs duration and with a separation of about 1 μs. The total length of the train of spikes depends principally on the duration of the exciting flashtube source, which may be about 1 ms. Peak powers within

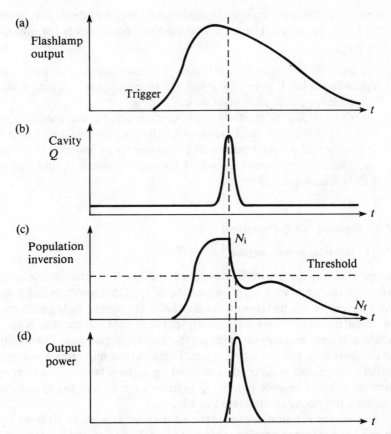

Fig. 3.11 Schematic representation of the variation of the parameters: (a) flashlamp output; (b) cavity Q; (c) population inversion; (d) output power as a function of time during the formation of a Q-switched laser pulse.

the 'spikes' are typically of the order of kilowatts. When the laser is Q-switched, however, the result is a single 'spike' of great power, usually in the megawatt range with a duration of 10–100 ns. It should be noted that, although there is a large increase in the peak power, the total energy emitted is less than in non-Q-switched operation due to losses associated with the Q-switching mechanism.

A word about the nomenclature: Q-switching refers to changing the Q *value* of the cavity. As we saw in Section 3.1, the Q value is inversely proportional to the energy dissipated per cycle (Eq. 3.3). In a high-loss situation therefore Q is small, while when the loss is removed Q 'switches' to higher values.

We may imagine Q-switching to be carried out by placing a closed shutter within the laser cavity, thereby isolating the cavity from the laser medium. After the laser has been pumped the shutter is opened, thus restoring the Q of the cavity. There are two obvious requirements for effective Q-switching:

(a) the pumping rate must be faster than the spontaneous decay rate of the upper lasing level, otherwise it will not be possible to build up a sufficiently large population inversion;

(b) the Q-switching mechanism must operate rapidly compared to the build-up of the laser oscillations, otherwise the latter will build up only gradually and a longer pulse will be obtained with lower peak power. In practical terms this means that ideally the switch should operate within a nanosecond or so.

3.7.1 Methods of Q-switching

3.7.1.1 Rotating-mirror method

This method was the first to be developed and involves rotating one of the cavity mirrors at a very high angular velocity. Obviously optical losses within the cavity will be large except for the brief interval during each rotation when the mirrors are very nearly parallel. Just before this point is reached a trigger mechanism initiates the flashlamp pumping (we assume that the laser is of the insulating crystal type). As the mirrors are not quite parallel the population inversion can build up without laser action starting. When the mirrors become parallel Q-switching occurs and the Q-switched pulse then develops, as illustrated in Fig. 3.11.

The mirror rotation speeds involved may be as high as 1000 rev s^{-1}, and this implies that the cavity could be Q-switched every 10^{-3} s. However, it is impossible to actually operate the laser with this interval between the pulses because of the excessive heating which would occur in the laser rod. Rotating-mirror type Q-switches are relatively cheap, reliable and fairly

---

Example 3.8 Switching speed of rotating mirror Q switch

We suppose we have a mirror rotating at 1000 rev s^{-1}, and that the mirrors must be aligned to within 1 minute of arc for lasing to take place. The time for the Q switch to operate may then be equated to the time taken for the mirror to rotate through 1 minute of arc. Since $360°$ or 360×60 minutes of arc takes a time of $1/1000$ s Q-switching will take place in $10^{-3}/360 \times 60$ or 4.6×10^{-8} s. As we remarked earlier, for the best results the switch should operate within a few nanoseconds, and this is appreciably slower than that.

---

rugged, but they are basically slow switching devices (see example 3.8), which results in lower peak powers than are possible with other methods.

3.7.1.2 *Electro-optic Q-switching*

There are several nonmechanical switching techniques that may be used, one of the most useful being based on the Pockels effect. This effect concerns the behavior of polarized light as it passes through certain *electro-optic* materials which are subject to electric fields. Thus if we take such a crystal and allow light which is plane polarized along a particular crystal direction to pass through it, then, provided a field of appropriate magnitude (say $\mathscr{E}_0$) is applied along the beam direction, the beam will emerge with its plane of polarization rotated through 90°. With no electric field applied, however, there is no rotation. If such a crystal is placed inside a laser cavity together with a polarizer as in Fig. 3.12, then the combination can be made to act as a shutter.

Consider light emerging from the lasing medium; it will pass through the polarizer and hence become plane polarized. It then traverses the electro-optic crystal twice before returning to the polarizer. If the plane of polarization of the beam has been rotated through 90°, however, it will

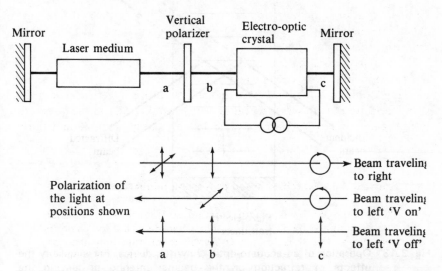

Fig. 3.12   Electro-optic crystal used as a Q switch. With the voltage *V* on, the electro-optic crystal acts as a λ/4 plate and converts the vertically polarized light at *b* into circularly polarized light at *c*. The reflected light is converted to horizontally polarized light and eliminated by the polarizer so that the cavity *Q* is low. With *V* off, the crystal is ineffective and the cavity *Q* is high.

be unable to pass through the polarizer and the shutter will be effectively closed. Since in fact two passes are made through the crystal we need only apply half the field referred to above (i.e. $\mathscr{E}_0/2$).† With no field applied the shutter is open. Hence by switching the field from $\mathscr{E}_0/2$ to zero at the appropriate time we can Q-switch the laser.

The voltages required to produce the appropriate fields are usually in the region of a few kilovolts and we must be able to switch them off in a time of the order of nanoseconds or less. This is not usually a problem.

3.7.1.3 Acousto-optic Q-switching

The acousto-optic effect is the change in the refractive index of a medium caused by the mechanical strains which accompany an acoustic wave as it travels through the medium. The strain, and hence the refractive index, will vary periodically with a wavelength equal to that of the acoustic wave. In effect the acoustic wave sets up a diffraction grating which can then be used to deflect a light beam. If light in the visible region is being used, then fused silica is a suitable medium. It should be noted that although we refer to an

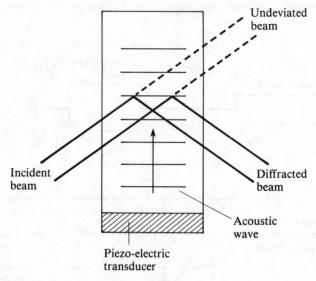

Fig. 3.13 Operation of an acousto-optic Q switch device. For simplicity the effects of refraction on the beams entering or leaving the transducer are ignored.

† It should not be taken that with $\mathscr{E}_0/2$ applied after one pass the emerging light has its polarization rotated through 45° – in fact *circularly polarized* light is produced. For a fuller description of the Pockels effect see Ref. 3.6.

acoustic wave the frequencies used in practice are ultrasonic (in the region of 50 MHz) and way above the limit of human hearing. In Fig. 3.13 we illustrate the mode of operation of an acousto-optic Q-switch. When the acoustic wave is present a significant fraction of the beam energy in the cavity is diffracted out of the cavity, thus introducing an additional loss mechanism and reducing the cavity Q value. When the acoustic wave is turned off diffraction ceases and the Q value returns to its former high level.

3.7.1.4 Passive Q-switching

Passive Q-switching relies on the action of so-called *saturable absorbers*, which are materials (often dye solutions) whose absorption decreases with increasing irradiance as shown in Fig. 3.14. The effect comes about because when we irradiate the solution dye molecules are excited from the ground to an excited state, thus reducing the ground-state population. Since the amount of absorption exhibited by the dye depends on the number of molecules in the ground state, increasing the total amount of irradiation must cause the overall absorption to fall. In most 'normal' materials under 'normal' irradiances the number of atoms or molecules in the excited state (compared to those in the ground state) is very small and absorption is practically independent of irradiance. In saturable absorbers, on the other hand, the molecules absorb radiation so strongly that appreciable numbers can be excited to the upper level, and significant changes made in the absorption of the dye. If the ground and excited state populations are almost equal, then the absorption becomes very small; in this case the dye is said to be 'bleached', or 'saturated'.

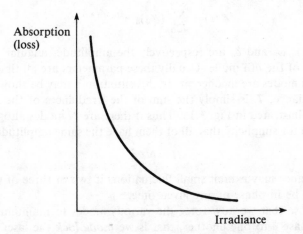

Fig. 3.14 Absorption as a function of incident light irradiance for a saturable absorber.

Consider now the effect of placing such a material within the cavity of a pulsed laser. (The dye must have an absorption band at the lasing transition frequency.) Initially, at low light levels, the dye is opaque, thereby preventing laser action and allowing a large build-up of population inversion. However, as the light irradiance builds up within the cavity more and more of the dye's excited states become populated and the dye begins to bleach. This is turn leads to an increase in irradiance and a further bleaching of the dye, and so on. In a very short time the dye can switch from being highly absorbing to being almost transparent, thus allowing the formation of a giant pulse.

Passive Q-switching has the great advantage of being extremely simple to implement, involving nothing more than the dye in a suitable solvent held in a transparent cell (although, as might be expected, the concentrations have to be chosen with some care). Suitable materials include cryptocyanine for ruby and sulfur hexafluoride for CO_2 lasers.

3.8 MODE LOCKING

Whereas in Q-switched pulsed lasers a single 'giant' optical pulse is produced during each pumping pulse, in a so-called mode-locked laser a train of extremely narrow, equally spaced (in time) pulses is produced. As we saw in Sections 1.10 and 3.1, a laser cavity may support many different modes oscillating simultaneously. The output of such a laser as a function of time depends on the relative phases, frequencies and amplitudes of the modes, and the total electric field as a function of time may be written as

$$\mathcal{E}(t) = \sum_{n=0}^{N-1} (\mathcal{E}_0)_n \, e^{i(\omega_n t + \delta_n)}, \tag{3.20}$$

where $(\mathcal{E}_0)_n, \omega_n$ and δ_n are respectively the amplitude, angular frequency and phase of the nth mode. Usually these parameters are all time varying, so that the modes are incoherent. In this situation it may be shown that the total irradiance, I, is simply the sum of the irradiances of the individual modes as illustrated in Fig. 3.15. Thus if there are N modes altogether and we assume for simplicity that all of them have the same amplitude $\mathcal{E}_0$, then

$$I = N\mathcal{E}_0^2. \tag{3.21}$$

The irradiance may exhibit small fluctuations if two or three of the modes happen to be in phase at any given time.

Suppose that we now force the various modes to maintain the same relative phase δ to one another, that is we *mode lock* the laser such that $\delta_n = \delta$. The total irradiance must now be found by first adding the individual electric fields. Using Eq. (3.20), the resultant electric field can now be

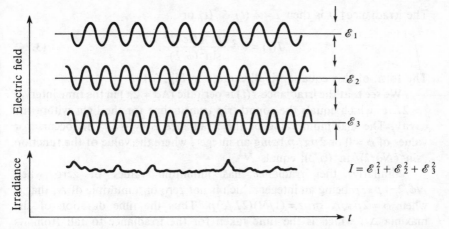

Fig. 3.15 The effect of adding together laser cavity modes whose phases are randomly related to each other. The resulting irradiance consists of small irregular fluctuations about a mean value.

written as

$$\mathscr{E}(t) = \mathscr{E}_0 \, e^{i\delta} \sum_{n=0}^{N-1} e^{i\omega_n t}. \qquad (3.22)$$

For convenience let us write the angular frequency ω_n as $\omega_n = \omega - n \, \Delta\omega$, where ω is the angular frequency of the highest frequency mode and $\Delta\omega$ is the angular frequency separation between modes, which from Eq. (1.27) we can write as

$$\Delta\omega = \pi \frac{c}{L}.$$

Equation (3.22) for $\mathscr{E}(t)$ can then be rewritten as

$$\mathscr{E}(t) = \mathscr{E}_0 \, e^{i\delta} \sum_{n=0}^{N-1} e^{i(\omega - n \, \Delta\omega)t}$$

$$= \mathscr{E}_0 \, e^{i(\omega t + \delta)} \sum_{n=0}^{N-1} e^{-\pi i nct/L}$$

or

$$\mathscr{E}(t) = \mathscr{E}_0 \, e^{i(\omega t + \delta)} (1 + e^{-i\phi} + e^{-2i\phi} + \cdots + e^{-(N-1)i\phi}). \qquad (3.23)$$

where $\phi = \pi ct/L$. The term in brackets in Eq. (3.23) is a geometric progression, and we can write

$$\mathscr{E}(t) = \mathscr{E}_0 \, e^{i(\omega t + \delta)} \frac{\sin(N\phi/2)}{\sin(\phi/2)}.$$

The irradiance† I is then $I = \mathscr{E}(t)\,\mathscr{E}^*(t)$ or

$$I(t) = \mathscr{E}_0^2\,\frac{\sin^2(N\phi/2)}{\sin^2(\phi/2)}. \tag{3.24}$$

The form of this equation is illustrated in Fig. 3.16.

We see that the irradiance $I(t)$ is periodic ($\Delta\phi = 2\pi$) in the time interval $t = 2L/c$. which equals the round trip transit time for the light within the cavity. The maximum value of the irradiance is $N^2\mathscr{E}_0^2$. This occurs for values of $\phi = 0$ or $2p\pi$, p being an integer, where the value of the function $|\sin^2(N\phi/2)/\sin^2(\phi/2)|$ equals N^2.

Similarly, the irradiance has minimum values of zero when $N\phi/2 = p\pi$, p being an integer which is not zero or a multiple of N, that is when $\phi = 2p\pi/N$ or $t = (1/N)(2L/c)p$. Thus the time duration of the maxima Δt, which is the time taken for the irradiance to fall from its

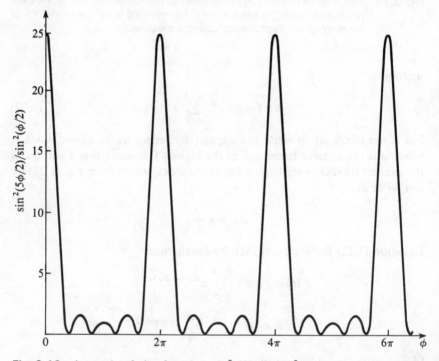

Fig. 3.16   A graph of the function $\sin^2(N\phi/2)/\sin^2(\phi/2)$ for N taking the value 5. Larger values give rise to higher narrower main peaks. Such plots represent the temporal variation in the output of a mode-locked laser with N oscillating modes.

† Strictly speaking, the irradiance is given by $(\mathscr{E}_v\mathscr{E}_r/\mu_r)^{1/2}\mathscr{E}(t)\,\mathscr{E}^*(t)$, but for simplicity we have ignored the constant multiplying factor throughout. (See, for example, Ref 1.1a, Section 19.5).

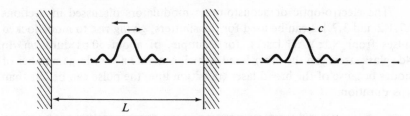

Fig. 3.17 Packet of energy resulting from the mode locking of N modes, bouncing to and fro between the laser mirrors. Each time the packet is incident on the output mirror a mode-locked pulse is emitted.

maximum value to an adjacent zero ($\Delta p = 1$), is $(1/N)(2L/c)$. We can see, therefore, that the output of a mode-locked laser consists of a sequence of short pulses, separated in time by $2L/c$, each of peak power equal to N times the average power (or N times the power of the same laser with the modes uncoupled). The ratio of the pulse spacing to the pulse width is approximately equal to the number of modes, that is $(2L/c)/|(2L/c)(1/N)| = N$. Thus to obtain high-power, short-duration pulses there should be a large number of modes; this depends on a broad laser transition and a long laser cavity.

The situation can be visualized as a short wave packet that bounces back and forth between the cavity mirrors; the pulses emitted by the laser appear each time the wave packet is partially transmitted by the output mirror, as indicated in Fig. 3.17. This physical picture is particularly useful when describing the active mode-locking mechanism used with argon ion and Nd : glass lasers.

3.8.1 Methods of mode locking

Mode locking is achieved by forcing the longitudinal modes to maintain fixed phase relationships. This can be accomplished by modulating the loss (or gain) of the laser cavity at a frequency equal to the intermode frequency separation $\Delta \nu = c/2L$ (or $\Delta \omega = \pi c/L$). Let us imagine that the loss modulation is provided by a shutter placed near to one of the mirrors. The shutter is closed (corresponding to very high losses) most of the time and is opened only very briefly every $2L/c$ seconds (corresponding to the cavity round trip time of the wave packet mentioned above). Now if the wave packet is exactly as long in time as the shutter stays open, and if it arrives exactly when the shutter is open, it will be unaffected by the presence of the shutter. Any parts of the wave packet, however, which arrive before the shutter opens or after it closes will be eliminated. Thus the phase relationships of the oscillating modes are continuously restored by the periodic operation of the shutter.

The electro-optic or acousto-optic modulators discussed in Sections 3.7.1.2 and 3.7.1.3 can be used for the shutters, giving rise to mode-locked pulses from Nd : YAG lasers, for example, of about 50 ps duration. In Nd : glass lasers, on the other hand, which generate a very large number of modes because of the broad laser transition line, the pulse can be less than 1 ps duration.

Example 3.9   Mode-locked pulses

Let us compare the pulse separation and pulse duration in a mode-locked Nd : YAG laser where the fluorescent linewidth is 1.1×10^{11} Hz and the laser rod is 0.1 m long. If we assume that the laser mirrors are very close to the ends of the rod, then the effective length of the laser cavity is nL, where n is the refractive index of the rod (1.82 for YAG). The longitudinal mode separation is $c/2nL = 8.2 \times 10^8$ Hz, thus the number of modes oscillating is $(1.1 \times 10^{11})/8.2 \times 10^8$) or about 133. The pulse separation is $2nL/c \simeq 1.3$ ns and the pulse duration $(1/N)(2nL/c) \simeq 10$ ps.

Mode locking may also be accomplished by using saturable absorbers. To appreciate how this takes place we suppose that the saturable absorber is placed up against one of the cavity mirrors. Initially the laser medium emits spontaneous radiation, which gives rise to random temporal fluctuations of the energy density. Some of these fluctuations, which can be of short duration, may be amplified by the laser medium and grow in irradiance to such an extent that the peak part of the fluctuation is transmitted by the saturable absorber with little attenuation. The low power parts of the fluctuation, however, are much more strongly attenuated and thus a high-power pulse can grow within the cavity providing the dye can recover in a time short compared with the duration of the pulse. Because of the nonlinear behavior of the dye the shortest and most intense fluctuations grow at the expense of the weaker ones. With careful adjustment of the concentration of the dye within the cavity an initial fluctuation may grow into a narrow pulse 'bouncing' to and fro within the cavity, producing a periodic train of mode-locked pulses.

Saturable absorbers provide a particularly simple method of mode locking high-power lasers such as Nd : glass and ruby; the so-called 9740 or 9860 dye solutions and cryptocyanine may be used as the saturable absorber for Nd : glass and ruby respectively. When a saturable absorber is used to mode lock a laser, then the laser is simultaneously Q-switched. The result is the production of a series of narrow ($\simeq 10$ ps), mode-locked pulses contained within an envelope which may be several hundred nanoseconds long. The peak power within the individual pulses may be enormous because of their very short duration.

3.9 FREQUENCY DOUBLING

Frequency-doubling materials are extremely useful since, as their name implies, they enable the frequency of a laser beam to be doubled (that is the wavelength halved). Thus the output of the Nd : YAG laser at 1.06 μm can be frequency doubled so that 0.53 μm radiation is obtained. The resulting radiation is still coherent, that is it still behaves exactly like laser radiation. Frequency doubling occurs only in those materials which have a nonlinear response to an electric field. To understand what we mean by this we must consider the net movement of charge within a solid when an external electric field is applied. The electrons bound to an atom, being negatively charged, are pulled in one direction while the atomic nuclei, being positively charged, are pulled in the opposite direction. The net result is a charge separation or electrical polarization of the material (see Fig. 3.18). The electrical polarization is in fact defined as the dipole moment per unit volume (the dipole moment being given by (charge) × (separation)). For most 'normal' materials and for relatively small applied fields the polarization (P) is linearly dependent on the applied field ($\mathscr{E}$). For non-linear materials, however, this is not the case; a graph of P versus $\mathscr{E}$ for such materials is shown in Fig. 3.19.

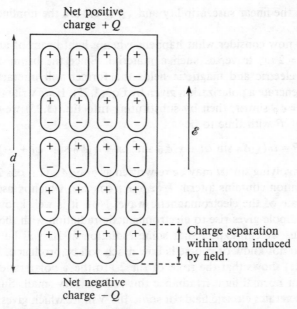

Fig. 3.18 The effect of an external electric field on an electrically polarizable medium. Charge separation occurs, resulting in a dipole moment of Qd. The induced polarization is the dipole moment per unit volume.

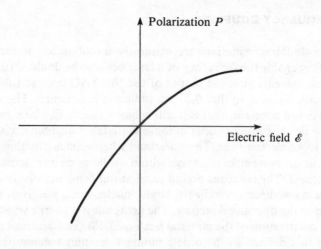

Fig. 3.19 Curve showing electrical polarization versus electric field for a nonlinear material.

In general we may write

$$P = \varepsilon_0(\chi_1 \mathscr{E} + \chi_2 \mathscr{E}^2 + \chi_3 \mathscr{E}^3 + \cdots) \qquad (3.25)$$

where χ_1 is the linear susceptibility and χ_2, χ_3 etc are the nonlinear optical coefficients.

Let us now consider what happens when a light beam of angular frequency $\omega(= 2\pi\nu)$ traverses such a material. Since the beam consists of oscillating electric and magnetic fields the former will interact with the crystal to generate a polarization given by Eq. (3.25). If we write this electric field as $\mathscr{E} = \mathscr{E}_0 \sin \omega t$, then by substituting into Eq. (3.25) we obtain the variation of P with time to be

$$P = \varepsilon_0(\chi_1 \mathscr{E}_0 \sin \omega t + \chi_2 \mathscr{E}_0^2 \sin^2 \omega t + \chi_3 \mathscr{E}_0^3 \sin^3 \omega t + \cdots)$$

The term involving $\sin^2 \omega t$ may be re-written as $\frac{1}{2}\varepsilon_0\chi_2\mathscr{E}_0^2 (1 - \cos 2\omega t)$. Thus the polarization contains a term $-\frac{1}{2}\varepsilon_0\chi_2\mathscr{E}_0^2 \cos 2\omega t$, which is oscillating at *twice* the rate of the electromagnetic wave. Now it is well known that an oscillating dipole gives rise to electromagnetic radiation with the same frequency; thus we can expect that some radiation at 2ω will be produced. What we do not know of course is how much will be produced. Inspection of Eq. (3.25) shows that the ratio of the 2ω to the ω polarization terms is $\chi_2\mathscr{E}_0/\chi_1$. For normal light irradiance this ratio is very small. Sunlight, for example, generates electric fields of some 100 V m^{-1}, which gives values for the above ratio of about 10^{-4}. For the ratio to equal unity we require fields of 10^6 V m^{-1}, which implies power densities of 10^9 W m^{-2}. Values as high as these were not available until the advent of the laser.

Frequency doubling or second-harmonic generation was first observed in 1961 by Franken *et al.* [3.7] who focused the 694.3 nm line from a ruby laser onto a quartz crystal and observed a very low-intensity output at a wavelength of 347.15 nm. The conversion efficiency from the lower to the higher frequency was typically 10^{-6}–10^{-4}%. The reason for these low conversion efficiencies is not just low laser power but is tied up with the optical properties of the material. In general the materials are dispersive, that is the refractive index (and hence speed of light) depends on the wavelength. The frequency-doubled light therefore travels at a different speed from that of the fundamental. As the latter is continuously generating the former on its passage through the crystal the frequency doubled light cannot then remain exactly in phase with itself. If the phase differences are sufficiently large, different parts of the frequency-doubled beam may get completely out of phase and cause destructive interference. A detailed analysis shows that the irradiance of the frequency-doubled beam undergoes fluctuations as a function of distance through the crystal with a periodicity of only a few microns or so.

Fortunately the problem can be overcome by a technique known as *index* or *phase* matching [3.8]. Thus it is usually possible to choose a direction in the crystal such that the velocity of the fundamental is the same as that of the second harmonic. The difficulty is to ensure that the beam travels *exactly* along this direction. Any deviation means that the two beams cannot remain in phase indefinitely. Good temperature stability is also often required since the refractive indices are temperature dependent. It is usually possible to maintain a near equality in the velocities over distances of some tens of mm or so. This enables the conversion efficiency to reach values as high as 50%. Typical materials used for frequency doubling include KDP (potassium dihydrogen phosphate, KH_2PO_4), KD^*P (basically KDP with the hydrogen replaced by deuterium) and lithium niobate ($LiNbO_3$).

3.10 PHASE CONJUGATION

In many instances it is highly desirable that a laser can be operated in a single longitudinal TEM_{00} mode with a Gaussian beam profile. In practice it is difficult to achieve this goal with many lasers. In flashlamp pumped doped insulator lasers, for example, appreciable radial temperature gradients can be set up within the laser rod, which give rise to a number of undesirable effects. Thermally induced stresses and thermal birefringence can both lead to depolarization of the radiation. In addition the thermal gradients can cause refractive index gradients in the rod which to a first approximation make it behave like a positive lens, this is known as *thermal lensing*. This in turn distorts the beam and can cause 'hot spots' to appear within the rod. In high-powered lasers such hot spots can lead to physical damage of the rod and thus limit the maximum output power obtainable.

The traditional approach to the problem of thermal lensing has been to use a compensating negative lens within the cavity with the same power as that induced in the rod. This certainly works but can only be completely effective under a fixed set of operating conditions. More complicated variable-power lens systems under microprocessor control are possible, but obviously add greatly to the complexity and cost of the system. It is also difficult to imagine such a system being able to respond to any very rapid changes in operating conditions.

A possible solution to these problems lies in the use of *phase-conjugate* mirrors. When a light beam is reflected from such a mirror it gives rise to what is known as a phase-conjugate beam. To understand what this is we consider a monochromatic beam propagating along the z axis, where the amplitude is given by

$$\mathscr{E}(x, y, z, t) = A(x, y)\cos(\omega t - kz + \phi(x, y)). \qquad (3.26)$$

If both the amplitude term $A(x, y)$ and the phase term $\phi(x, y)$ are independent of x and y, then this equation represents a plane wave traveling along the positive z direction. The amplitude term allows for a variation of field in the x, y plane and the term $\phi(x, y)$ indicates how far the phase departs from that of a plane wave. The phase-conjugate beam to that given by Eq. (3.26) is then defined to be

$$\mathscr{E}^c(x, y, z, t) = A(x, y)\cos(\omega t + kz - \phi(x, y)). \qquad (3.27)$$

We may obtain a feel for what such a beam looks like by noting that Eq. (3.27) may be obtained from Eq. (3.26) by replacing t by $-t$. For this reason another name sometimes given to a phase-conjugate beam is a *time-reversed* beam. As far as the variation of electric field with x and y is concerned, the two beams are identical, but of course the phase-conjugate beam is traveling in the opposite direction. In Fig. 3.20 (a and b) we show the waveform resulting when an initially plane wave passes through a phase-distorting medium, is reflected from a phase-conjugate mirror, and then repasses through the distorting medium. We see that the beam regains its original form. We may contrast this with the behavior of an ordinary mirror, Fig. 3.20(c), when the phase distortion is effectively doubled after two passes through the distorting medium.

Thus if we have a laser cavity where one of the mirrors is a phase-conjugate mirror (Fig. 3.21) then any distortion introduced by the laser medium can, in principle, be compensated for completely. Furthermore, the compensation is applied very rapidly, the limiting factor being the time it takes the beam to make a double transit through the distorting medium. Another interesting feature that arises is that the cavity is stable regardless of either the radius of curvature of the output mirror or the cavity length.

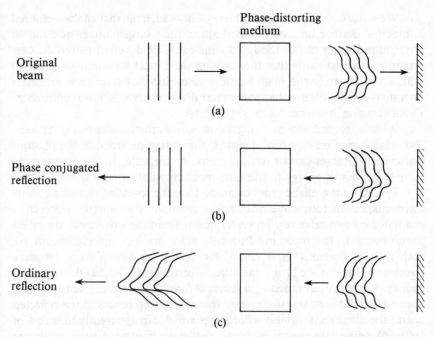

Fig. 3.20 Illustration of the behavior of a phase conjugate mirror. In (a) an originally plane wave suffers phase distortion after passing through a distorting medium. If this distorted beam is reflected from a phase conjugate mirror then, after re-passing through the distorting medium, as in (b), a plane wave is re-generated. In contrast, if reflection is from an ordinary mirror, as in (c), then the phase distortion is effectively doubled.

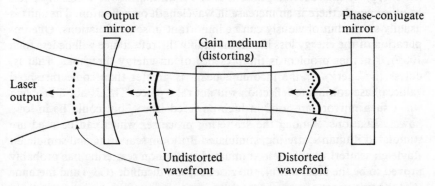

Fig. 3.21 Laser cavity incorporating a phase conjugate mirror, giving rise to an undistorted output beam.

We must now turn to the problem of how such mirrors can be achieved in practice. Rather surprisingly, perhaps, quite a large number of different physical processes can be used in a wide range of different materials. One essential requirement is that the medium used must be *nonlinear* (Section 3.9). Unfortunately the mathematical description of how such processes operate is not possible in the space at our disposal here. A more comprehensive discussion is contained in Ref. 3.9.

We may regard phase-conjugate mirrors as photon-scattering devices. Two main types may be distinguished, depending on whether the photon-scattering processes can be termed elastic or inelastic. In the former type there is no loss of energy to the laser medium, whilst in the latter there is.

Typical of the elastic types of process are the so-called three- and four-wave mixing. In four-wave mixing, for example, the 'mirror' material is irradiated by two relatively powerful beams from the side (these are called *pump beams*). The incoming ('probe') beam and the reflected beam are both relatively weak (Fig. 3.22). If the two pump beams have the same frequency as the probe beam, then the reflected beam also has the same frequency (hence the term used – *degenerate four-wave mixing*). Since it turns out to be possible to transfer energy from the pump beams to the reflected beam, the mirror can exhibit reflectances which are apparently in excess of 100%. Amongst the mirror materials that have been used successfully are SF_6 (at 10.6 μm), Si (at 1.06 μm), CdS (at 694 nm) and $BaTiO_3$ (at 632.8 nm). Although such mirrors have some very useful properties, the necessity for two pump beams makes it rather unlikely that they will ever be used as laser mirrors in high-power laser systems. However, they may very well find a place in image processing and holography systems.

The other type of mirror, which relies on inelastic photon-scattering processes, involves no other beams apart from the incoming and reflected ones. There are, however, some penalties for this simplicity. Firstly, all the processes involve some form of energy loss to the solid and consequently the energy of the reflected photons is less than that of the incoming ones. In other words there is an increase in wavelength on reflection. The shift is usually small, but obviously can be important in some situations. One implication of the energy loss is that inevitably the reflectance will be less than 100%. Another problem is the presence of an energy threshold. That is, unless the energy of the incoming beam is greater than some threshold value, phase-conjugate reflection will not take place. This is not a problem when such mirrors are used in high-powered lasers, but could be in low-power situations. Among the scattering processes which can be used are stimulated Raman scattering, stimulated Brillouin scattering and stimulated Rayleigh scattering. Of these stimulated Brillouion scattering has probably proved to be the most useful, the gases carbon disulfide (CS_2) and methane (CH_4) being most often used as the mirror media. The gas is usually held under pressure in a suitable cell. For example at a wavelength of 1.06 μm

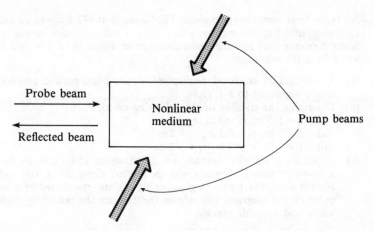

Fig. 3.22 Schematic diagram of a phase conjugate mirror using four-wave mixing.

(i.e. in a Nd : YAG laser) and with a beam irradiance of 10^{13} W m^{-2}, mirror reflectances of 80% have been obtained using methane at a pressure of 9×10^6 Pa. The relatively high beam irradiances required may be obtained by focusing the laser beam onto the gas cell with a lens. Several recent experiments [3.10] have confirmed the potential of these techniques in compensating for distortions in the outputs of high-power solid-state lasers.

PROBLEMS

3.1 A HeNe laser has a mirror separation of 0.5 m. Given that the width of the gain curve is 1500 MHz, estimate the maximum number of mode frequencies possible in (a) a confocal cavity ($r_1 = r_2 = L$) and (b) a cavity where $r_1 = r_2 = 2L$.

3.2 Estimate the linewidth of a single-mode HeNe laser where the cavity length is 1 m and where the mirror reflectances are 0.99 and 0.96.

3.3 A HeNe laser operating on a single TEM$_{00}$ mode has a meter long cavity based on aluminum. Estimate the frequency drift resulting from a 0.5°C change in ambient temperature. Take the thermal expansion coefficient of aluminum to be 2.5×10^{-5} K^{-1}.

3.4 Show that if the irradiance of a Gaussian beam is written $I = I_0 \exp(-2r^2/w^2)$, where r is measured from the center of the beam, then the total amount of power carried by the beam is $I_0 w^2/2$. A 100 W CO$_2$ CW laser operating in a single TEM$_{00}$ mode is focused down to a spot where the beam radius (i.e. w) is 0.5 mm. Calculate the irradiance at the center of the spot.

3.5   An HeNe laser operating in a single TEM_{00} mode at 632.8 nm has a mirror separation of 0.5 m with mirrors where $r_1 = r_2 = 1$ m, calculate the minimum beam diameter (w_0) and the beam diameter at distances of 1 m and 10 m away from the minimum.

3.6   (a) Verify that the confocal, hemispherical, and plane parallel cavities are stable according to Eq. (3.9).
   (b) Determine the stability of the following cavities:
   (i) $L = 1.5$ m, $r_1 = 3$ m, $r_2 = 2$ m
   (ii) $L = 1$ m, $r_1 = 0.5$ m, $r_2 = 2$ m
   (iii) $L = 1$ m, $r_1 = 3$ m, $r_2 = -2$ m.
   (c) Construct a 'stability diagram' for the situations of (a) and (b). This is a two-dimensional diagram with g_1 plotted along the x axis and g_2 plotted along the y axis. A given cavity is thus represented by a single point on the diagram. Indicate on the diagram the boundary between stable and unstable regions.

3.7   Given that the red cadmium line, of wavelength 643.8 nm, has a width of 0.3 nm, estimate the coherence length.

3.8   Given that the halfwidth of the 10.6 μm transition of a low-pressure CO_2 laser is 60 MHz, calculate the coherence length of the laser. Show that, if the cavity length is 1 m, then not more than one longitudinal mode will oscillate.
   Given that the mirror reflectances are 1 and 0.95, calculate the Q value of the cavity and use this to estimate the expected maximum coherence length. Why do these two results differ?

3.9   A Q-switched Nd:YAG laser ($\lambda = 1.06 \mu$m) emits pulses of energy 10 J. Estimate how many more Nd ions need to be in the initial lasing state than in the final lasing state just prior to each pulse (assume that each ion in the upper state emits only once during the duration of the pulse).

3.10 Plot the irradiance versus time relationship expected from Eq. (3.24) for 2, 3 etc. mode-locked pulses. You may find it useful to write a short computer program to do this. Show that as the number of mode-locked pulses increases the main pulses become narrower and more intense.

3.11 Calculate the pulse width expected from a mode-locked Nd:Glass laser, assuming that the laser cavity is 0.5 m long, the laser rod is 0.2 m long and that there are 3000 participating longitudinal modes. Calculate also the separation between pulses and the coherence time and coherence length of the pulses. Take the refractive index of the rod to be 1.52.

REFERENCES

3.1   J. T. Verdeyen, *Laser Electronics,* Prentice-Hall, Englewood Cliffs, N.J., 1981, Section 6.4.
3.2   M. Born and E. Wolf, *Principles of Optics,* Pergamon Press, Oxford (6th edn), 1980, Section 8.5.2.
3.3   A. Yariv, *Optical Electronics* (3rd edn), Holt, Rinehart and Winston, New York, 1985 Sections 2.1, 2.7 and 4.4.

3.4 J. T. Verdeyen, *Laser Electronics,* Prentice-Hall, Englewood Cliffs, N.J., 1981, Section 5.1.

3.5 A. Yariv, *Optical Electronics* (3rd edn), Holt, Rinehart and Winston, New York, 1985, Sections 10.7 & 10.8.

3.6 J. Wilson and J. F. B. Hawkes, *Optoelectronics: An Introduction,* Prentice-Hall International, London, 1983, Section 3.4.

3.7 P. A. Franken, A. E. Hill, C. W. Peters and G. Weinreich, 'Generation of Optical Harmonics', *Phys. Rev. Letters,* **7**, 118–119, 1961.

3.8 J. Wilson and J. F. B. Hawkes, *Optoelectronics: An Introduction,* Prentice-Hall International, London, 1983, Section 3.9.

3.9 D. M. Pepper, 'Nonlinear Optical Phase Conjugation', *Opt. Eng.,* **21**, 156–183, 1982.

3.10 D. A. Rockwell and C. R. Giuliano, 'Coherent Coupling of Laser Gain Media Using Phase Conjugation', *Opt. Lett.,* **11**, 147–149, 1986.

Additional information on the topics covered in this chapter may be obtained from the following:

G. H. C. New, 'The Generation of Ultrashort Laser Pulses', *Rep. Prog. Phys.,* **46**, 877–971, 1983.

O. Svelto, *Principles of Lasers* (2nd edn), Plenum, New York, 1982.

P. W. Smith, M. A. Duguay and E. P. Ippen, 'Mode Locking of Lasers', *Progress in Quantum Electronics*, **3**, 109–229, 1974.

K. Thyagarajan and A. K. Ghatak, *Lasers: Theory and Applications,* Plenum, New York, 1981.

J. T. Verdeyen, *Laser Electronics*, Prentice-Hall, Englewood Cliffs, N.J., 1981.

A. Yariv, *Optical Electronics* (3rd edn), Holt, Rinehart and Winston, New York, 1985.

A. Yariv and J. E. Pearson, 'Parametric Processes', *Progress in Quantum Electronics*, **1**, 1–49, 1969.

4

Metrological and Scientific
Applications

Optical methods of measuring such parameters as distance, alignment, angle and flatness have been used for many years in industrial metrology and surveying. Their use prior to the advent of lasers was restricted, however, by the light sources available, to telescopic methods of alignment, precise comparison of nearly equal optical path lengths and the measurement of longer distances not exceeding a few kilometers.

The introduction of lasers, especially visible wavelength gas lasers, has dramatically increased the scope of optical metrology and often greatly simplified its use. Thus, for example, as the beams from such lasers are highly collimated because of their spatial coherence (see Section 3.4), alignment can be carried out simply by pointing the beam in the direction of interest. Similarly the temporal coherence of gas laser radiation and its brightness enables interferometric measurements to be made over much longer distances and in normal lighting conditions.

Apart from the measurement of small and large distances and alignment, lasers are now used routinely for a large number of metrological measurements, including the measurement of the velocity of solid objects and fluid flows, rotation, geometrical and mechanical parameters, deformation, vibration, strain and surface roughness. The narrow linewidth and tunability of laser radiation has also had considerable impact on spectroscopic measurements, so that atomic and molecular energy level structures can be investigated with a much improved accuracy.

4.1 OPTICAL ALIGNMENT

Perhaps the simplest applications of lasers such as the HeNe laser is in producing a visible line which can be used for positioning an object, surveying, guidance of equipment in construction or for aiming other lasers or optical instruments. The use of a beam of light for alignment, often called optical tooling, has many advantages compared to mechanical alignment methods which are slow, cumbersome and often require more than one operator. Optical tooling has developed since the advent of the laser so that as well as alignment, tasks such as angular alignment, definition of planes, leveling and fixing of right angles can be readily performed.

The brightness of a 1–5 mW HeNe laser is sufficient as the beam is easily visible in an ambient background of workshop lighting or daylight up to distances of several hundred meters from the laser. For such lasers operating in the TEM_{00} mode the intensity profile remains Gaussian at all distances from the laser and the beam divergence angle θ is thus (see Eq. (3.16b)), $\theta = \lambda/\pi w_0$, where w_0 is the minimum beam radius within the laser cavity. In practice we may take $w_0 \simeq a$, where a is the radius of the exit aperture of the beam. This defines the half angle of the cone into which the light beam diverges far from the laser. For a HeNe laser the beam has a diameter of about 1 mm at the exit mirror, so the corresponding divergence angle is $\theta \simeq 10^{-3}$ rad or $0.06°$ (see Example 3.3).

The accuracy of laser alignment is limited by the angular divergence of the beam, and, as we saw in Section 3.3, the divergence can be reduced by expanding the beam.

Example 4.1 Accuracy of optical alignment

Let us suppose that it is required to align an object to an accuracy of 1 mm at a distance of 10 m using an HeNe laser. We need to calculate the corresponding beam divergence angle and degree of beam expansion required.

1 mm in 10 m corresponds to an angle of 10^{-4} radian. To reduce the beam divergence to this figure the beam diameter must be expanded to a value of

$$\frac{2 \times 2 \times 632.8 \times 10^{-9}}{\pi \times 10^{-4}} \simeq 8.1 \times 10^{-3} \text{ m}$$

Thus a beam of 1 mm diameter needs to be expanded by a factor of about eight.

The utility of optical 'straight edges' is obvious. They are used for defining straight lines for surveying and civil engineering projects such as pipeline construction and those involving the guidance of machinery for laying drainage pipes and boring tunnels. Other alignment functions include the assembly of large structures such as aircraft and ships, the erection of buildings and the alignment of high-power lasers used for cutting, drilling and welding, as these usually have outputs in the infra red.

Silicon
photodiodes

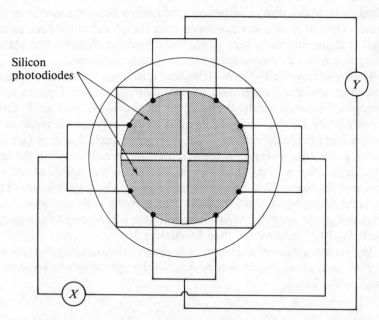

Fig. 4.1   A typical quantrant detector. The area of each of the four
photodiodes may be of the order of 20 mm² and their separation
may be of the order of 0.1 mm. The magnitudes and signs of the X
and Y signals enables the position of the laser spot to be determined.

Very accurate settings in the direction of alignment can be obtained
using a quadrant detector as illustrated in Fig. 4.1; if necessary feedback
loops can be incorporated to maintain the alignment. Commercial instruments can give an angular precision of better than 1 μrad. Expressed
another way it is possible to measure displacements on a quadrant detector
attached to a workpiece as far away as 100 m to better than 0.025 mm.
This kind of alignment system has been used to monitor the movement of
large structures such as dams. A laser beam is aimed along the top of the
dam at a reference target and is split by beam-splitting mirrors along the
way so that portions of the beam are reflected to nearby detectors to monitor
any movement.

By rotating the laser beam using, for example, a rotating pentaprism,
a plane may be defined; some manufacturers market laser levels which, providing they are initially set within about 5° of level, adjust themselves
automatically to define a level plane some 500 m in diameter for construction work. A pentaprism deviates the beam by 90° irrespective of the precise
orientation of the prism and may thus be used to establish a 90° angle.

4.2 MEASUREMENT OF DISTANCE

Short to intermediate distances can be measured with great accuracy using interferometric techniques, while for larger distances beam-modulation telemetry or time-of-flight methods may be used.

4.2.1 Interferometry

The classical method of measuring distance and small displacements is the Michelson interferometer (see also Section 3.4), which was designed in 1882 to detect possible changes in the speed of light in different directions relative to the earth's motion through space. Variants of the basic instrument, which is shown in Fig. 4.2, are used to measure surface flatness and to test optical components. In interferometric techniques distance is measured in terms of the wavelength of the light used.† Accuracies of a tenth of a wavelength are quite easily achieved while, with the aid of modern electronic and computing techniques, resolutions of $\lambda/100$ can be obtained in analyzing test surfaces.

In the Michelson interferometer (Fig. 4.2) light from an extended monochromatic source is made roughly parallel by the lens L_1. The light then falls on a semi-reflecting mirror (or beam splitter) M so that some of the light passes through M and is reflected first by M_2 and then by M so as to enter the telescope T. The rest of the light is reflected at the rear face of M, then by M_1, from where it passes through M to the telescope. The two beams of light entering the telescope are coherent if the path difference is less than the coherence length (Section 3.4) and interference fringes can then be seen through the telescope. The compensator plate C, which is a plate of glass of identical thickness to M, is often included to ensure that the two *arms* of the interferometer can be made *optically equal*. That is, the two beams have the same path length in glass, so that dispersion occurs equally in both arms.

We may regard the fringes as being formed by the thin film of air formed between M_1 and M_2', which is the reflection of M_2 in M. Thus if M_1 and M_2' are exactly parallel (that is, M_1 and M_2 are perpendicular to each other) a system of circular fringes of equal inclination is formed according

---

† It is perhaps noteworthy that in October 1983 the basis of length measurement underwent a major revision – the meter was redefined. It is now based on the speed of light as a fixed constant and uses lasers as reference standards of frequency and wavelength. The meter is now taken as the length of the path traveled by light in vacuum during a time interval of $(299\ 792\ 458)^{-1}$ s.

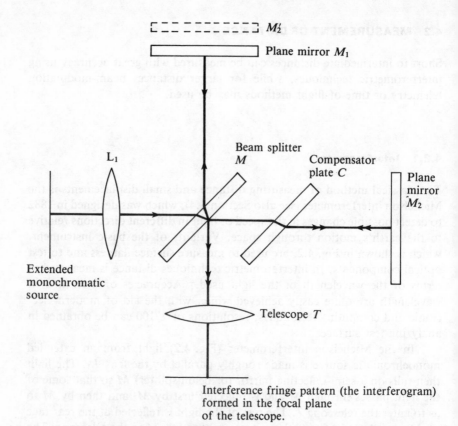

Interference fringe pattern (the interferogram) formed in the focal plane of the telescope.

Fig. 4.2   The Michelson interferometer. Mirror M_1 is fixed while mirror M_2 can move along the direction MM_2. Interference fringes appear to form in the parallel-sided air film between M_1 and M_2' which is the image of M_2 in the beam splitter M. The extended source can be replaced by a laser and beam expander.

to

$$p\lambda = 2D \cos \theta, \qquad (4.1)$$

where p is an integer, θ is the angle of reflection within the thin film ($\theta \simeq 0$) and D is the separation of M_1 and M_2' (see Problem 4.1). If, however, one of the mirrors is inclined at a small angle to the axis of the arm, then straight-line fringes of equal thickness are formed.

One of the mirrors, say M_2, is free to move along the axis of the arm, whilst remaining perpendicular to it. If M_2 is moved, then the optical path (and hence the phase) of the light reflected from it will change relative to that reflected from M_1 and the interference pattern will cross the field of view. That is, D changes, so that if θ is constant p will change by one each time D changes by $\lambda/2$ a fringe will pass a reference point in the fringe system (assuming that incidence is nearly normal, so that $\theta \simeq 0$).

Example 4.2   Fringe shift corresponding to a mirror movement D

Suppose the mirror M_2 moves 0.1 m, how many fringes of 632.8 nm HeNe laser radiation will cross a reference point in the field of view? From Eq. (4.1), assuming $\theta \simeq 0$, then

$$\delta p = \frac{2\,\delta D}{\lambda} = \frac{2 \times 0.1}{632.8 \times 10^{-9}} = 3.16 \times 10^5 \text{ fringes.}$$

Using laser sources such large mirror displacements are quite conceivable though the fringe shift must be counted electronically.

We can therefore measure the distance moved by M_2 in terms of fringe shifts. To measure an unknown distance, M_2 is aligned with one end (using a microscope for example) and the fringe shift counted as M_2 is moved until it coincides with the other end of the distance being measured.

Prior to the advent of the lasers such measurements were limited by the coherence length of available light sources. Michelson, using the 643.8 nm red line of cadmium was able to measure distances of only a few millimeters. A well-designed single-frequency HeNe laser can give acceptable fringes at very much greater distances. The practical limits are set by the difficulty of avoiding vibrations and atmospheric disturbances rather than by the coherence length of the laser. The distance measured is, of course, an optical path length. That is, it is the geometrical path multiplied by the refractive index of air, which changes due to pressure and temperature fluctuations. These fluctuations result in random fringe shifts, which limit the accuracy obtainable to about 1 part in 10^6.

The long coherence length, which permits direct fringe counting while M_2 traverses long distances, also causes problems. Firstly undesirable reflections from other surfaces, for example the air–glass interface at the front of the beam splitter, give rise to spurious interference patterns. Laser interferometers are thus designed with a minimum number of surfaces and, where possible, optical elements are thick and wedge shaped so that spurious beams are thrown to the side and do not reach the detector. Secondly, the laser is a resonant structure and any light reflected back from the interferometer into the laser may modulate the laser output wavelength and amplitude. In general these parameters then become unstable and vary with the position and alignment of the moving mirror M_2. The laser can be isolated from such reflections, though a better solution is to use a design in which no light is reflected back into the laser.

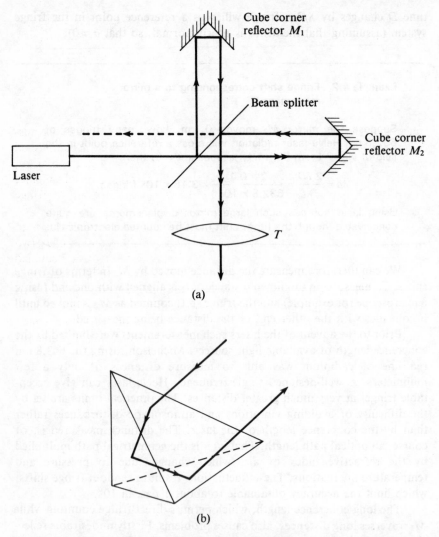

Fig. 4.3 (a) A simplified diagram of the Michelson interferometer showing
how the use of cube corner reflectors displaces the returning beams
so that they cannot re-enter the laser cavity. (b) Schematic diagram
of a cube corner retroreflector. The incident light reflects once off
each side face and emerges along a path parallel (to within a few arc
seconds) to that of the incident light.

One way of achieving this is to replace the plane mirrors M_1, M_2 with
cube corner reflectors as shown in Fig. 4.3(a) and (b). Cube corners have
the property of reflecting an incident beam back along a direction parallel
to its incident path but displaced from it. An added advantage of cube cor-

ner reflectors is that they simplify alignment of the interferometers as two angular degrees of freedom of each mirror are replaced by two lateral ones.

4.2.1.1 *Reversible counting*

A practical instrument must be capable of reversible fringe counting so that measurements can be made with mirror M_2 moving both away from and towards the beam splitter and, more important, so that no fringes are mis-counted in the presence of vibrations. In principle this can be accomplished by obtaining two signals from the interferometer that are in quadrature, that is, one varying sinusoidally while the other varies consinusoidally. These signals can be used to determine the direction and rate of fringe movement.

A simple way (though of limited application) of achieving this is to ensure that the fringe spacing is reasonably large (~ 2 mm) and to place two detectors as shown in Fig. 4.4. The outputs from the detectors are coupled to the X and Y inputs of an oscilloscope respectively so that the trace becomes a circle. As the fringes move relative to the detectors the sense of rotation of the circle gives the direction of movement, while the rate of rota-tion of the circle gives the rate of fringe movement, that is the movement of mirror M_2. This method is unsatisfactory in that slight misalignment of

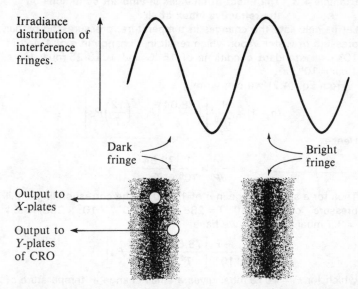

Fig. 4.4   Arrangement of two photodetectors relative to an interference fringe pattern to provide for reversible counting as the fringes move relative to the detectors. The two detector signals are connected to the X and Y plates of a CRO.

the mirrors will change the fringe spacing and hence the phase relationships of the detector outputs, possibly causing counting errors. A variety of more useful methods have been developed to obtain the quadrature signals [4.1].

4.2.1.2 Refractive index correction

In any interferometric measurement the length corresponding to a given fringe count obviously depends on the wavelength of the light used and hence on the refractive index of the air as $n = \lambda_0/\lambda_a$, λ_0 and λ_a being the wavelength in vacuum and air respectively. The refractive index of air is a function of pressure, temperature, composition (principally the presence of water vapor) and wavelength. In normal conditions the refractive index varies only slightly from unity and, for most purposes, the refractive index at the HeNe wavelength ($\lambda_0 = 632.991$ nm) is given by

$$(n - 1) \times 10^6 = \left(\frac{78.64}{T}\right) P_t - \left(\frac{12}{T}\right) P_w \qquad (4.2)$$

where P_t is the total pressure and P_w is the partial pressure of water vapor in millibars, while T is the temperature in K [4.2].

Example 4.3   The effect of changes in ambient conditions on the refractive index of air

Let us calculate the changes in temperature, pressure and partial pressure of water vapor which result in a change in n of 1 part in 10^6 near standard conditions of $15°C$ and 1013.25 mbar (note 1 bar $= 10^5$ Pa).

From Eq. (4.2) we can write

$$(n - 1) = \frac{1}{10^6} \left[\left(\frac{78.64}{T}\right) P_t - \left(\frac{12}{T}\right) P_w \right]$$

Hence

$$\frac{\partial n}{\partial P_t} = \frac{1}{10^6} \frac{78.64}{T}.$$

Thus for a small change in n of 1×10^{-6}, the corresponding small pressure change, at $T = 288$ K, is $10^{-6} \times 10^6 \times 288/78.64 = 3.7$ mbar. Similarly we have

$$\frac{\partial n}{\partial T} = \frac{-1}{10^6} \left[\frac{78.64}{T^2} P_t + \frac{12}{T^2} P_w \right],$$

which for $P_t = 1013$ mbar gives a small change in temperature of 1.0 K for a change of 1×10^{-6} in n. We may ignore the second term as the saturation vapor pressure of air at $15°C$ is only 17 mbar. Finally $\delta P_w = 24$ mbar also gives $\delta n = 1 \times 10^{-6}$.

Thus we see that fluctuations of the atmospheric conditions affect the refractive index n and hence the wavelength of the light λa. This in turn affects the conversion of fringe count to length. In many measurements variations of temperature and partial pressure of water vapor are relatively unimportant in comparison to changes in the total pressure. For accurate work, however, all of these parameters, especially the pressure, must be monitored continuously. Commercially available interferometers often include pressure, temperature and humidity sensors, the outputs of which are automatically included in the conversion of fringe count to length.

The variation of the refractive index of air with wavelength is small in the visible, for example, it changes only from 1.000 283 at 400 mn to 1.000 276 at 700 nm for dry air under standard conditions. Corrections for change of source wavelength can be readily made.

4.2.2 Surface topography and optical component testing

It is appropriate to consider topics such as the evaluation of surface topography and component testing under this section as again we are concerned, in effect, with the evaluation of optical path. Interferometers, such as the Fizeau and variants of the Michelson, have long been used for these purposes. Laser light, however, despite problems of spurious fringe patterns, has greatly simplified and broadened the techniques used. Again the incorporation of electronics and microcomputers has permitted much of this work to be done on a routine basis, resulting in improvements in the quality and reduction in the cost of precision optical components. Of particular importance in this respect is the fact that optics can be tested in the presence of turbulence by making many measurements and taking average values to reduce the effects of the turbulence to acceptable levels. Similarly computers are playing a role in reducing the quality demanded for accessory optics in optical testing. Formerly all accessory optics had to be of a better quality than the components under test. Now it is routine to calibrate the quality of the accessory optics and subtract the test error in the data analysis.

The Fizeau interferometer is the classical instrument for measuring the variation between a test and reference surface. Typically the test surface is placed in contact with a high quality reference surface, as illustrated in Fig. 4.5. Small air wedges usually exist between the two surfaces and interference fringes are formed with coherent light. If the two surfaces were perfectly flat and inclined at a small angle, then straight-line fringes of equal thickness would be formed. Surface height variations between the surfaces, however, cause the fringes to bend and produce a 'contour map' of the variation. Moving transversely from one fringe to the next corresponds to

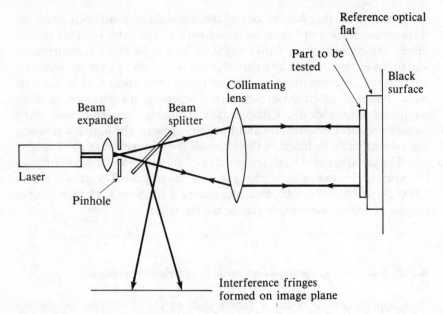

Fig. 4.5 Schematic diagram of a Fizeau interferometer using a laser source.

a change in separation of the surfaces of $\lambda/2$ so that we may write

$$\text{surface separation} = \frac{\delta}{s} \frac{\lambda}{2},$$

where s is the average fringe separation and δ is the deviation in the spacing of the fringes as shown in Fig. 4.6. δ/s can be measured to better than one tenth with the naked eye so it is easily possible to detect surface height variations of $\lambda/20$ (~ 30 nm).

The 'sign' of the surface defect, that is, hill or hollow in the test surface, can be determined by applying slight pressure to the component. Then if the defect is a hollow the fringes will move to the apex of the wedge, while if it is a hill the fringes will move away from the apex (see Fig. 4.6).

The advantage of using a laser in these measurements, which are commonly performed on machined metal components as well as optical components, is that the long coherence length of the light enables the test and reference surfaces to be separated as shown in Fig. 4.7. This prevents the surface from being damaged.

The Twyman Green variation of the Michelson interferometer can also be used to test surfaces as illustrated in Fig. 4.8. The laser beam is expanded, using for example a microscope objective, and then collimated and passed to the beam splitter. Part of the light is transmitted to the reference plane and part to the test surface (initially assumed to be plane). Both beams are

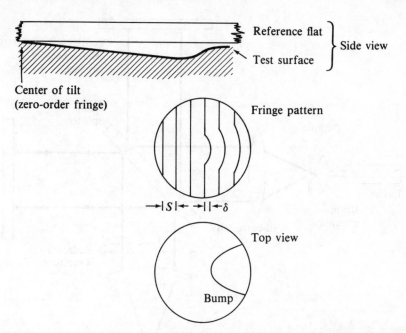

Fig. 4.6 The Fizeau fringe system corresponding to a bump on the test surface.

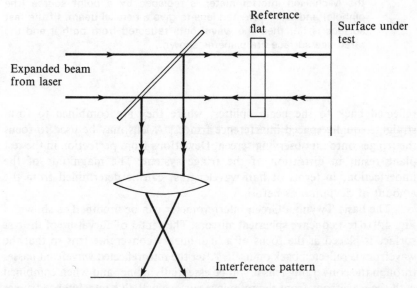

Fig. 4.7 Non-contact Fizeau interferometer for testing surfaces. The long coherence length of laser radiation enables an interference pattern to be formed even when the reflecting surfaces are well separated.

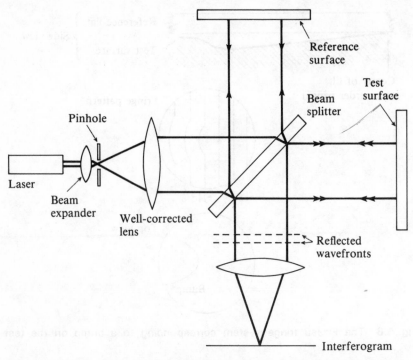

Fig. 4.8   The basic Twyman–Green interferometer – the extended source in the Michelson interferometer is replaced by a point source (the pinhole) and well-corrected lens to give a parallel beam. (If the test surface is flat then the wavefronts reflected from both it and the reference surface are plane as shown.)

reflected back to the beam splitter, where they are combined to form straight, equally spaced interference fringes. A lens may be used to focus the fringes onto an observing screen. Deviations from perfection in the test plane result in distortion of the fringe system. The magnitude of the imperfection, in terms of half-wavelengths, can be determined from the amount of deviation as before.

The basic Twyman Green interferometer can be modified as shown in Fig. 4.9 to test concave spherical mirrors. The center of curvature of the test surface is placed at the focus of a high-quality converging lens so that the wavefront is reflected back on itself. After the retroreflected wavefront passes through the converging lens it will be essentially plane, and when combined with the wavefront from the reference surface will give interference fringes similar to those formed by two flat surfaces. In this case any distortion of the fringes will indicate how the spherical mirror differs from the desired

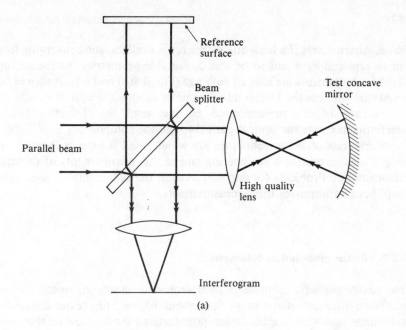

(a)

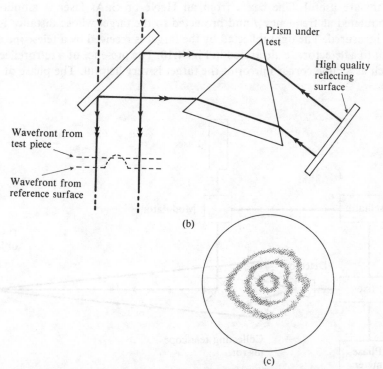

(b)

(c)

Fig. 4.9 The Twyman–Green interferometer modified to test (a) a concave mirror and (b) a prism. (c) illustrates the appearance of the interferogram assuming a defect in the prism under test in (b).

shape. Alternatively if a high-quality mirror is available the converging lens can be replaced by a lens to be tested. Suitable geometries for the testing of other components are easy to envisage (Fig. 4.9(b) and (c)). It should be noted that whereas the Fizeau interferometer enables the optical quality of the surface of a component to be measured the Twyman Green interferometer tests the optical path through the component.

Variations of these techniques are widely used for the calibration of gauges used in precision engineering and in the measurements of thermal expansion (see Problems 4.4 and 4.5). Again, the availability of laser light simplifies and improves these measurements.

4.2.3   Beam-modulation telemetry

Due to atmospheric turbulence interferometric measuring methods are limited to distances of not more than about 100 m. For greater distances, techniques involving amplitude (or polarization) modulation of the laser beam are useful. The beam from an HeNe or GaAs laser is amplitude modulated at frequency f and projected to the target whose distance is to be measured. The light reflected by the target is received by a telescope and sent to a detector, as illustrated in Fig. 4.10. The presence of a retroreflector such as a cube corner mirror at the target is very helpful. The phase of the

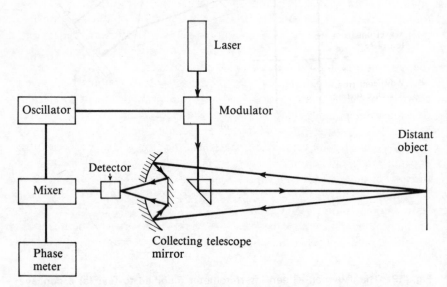

Fig. 4.10 Schematic diagram of a beam modulation distance measurement system.

modulation of the returning beam is different from that of the emitted beam because of the time taken for the light to travel to the target and back. The phase shift ϕ is related to the path length $2L$ by

$$\phi = \frac{2\pi}{\lambda_0}(2n_gL),\tag{4.3}$$

where n_g is the group refractive index of the atmosphere averaged over the path and λ_0 is the modulation wavelength in vacuum. The use of a modulated beam requires that the group refractive index should be used rather than the ordinary phase refractive index, n, which we have used previously in discussing interferometric measurements. The difference arises because in the modulated beam the energy associated with the wave propagates at the group velocity rather than the phase velocity, which is the velocity of propagation of the phase of the wave. In a dispersive medium the two velocities are not the same and are related by [4.3]

$$n_g = n + \frac{1}{\lambda_0}\frac{dn}{d(1/\lambda_0)} = n + \lambda_0\frac{dn}{d\lambda_0}.\tag{4.4}$$

The value of n_g at $15°C$ and 1013.25 mbar is $1.000\ 284\ 507\ 3$.

The phase difference ϕ of Eq. (4.3) can be written as

$$\phi = 2\pi(p+q)$$

where p is a large integer ($\simeq 10^5$, for $L \simeq 10$ km and a modulation frequency $\simeq 1$ GHz) and q a fraction less than unity. The phase comparison gives q but not p. To determine p and hence the absolute value of $p+q$ the measurement is repeated with different values of the modulation frequency, which for highest accuracy should be in the microwave range, that is $\sim$ GHz, and the method of exact fractions [4.4] is then used to calculate the integral multiples of 2π and hence the distance L.

Amplitude modulation may be performed using simple mechanical choppers while the phase (or polarization) modulation produced by electro- or acousto-optical modulators such as the Pockels and Bragg cells (see Section 3.7.1) can be converted into an amplitude modulation by the use of subsidiary fixed polarizers. The Pockels cell (Section 3.7.1.2) consists of a crystal such as potassium dihydrogen phosphate (KDP) which will change the state of polarization of a beam of light passing through the crystal when a voltage is applied. Thus if an alternating voltage is applied to the cell the state of polarization of the transmitted light will change at the same frequency as the alternating voltage. If this light is then incident on a linear (or plane) polarizing element the irradiance of the light transmitted will also vary.

The narrow bandwidth (that is, its spectral purity) of laser radiation provides for high discrimination against stray light by using appropriate wavelength filters, so that this system can be used in daylight with a high signal-to-noise ratio. Similarly, the small beam divergence allows a high degree of target selectivity. Allowing for the various losses involved in the system, ranges up to 10 km can be measured in daylight with quite low-power lasers (~ few mW). Losses include geometrical attenuation due to spreading of the beam by atmospheric turbulence (this is larger than the intrinsic divergence due to the optics), instrumental attenuation due to absorption and reflection in the optics, losses at the modulator, aerosol and Rayleigh scattering (see Section 7.1.2.4) and absorption by atmospheric gases.

Beam-modulation instruments have been developed with accuracies of better than 1 in 10^5 for military ranging, 1 in 10^6 for geodetic survey applications while even higher accuracies have been obtained for geophysical measurements of earth strain. The principal limitation to the ultimate accuracy of these techniques is the uncertainty in the average velocity of propagation because of the effects of atmospheric inhomogeneities and turbulence in the atmosphere. Not only do these affect the average value of n_g but also gradients in refractive index cause L to be larger than the true straight-line distance being measured. These uncertainties apply also to the pulse–echo method used, for example, in the measurement of very large distances, which is described in the next section.

4.2.4 Pulse–echo techniques

Distance can also be measured by timing the round-trip transit time for a very short pulse of light reflected from a distant target. The system consists of a pulsed laser, preferably Q-switched, a telescope to collect the reflected light, a photodetector and an accurate timer. A typical hand-held military rangefinder incorporates an Nd : YAG or glass laser. The laser emits 15 mJ pulses of energy which are 8 ns long. A silicon avalanche photodiode is used to detect the reflected pulses while a computer times the precise interval between the transmission of the output pulse and detection of the pulse reflected from the selected target. Accuracies of ± 5 m in ranges of 5–10 km are readily achievable.

Following the introduction a few years ago of nanosecond interval timers, airborne laser profiling of the earth's surface for mapping, surveying, forest inventories etc. can be undertaken [4.5]. The system often uses a gallium arsenide injection laser because of its ease of modulation and inherent safety. The laser typically emits 4000 pulses per second with a pulse width of 10 ns and a rise time of about 1 ns. The detector is a silicon avalanche photodiode (see Section 7.1.3) and timing can be done correct to ± 0.5 ns enabling a profile accuracy of better than 0.15 m to be obtained.

Greater accuracies can be obtained if retroreflectors are mounted on the target. Using retroreflectors left on the surface of the moon during

Apollo space missions the lunar distance has been measured to an accuracy of about ±0.15 m. [4.6]

This technique, which is often known as *optical radar* or lidar (light detection and ranging) is quite widely used and has been extended to atmospheric studies. By measuring the amount of backscattered light the presence of air turbulence can be detected and the amounts of various atmospheric pollutants can be measured. Using more sophisticated techniques the actual pollutants such as CO, NO, N_2O, SO_2, H_2S, can be identified. This involves measuring the frequency shift of the backscattered light from, for example, a frequency-doubled Nd : YAG laser due to the Raman effect, which consists of the appearance of extra spectral lines near the wavelength of the incident line when light is scattered by molecules of gases, liquids or solids. The new lines are characteristic of the molecules which can then be identified (see Refs. 4.7 and Section 4.6).

Carbon dioxide lasers are widely used in lidar systems because the strong emission at 10.6 μm corresponds to a wavelength region of low absorption (that is, an atmospheric window) and to the peak sensitivity of HgCdTe photodetectors. Also high-power Q-switched pulses can be readily generated.

In addition to information on the range of the target, the target velocity can also be obtained from the Doppler frequency shift in the returned pulse; thus we have laser Doppler velocimetry which is discussed in the next section.

4.3   LASER DOPPLER VELOCIMETRY

If the mirror M_2 of the Michelson interferometer (Fig. 4.2) is moved continuously along its optic axis at velocity v, the the interference fringes move across the plane of observation at a frequency $f = 2v/\lambda$. The output of a photodetector placed in this plane will vary at frequency f and v can be determined if λ is known.

This result can be interpreted from the rate of change of the separation between mirror M_1 and the image M_2' in terms of half-wavelengths. Alternatively we may regard M_2 as a moving source of waves, that is, the light reflected from it will undergo a Doppler frequency shift given by

$$\nu' = \nu(1 \pm 2v/c) \tag{4.5}$$

relative to the light reflected from the stationary mirror M_1. (As far as an observer is concerned the velocity of M_2', the image of M_2 in the beam splitter M, appears to move at velocity $2v$ when the actual velocity of M_2 is v). Thus when the light waves reflected from the two plane mirrors are mixed beats will be formed of frequency $f = \nu - \nu' = 2v\nu/c$ or $f = 2v/\lambda$ as before. This then is the basis of laser Doppler velocimetry (LDV).

Example 4.4   Frequency shift in the light reflected from a moving object

Let us calculate the frequency shift in the 632.8 nm HeNe laser line reflected from a car traveling at 20 m s^{-1}. We have

$$f = \nu - \nu' = \frac{2\nu\upsilon}{c} = \frac{2\upsilon}{\lambda}$$

$$= 40/632.8 \times 10^{-9} = 6.32 \times 10^{7} \text{ Hz}.$$

Note that this is about 1 part in 10^{7} of the frequency of the laser output. Clearly the laser must be stabilized so that the frequency drift is much less than this (Section 3.2).

In practice the moving mirror could be replaced by any surface or even by impurity particles such as specks of dust, algae or air bubbles in gaseous or liquid flows. The impurities act as scattering particles and their mean velocity which, if the particles are small enough, is the same as the velocity of the fluid and is given by the mean Doppler shift $(\nu - \nu')$ of the received signal.

The technique has the great advantage of being non-invasive and although it was used before the development of lasers, the highly coherent output of lasers has made possible the development of almost ideal Doppler velocimeters. These require no calibration and give a reading which is linear with velocity in liquids and gases. Simultaneous measurements of turbulence and flow pulsations are also possible with good accuracy.

The first use of LDV was reported by Yeh and Cummings in 1964 [4.8]; their method, which is often called the reference-beam technique and is illustrated in Fig. 4.11(a), suffers from a poor signal-to-noise ratio and sensitive alignment has to be achieved and maintained. The position of the photodetector (and hence the reference-beam detector) determines the component of velocity measured. These disadvantages have been overcome with the development of the dual-beam technique shown in Fig. 4.11(b). In this arrangement two beams of equal irradiance are focused by a lens into the fluid flow whose velocity is to be measured; the region where the beams cross becomes the measurement region.

When a particle (present in a fluid for example) passes through the measurement region it scatters light from each beam. The light has its frequency shifted so that when the two scattered beams are mixed or heterodyned a suitable detector will see only the difference frequency $\Delta\nu$. If $\mathbf{k}_1$ and $\mathbf{k}_2$ are unit vectors in the directions of the incident beams, k_s is a ray of scattered light and $\mathbf{v}$ is the particle velocity (see Fig. 4.12) then the frequency shift of the first beam is given by [4.9]

$$\nu_1' = \nu\left(1 + \mathbf{v} \cdot \left(\frac{\mathbf{k}_s - \mathbf{k}_1}{c}\right)\right)$$

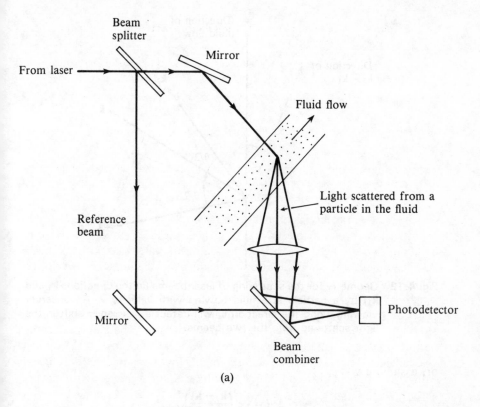

(a)

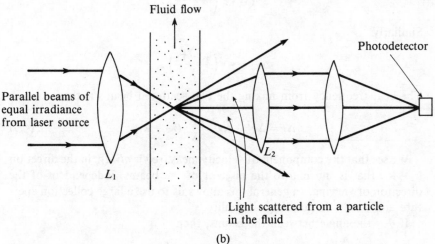

(b)

Fig. 4.11 Schematic of laser Doppler velocimeter: (a) the reference beam method which requires extremely careful alignment of the reference and scattered beams as they enter the photodetector; (b) the dual-beam method.

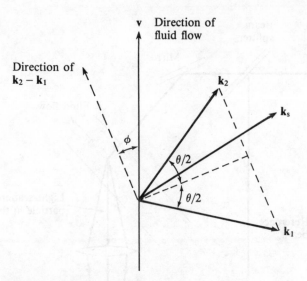

Fig. 4.12 Geometry for the scattering of laser beams (in the directions k_1 and k_1) by a particle in a fluid flowing with velocity v. An observer viewing along the direction k_s will detect a frequency shift in the light scattered from the two beams.

or, assuming $v \ll c$,

$$\Delta \nu_1' = \mathbf{v} \cdot \left(\frac{\mathbf{k_s} - \mathbf{k_1}}{\lambda} \right).$$

Similarly

$$\Delta \nu_2' = \mathbf{v} \cdot \left(\frac{\mathbf{k_s} - \mathbf{k_2}}{\lambda} \right).$$

The beat frequency from mixing the two scattered beams is then

$$\Delta \nu = \Delta \nu_1' - \Delta \nu_2' = \frac{\mathbf{v}}{\lambda} \cdot (\mathbf{k_2} - \mathbf{k_1}) \qquad (4.5)$$

We see that the component of velocity measured is *always* in the direction $k_2 - k_1$, that is, normal to the bisector of the beams, independent of the direction of viewing. In general this allows us to use a large collection aperture and results in good signal quality.

If θ is the angle between the beams, then

$$\Delta \nu = \frac{2v}{\lambda} \cos \phi \sin \frac{\theta}{2}, \qquad (4.7)$$

where ϕ is the angle between the direction of $(k_2 - k_1)$ and the direction of fluid flow.

An alternative explanation of the dual-beam method is as follows. If the two incident beams are coherent, then their intersection will result in the formation of a set of interference fringes in the plane of the beams at the crossing point. The fringes will be parallel to the bisector of the beams, that is, normal to the direction of the component of flow being measured. A particle passing through the alternate bright and dark bands will scatter light whose irradiance will vary, the rate of variation being proportional to the particle velocity.

The fringe separation d is given by (see Problem 4.7)

$$d = \frac{\lambda}{2 \sin(\theta/2)}.$$

The particle velocity is given by $v = df$, where f is the frequency of the photodetector output signal; f is the same as the Doppler frequency so that

$$v = d \, \Delta\nu = \frac{\lambda}{2 \sin(\theta/2)} \, \Delta\nu$$

as given in Eq. (4.7) above, with $\phi = 0$.

A typical dual-beam optical system is shown in Fig. 4.13; the lenses, beam-splitting prism and photodetector (a photomultiplier or pin photodiode can be used) are mounted on an optical bench. This system is referred to as the forward-scatter arrangement and provides the best signal quality, but obviously requires optical access to the flow in two directions. Conversely, in the case of backscatter arrangements all the optics are on one side of the flow but the signal irradiance is much less than in the forward scatter arrangement. The lenses L_1 and L_2 can be linked together so as to share a common focus. Then by moving them as a unit the fluid flow can be traversed and the velocity profile determined.

Light from a low-power (~ 5 mW) HeNe laser passes through a beam splitter which gives two parallel beams of similar power. The direct beams are prevented from reaching the photodetector by the aperture A, so that only the scattered light is focused onto the detector by lens L_3. This enhances the signal-to-noise ratio and prevents the relatively high power of the direct beams from causing fatigue in the photocathode.

The output from the photodetector is fed to a spectrum analyzer whose output is recorded on a storage oscilloscope or chart recorder. The detector cannot respond directly to signals at the frequency of visible light and the alternating signal in the detector output consists of difference terms of the form indicated by Eq. (4.7). The record consists of an approximately Gaussian-shaped curve centered on the Doppler frequency. The spread in the width of the peak is due to instrumental effects and possibly velocity fluctuations. Finding the velocity necessitates estimating the center of the peak, which can be done to an accuracy of about 1%. This can be improved by more sophisticated signal-processing techniques (see, for example, Ref. 4.9b).

The applications of LDV are many and varied; the technique has been used for measurements in wind tunnels, internal combustion engines, near flames, of the velocity of moving parts of machinery, propellors and the like. It has also been used for the measurement of the velocity of blood flow; indeed the dynamic range extends from micrometers per second to several times the speed of sound.

Although for many applications HeNe lasers are ideal, in backscatter configurations where more power is required argon lasers with outputs of a few watts have been used. The argon laser has two strong wavelengths which can conveniently be used for measurements of two flow components.

Since the scattering efficiency increases as the wavelength decreases, HeCd lasers ($\lambda = 446$ nm) may be used instead of the red line of HeNe lasers if they become more cost effective or alternatively the green line ($\lambda = 543.5$ nm) of HeNe may be used. Measurements at large distances, approaching a kilometer or so have been made in the atmosphere using CO_2 lasers. In this case the reference-beam mode is used to measure the velocity along the optic axis.

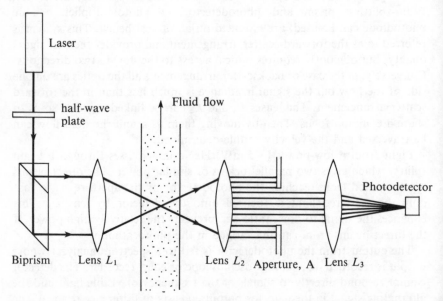

Fig. 4.13   Schematic of a typical forward scatter laser Doppler velocimeter. Moving the linked lenses L_1 and L_2 permits the velocity profile across the flow to be measured. The irradiances of the two beams can be set equal to give the best signal by rotating the half-wave plate.

4.4 SURFACE VELOCITY MEASUREMENTS USING SPECKLE PATTERNS

The Doppler technique can be used for the measurement of the velocity of solid surfaces, though the method is better adapted to solids with smooth surfaces, which will give rise to a relatively well-collimated reflected beam. For surfaces which are optically rough, that is have variations in height which are more than about a wavelength of the illuminating light, a method based on 'speckle pattern' is better.

Speckle pattern is the name given to the granular appearance of laser light reflected from a rough surface. The light reflected from neighboring small irregularities present on the surface can interfere to produce local bright and dark areas. Such effects are, in fact, present when a surface is illuminated with incoherent light sources. The pattern changes randomly and rapidly compared to the response time of the eye, however, so the surface appears to be uniformly illuminated. The high coherence of laser light, on the other hand, results in surfaces appearing to have a granulated, speckled texture.

If the surface moves relative to the observer the whole speckle pattern also appears to move, the apparent velocity of the pattern being twice that of the relative motion. If such movement is recorded by a photodetector with a small aperture, then the movement of one bright speckle past the aperture gives rise to an output pulse from the detector. If, as shown in Fig. 4.14, a grating is placed in front of the photodetector, then as the surface is moved a bright speckle produces a series of pulses. The frequency

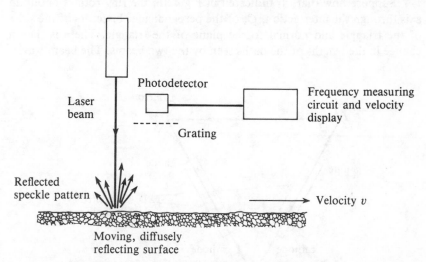

Fig. 4.14 Schematic diagram of a system for measuring the velocity of a rough solid surface using the speckle pattern of reflected laser radiation.

of these pulses is $f = 2v/d$, where d is the grating spacing and v the velocity of the surface.

In practice there will be a large number of bright speckles passing the grating, each giving rise to a series of pulses. Although the series of pulses have random phases they all have the same frequency. Thus measurement of the center frequency of the output of the photodetector permits the velocity of the surface to be measured.

This provides a useful non-contact method of measuring the velocity of surfaces with a variety of textures and colors. It has been used in the velocity range from about $0.1 \, \mathrm{m \, s^{-1}}$ to $10 \, \mathrm{m \, s^{-1}}$.

4.5   ANGULAR ROTATION

The measurement of the rate of rotation using laser gyroscopes is now quite well established and the so-called ring-laser gyro is being installed in military and commercial aircraft. The gyro has a ring configuration, usually an equilateral triangle, in which two laser beams travel in opposite directions, as illustrated in Fig. 4.15. There is a gain medium, usually HeNe, in at least one of the arms of the triangle. The wavelength of operation then adjusts itself so that the total distance around the ring is an integral number of wavelengths. Any change in length of the ring results in a change in the wavelength.

Suppose now that, as indicated in Fig 4.16, the ring rotates about an axis through the intersection, O, of the perpendicular bisectors of the sides of the triangle and normal to the plane of the triangle. There is then a change in the lengths of the paths seen by the two beams. The beam travel-

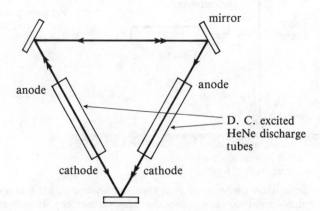

Fig. 4.15   Schematic of the ring laser gyroscope.

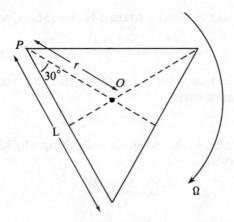

Fig. 4.16 Geometry of the ring laser gyroscope.

ing in the same direction as the rotation has to travel slightly further on each traversal of the ring, and the beam traveling in the opposite direction travels slightly less on each traversal than the path covered at rest. Consequently the two counter-rotating beams have slightly different wavelengths and frequencies to satisfy the condition that the round-trip path length should be an integral multiple of wavelengths. We shall now show that the difference in frequencies, which can be detected by beating the two beams together, is a measure of the rate of rotation.

Let us consider light leaving point P on the triangular path, which is rotating about O with angular velocity Ω, and making one complete transit of the triangle (Fig. 4.16). The time for the transit is

$$t = 3L/c = S/c,$$

where L is the side length and $S = 3L$ the total perimeter of the triangle.

During this time point P moves a distance

$$d = \Omega r t = \frac{\Omega r S}{c},$$

where r is the distance from O to P, which is simply $L/2 \sec 30°$ or $L/\sqrt{3}$. The change in path length δS seen by the beam is the component of the movement of P along the direction of the beam, that is

$$\delta S = d \cos 60° = d/2.$$

Therefore substituting for d and r we have

$$\delta S = \frac{\Omega S L}{2\sqrt{3}c} = \frac{\Omega\sqrt{3}L^2}{2c}.$$

Now the area of the equilateral triangle is $A = \sqrt{3}L^2/4$, so that

$$\delta S = \frac{2\,\Omega A}{c}. \tag{4.8}$$

To satisfy the condition that the path length is an integral number of wavelengths we must have

$$n\lambda = 3L = S,$$

where n is an integer, so that when the path changes by δS the wavelength changes by $\delta\lambda$, where

$$\delta\lambda = \frac{\delta S}{n} = \frac{\lambda \delta S}{S}.$$

The corresponding frequency change is given by

$$\frac{\delta\nu}{\nu} = \frac{\delta\lambda}{\lambda} = \frac{\delta S}{S}.$$

Each of the two beams suffers the same frequency shift, but in opposite senses so that the beat frequency f is $f = 2\delta\nu = 2(\delta S/S)\nu$, which on substituting for δS for Eq. (4.8) gives

$$f = \frac{4\Omega A\nu}{cS} = \frac{4\Omega A}{\lambda S}. \tag{4.9}$$

Equation (4.9) is the basic equation used for angular rotation rate measurement. It applies quite generally to any path with an enclosed area A and perimeter S. (This is often referred to as the Sagnac effect; Sagnac successfully demonstrated a rotating ring interferometer in 1913.)

In principle laser gyros should be very sensitive and accurate with a fundamental limit of less than 10^{-6} degrees per hour. In practice the performance is less than this, the limits being set by the accuracy of fabrication, cleanliness and a phenomenon called 'lock-in'. This occurs if the rotation rate is very small when it is found that the frequency difference falls to zero. It is caused by the frequencies of the two counter-rotating beams acquiring the same value in the same way that coupled oscillators operating at slightly different frequencies lock together. This problem can be overcome and rotation rates of less than 0.003 degrees per hour measured.

The construction of a laser gyro in principle is quite straightforward. The equilateral triangular ring can be machined out of a block of quartz; indeed, three axis systems required for navigational purposes have been fabricated in a single block, though in practice three separate plane systems are often used. Corner mirrors and electrodes can then be attached to the block. Readout is obtained by extracting part of each of the counter-rotating beams from one of the mirrors and then combining the two parts at a detector as shown in Fig. 4.17.

Example 4.5   Frequency shift in a ring laser gyro

Let us calculate the frequency shift corresponding to a rotation rate of 0.1° h^{-1} in a triangle with 0.1 m side length assuming $\lambda = 632.8$ nm.

0.1° h^{-1} corresponds to $= 4.85 \times 10^{-7}$ rad s^{-1}

The area of the triangle is $\sqrt{3} \times 10^{-2}/4$ m^2, so that from Eq. (4.9)

$$f = \frac{4\Omega A}{S\lambda} = \frac{4.85 \times 10^{-7} \times \sqrt{3} \times 10^{-2}}{0.3 \times 632.8 \times 10^{-9}},$$

that is, $f = 0.044$ Hz.

If the apex of the prism shown in Fig. 4.17 is not exactly 90°, the two beams form an interference pattern. If the gyro is stationary, then the fringe pattern too is stationary, while if the gyro is rotating the fringe pattern moves at the beat frequency rate. By positioning two detectors 90° (that is a quarter of a fringe) apart the sense of the fringe movement and hence the direction of rotation can be determined as outlined in Section 4.2.1.1.

Recently laser gyros involving semiconductor lasers and optical fibers

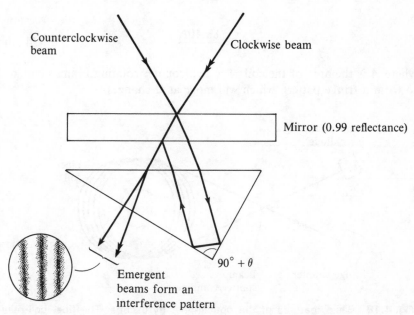

Fig. 4.17 Laser gyroscope readout optics. The angle θ is a few arc seconds and the interference fringes are of the order of 3 mm apart.

have been developed. The light from the laser is split and the two parts traverse a coiled optical fiber in opposite directions. When the coil is rotated the light traversing the fiber coil in the direction of rotation remains in the fiber for a slightly longer time than the light traveling in the opposite direction. The two beams emerge from the coil with a phase difference $\Delta\phi$, which may be evaluated as follows. Consider the light from a semiconducting laser being divided by a beam splitter and entering the two ends of a coil of optical fiber of radius R, having N turns as shown in Fig. 4.18. If the angular velocity of the coil is Ω, then the apparent velocity of the light traveling in the direction of rotation is $c - R\Omega$, while that of the counter-rotating beam is $c + R\Omega$. Thus the two beams traverse the coil in times t and t', where

$$t = \frac{2\pi RN}{c - R\Omega} \quad \text{and} \quad t' = \frac{2\pi RN}{c + R\Omega}.$$

The phase difference of the two beams as they emerge is then $2\pi\nu\,(t' - t)$, that is,

$$\Delta\phi = 4\pi^2\nu RN\left(\left(\frac{1}{c + R\Omega}\right) - \left(\frac{1}{c - R\Omega}\right)\right).$$

Then using the binomial theorem, assuming $c \gg R\Omega$, we have

$$\Delta\phi = \frac{4\pi^2\nu RN}{c}\left(\frac{2R\Omega}{c}\right)$$

or

$$\Delta\phi = \frac{8\pi A\Omega N}{c\lambda}, \tag{4.10}$$

where A is the area of the coil. The two counter-rotating beams combine to form a fringe pattern which will move as Ω changes.

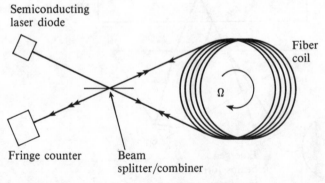

Fig. 4.18   Basic features of the optical-fiber gyroscope. The fiber coil may comprise several hundred turns and have a radius of about 0.1–0.2 m.

The fiber optic gyro (see Ref. 4.10) is probably cheaper and smaller than the ring laser gyro but less accurate (neither instrument, of course, is a gyro in the strict sense of the word). Both types enjoy the advantages over mechanical gyros of ruggedness, freedom from moving parts with a consequent absence of wear, and freedom from the need for a gimbal mount.

4.6 LASER SPECTROSCOPY

Spectroscopy studies the interaction of light with matter and thereby provides much information on the energy-level structures of the constituent atoms or molecules. In absorption spectroscopy, for example, nearly monochromatic radiation is passed through a sample and the amount transmitted is measured as a function of the wavelength of the radiation. The radiation is more strongly absorbed when the photon energy corresponds to some difference between the energy levels of the material under study. A typical absorption spectrum is shown in Fig. 4.19.

The conventional way to obtain the monochromatic radiation is to use a high-intensity broad-band source (such as a quartz halogen or high-pressure xenon lamp) in conjunction with a monochromator. Critical factors in such an arrangement are the bandwidth and power of the radiation emerging from the monochromator. For a grating monochromator the

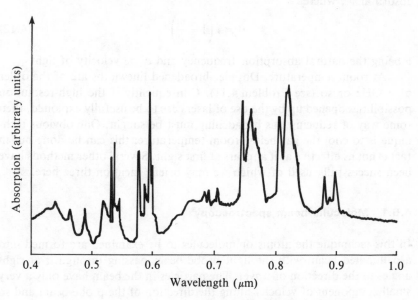

Fig. 4.19 Optical absorption spectrum of Nd: YAG.

bandwidth $\Delta\nu$ at a frequency ν can be written [see Ref. 4.11]

$$\Delta\nu = \frac{\nu}{qN}, \tag{4.11}$$

were N is the total number of lines on the grating and q is the order of the spectrum. For visible radiation $\nu \approx 10^{14}$ Hz and taking $q = 3$ and $N = 150\ 000$ we obtain $\Delta\nu \sim 2$ GHz. Available powers from such an arrangement are usually below 1 nW. We may compare these figures with those from a single-mode HeNe laser, where the linewidth can be less than 1 MHz with beam powers of the order of 1 mW. Unfortunately the HeNe laser can be tuned only over the comparatively narrow frequency range of about 1500 MHz, which corresponds to the natural linewidth.

Of course lasers that are tunable over much wider frequency ranges are readily available, for example dye lasers (Section 2.4) and lead salt lasers (Section 2.2), although these generally exhibit larger linewidths than the HeNe laser. Thus the greatly increased source power and smaller bandwidths of lasers has led to improvements in resolution, accuracy and sensitivity by many orders of magnitude compared to traditional spectroscopic methods. However, source linewidth has not been the only limiting factor on resolution in the past. Absorption lines in gases are broadened due to the Doppler affect (Section 3.2) caused by the thermal motion of the absorbing atoms or molecules. Although each atom or molecule absorbs radiation over a very narrow range of frequencies (the 'natural' linewidth), if it is moving at a relative velocity v_r away from an observer it appears to absorb at ν', where

$$\nu' = \nu\left(1 - \frac{v_r}{c}\right), \tag{4.12}$$

ν being the natural absorption frequency and c the velocity of light.

At room temperature, Doppler-broadened linewidths are of the order of a GHz or so (see Problem 4.11). Consequently if the high-resolution possibilities opened up by the use of lasers are to be usefully exploited, then some way of reducing this broadening must be sought. One obvious technique is to cool the gas below room temperature: this can be done but in fact is not as effective as it appears at first sight. Several other methods have been successfully used of which we may briefly mention three here.

4.6.1   Molecular-beam spectroscopy

In this technique the atoms or molecules to be examined are formed into a collimated beam with the light probe beam passing through it at right angles to the direction of travel. The particles in the beam have only a very small component of velocity along the direction of the probe beam and so the Doppler broadening is considerably reduced.

4.6.2 Saturation spectroscopy

Here the laser output is split into two beams which travel through the target material in opposite directions. One of the beams (the 'saturating' beam) is made much more intense than the other (the 'probe' beam) and is also amplitude modulated. When the frequency of the saturating beam corresponds to a transition in the material it tends to equalize the ground and excited state populations. Provided that both saturating and probe beams can interact with the same group of molecules, then the material will become transparent to the probe beam. This can only happen when the laser frequency corresponds to the exact center of the transition when its output is absorbed by molecules having a zero velocity component along the beam direction. Under these conditions the probe beam then also becomes amplitude modulated. When the laser is tuned away from the line center the probe beam cannot interact with the group of molecules that are saturated by the saturating beam and so the probe beam is not then amplitude modulated.

4.6.3 Two-photon spectroscopy

As in saturation spectroscopy two-photon spectroscopy uses two beams from the same laser which traverse the material under examination in opposite directions. In this case, however, the two beams have equal irradiances.

As far as a particular molecule is concerned the two beams appear to have frequencies of $\nu(1 + v_r/c)$ and $\nu(1 - v_r/c)$ where v_r is the velocity component of the molecule along the beam direction (see Eq. (4.12)). If the molecule can absorb a photon from both beams *simultaneously*, then the energy available is just $2h\nu$, which is independent of v_r. The occurrence of such an absorption can be detected either by monitoring the amount of absorption taking place in one of the beams or by looking for the appearance of fluorescence induced by the transition. This type of spectroscopy differs from saturation spectroscopy in that all atoms in the interaction region can take part in the absorption. Furthermore this process enables the regions accessible to laser radiation to be considerably increased since the laser photon energy is effectively doubled.

In addition to conventional absorption spectroscopy many other types of spectroscopy have benefited from the introduction of laser sources. A particularly noteworthy example is in Raman spectroscopy (see Section 4.2.4 and also Ref. 4.12). Here the sample is illuminated by a powerful beam of monochromatic radiation. A proportion of this radiation is scattered and also 'frequency shifted' by the sample so that its frequency becomes $\nu \pm \Delta\nu_s$, where $\Delta\nu_s$ corresponds to some transition within the material. This is known as the Raman effect. Thus in effect an incoming photon has its energy increased or decreased by the addition or subtraction of energy available from within the specimen. When the energy is decreased (i.e. $\nu = \nu - \Delta\nu_s$) the resulting spectral line is known as a Stokes line. Conversely an energy increase gives rise to an anti-Stokes line. The Raman effect is commonly used to investigate molecular vibrational and rotational energy levels so that $\Delta\nu_s$ is often relatively small. The efficiency of Raman scattering is low but it does increase as the frequency increases, so that, all else being equal, it is better to use as short a wavelength as possible. The spectral width of the exciting radiation obviously sets a limit to the smallest value of $\Delta\nu_s$ that can be observed and also to the resolution that may be achieved. The 'classical' source for Raman spectroscopy is the 435.8 nm line of a high-pressure mercury arc lamp. This line has a width of some 600 MHz, whereas, of course, laser linewidths are several orders of magnitude smaller. In addition lasers provide higher-power sources where the directionality and polarization are readily controllable. One of the most popular Raman sources is now the argon ion laser, but the availability of a wide range of alternative wavelength sources is another advantage of laser sources, since one can then choose a wavelength where the specimen is nonabsorbing. An example of this is the use of the Nd:YAG laser to investigate many semiconductor materials, such as GaAs, which are heavily absorbing at shorter wavelengths.

It is interesting to note that with a laser Raman source the scattered radiation is itself coherent, so that it is possible to use the Raman effect to extend yet further the range of coherent wavelengths available.

In the limited space available here it has been possible to review only a very few of the techniques involved in laser spectroscopy. For a more detailed discussion the reader may consult the references contained in Ref. 4.13. It is certainly no exaggeration to say that the widespread adoption of laser-spectroscopic techniques has resulted in order-of-magnitude improvements both in accuracy and sensitivity.

One possible large-scale commercial application of what is essentially a spectroscopic technique is that of the laser enrichment of uranium, which is discussed in the next section.

4.7 LASER URANIUM ENRICHMENT

In naturally occurring uranium the concentration of the isotope of mass number 235 (about 0.7%) is less than that required for use in the nuclear power industry (about 3%). The usual enrichment technique, that of gaseous diffusion, is expensive; laser enrichment promises a considerable reduction both in the capital and running costs. The idea behind laser

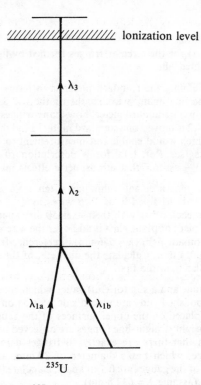

Fig. 4.20 Ionization of ^{235}U atoms using a three-step absorption process.

enrichment is relatively straightforward and relies on the slight differences between the energy levels of the different uranium isotopes (the so-called 'isotope shifts'). Isotope shifts arise because of the interaction of the electron cloud in an atom with its own nucleus. Different isotopes have very slightly different sized nuclei (because of the differing numbers of neutrons) which give rise to different interactions. The differences in absorption line positions are relatively small (say between 5 and 20 GHz); nevertheless they are larger than the linewidths available from suitable tunable laser sources (say between 0.1 and 1 GHz). One of the most favored schemes involves preferentially ionizing the ^{235}U atoms, which may then be separated out using an electrostatic field. Many different excitation routes are possible (uranium has between 10^4 and 10^5 possible transitions). Although the ionization could be carried out with the absorption of a single photon from an excimer laser, the most studied routes involve a three-step transition process using dye amplifiers pumped by copper or gold lasers. (In fact four separate wavelengths are required since a low-lying state is also significantly populated in uranium vapor – see Fig. 4.20). The cumulative isotope shifts on all these transitions result in very high selectivities.

PROBLEMS

4.1   Derive Eq. (4.1) for the circular fringes formed by light of wavelength, λ, in a parallel sided film.

4.2   One way of defining the standard meter is in terms of the wavelength of light. Calculate how many wavelengths of the 632.8 nm line of the HeNe laser there are in the standard meter; how many fringes cross the field of view as M_2 in Fig. 4.2 is moved one standard meter? Find the maximum linewidth of the laser which would enable this measurement to be made without subsidiary etalons (see Ref. 1.1a for a description of Michelson's original measurements) – assume that atmospheric effects may be ignored.

4.3   Interferometric measurement techniques often use a small angle wedge film rather than a parallel-sided film. Two wires, one of diameter 0.2 mm, are laid parallel to each other with their axes 50 mm apart on a sheet of plane glass; another piece of plane glass is laid over the wires and when illuminated with monochromatic light ($\lambda = 546$ nm) interference fringes are formed with a spacing of 0.054 mm. Calculate the diameter of the second wire assuming that it is smaller than the first.

4.4   A standard gauge and a slip (or end) gauge which consist of lengths of steel rod with flat polished ends are placed side by side on a flat glass plate. An optical flat is placed on the upper surfaces of the gauge and due to a small difference in height straight-line fringes are observed between the flat and the gauges. Given that there are exactly 10 fringes across the surface of the standard gauge, which has a diameter of 30 mm, and given that corresponding sides of the gauges are 0.1 m apart, calculate the difference in height of the gauges (assume $\lambda = 632.8$ nm).

Devise an interferometric method of comparing two gauges which avoids placing the ends in contact with another surface with its consequent risk of damage.

4.5   A block of material has two parallel faces 10 mm apart and rests on one of these faces. A plane glass plate is placed over it, supported by two copper blocks which are just over 10 mm high, leaving an air film between the lower glass surface and the upper face of the material. Interference fringes are formed with HeNe light ($\lambda = 632.8$ nm) reflected normally from these two surfaces and are viewed through a microscope. When the temperature of the whole system is raised by $100\,^{\circ}$C, 20.5 fringes cross the field of view. Given that the temperature coefficient of expansion of copper is $1.4 \times 10^{-5}\,^{\circ}\text{C}^{-1}$, calculate the possible expansion coefficients of the material. How would you determine which one is correct.

4.6   Show how a Twyman Green interferometer could be used to test a convex mirror and a biconcave lens.

4.7   Show that the fringe separation in the dual-beam laser Doppler velocimeter is given by $d = \lambda \, (2 \sin(\theta/2)^{-1}$.

4.8   The output from a photodetector used in an LDV when analyzed with a spectrum analyzer shows a peak at 65 kHz. Given that the two parallel beams are initially separated by 50 mm and the focusing lens has a focal length of 0.15 m, estimate the velocity of the fluid flow (take $\lambda = 632.8$ nm). (*Note*: In the case of liquids the calculation would have to allow for refraction at the walls of the containing tube.)

4.9 A measurement of distance requires an HeNe laser beam ($\lambda = 632.8$ nm) with a coherence length of 3 m. Estimate the maximum linewidth of the laser transition. Hence, assuming that frequency fluctuations are dominated by changes in length of the laser cavity, calculate the maximum fluctuations in temperature of the laser, assuming that the temperature coefficient of expansion of the cavity is $1 \times 10^{-6}\,^{\circ}C^{-1}$.

4.10 The most obvious feature of the optical absorption spectrum of Nd : YAG, as shown in Fig. 4.19, is that the absorption lines tend to be clustered together in groups. Assuming that each group corresponds to a transition between the spin–orbit split terms of Fig. 2.2, identify the transitions involved.

4.11 Assuming that in a gas the average thermal energy of a molecule is $\sim kT$, estimate the width of the Doppler broadened lines in nitrogen at room temperature. What linewidth would you expect if the gas were cooled down to 77K? Take the relative atomic mass of nitrogen to be 14.

REFERENCES

4.1 (a) J. N. Dukes and G. B. Gordon, 'A Two Hundred-foot Yardstick with Graduations Every Microinch', *Hewlett Packard Journal*, 2–8, August 1970. (*Note:* This journal contains some other articles relevant to this chapter).

(b) UK Patent Application No. 2012450.

(c) W. R. C. Rowley and D. C. Wilson, 'Design Tolerances in Laser Measurement Systems', *Symposium on Lasers and the Mechanical Engineer*, London, Nov. 1968, I.Mech.E., London, November 1968.

4.2 J. C. Owens, *Appl. Opt.* **6**, 51, 1967.

4.3 R. S. Longhurst, *Geometrical and Physical Optics.* (3rd edn), Longman, London, 1973, pp. 122–124.

4.4 R. S. Longhurst, *Geometrical and Physical Optics* (3rd edn), Longman, London, 1973, pp. 185–189.

4.5 J. Jepsky, 'Airborne Laser Profiling and Mapping', *Lasers and Applications*, 95–98, March 1985.

4.6 J. F. Faller and E. J. Wampler, 'The Lunar Laser Reflector', *Sci. Am.*, 38–49, 1970.

4.7 (a) P. Camagni and S. Sandroni (eds.) *Optical Remote Sensing of Air Pollution*, Elsevier, Amsterdam, 1984.

(b) R. M. Huffaker, 'Coherent Laser Radar', *Laser Focus*, 12–20, November 1980.

(c) J. G. Hawley, 'Dual-wavelength Laser Radar Probes for Air Pollutants, *Laser Focus*, March 1981.

4.8 Y. Yeh and H. Z. Cummings, 'Localised Fluid Flow Measurements with a He–Ne Laser Spectrometer', *Appl. Phys. Lett.*, **4**, 176–178, 1964.

4.9 (a) K. A. Blake and K. I. Jespersen, The NEL Laser Velocimeter National Engineering Laboratory, Dept. of Trade and Industry, May 1972.

(b) L. E. Drain, *Laser Doppler Technique*, Wiley Interscience, 1980.

4.10 (a) See for example: *Proceedings of the First International Conference of Fiber Optic Rotation Sensors*, Boston, November 1981.

(b) B. Yoon Kim and H. J. Shaw, Fiber-Optic Gyroscopes, *IEEE Spectrum* (USA), **23**(3), 54–60, 1986.

4.11 F. A. Jenkins and H. E. White, *Fundamentals of Optics* (4th edn), McGraw-Hill, New York, 1980, Section 17.9

4.12 D. A. Long, *Raman Spectroscopy*, McGraw-Hill, New York, 1977.

4.13 (a) G. W. Series, 'Laser Spectroscopy', *Contemp. Phys.* **25**, 3–29, 1984.

  (b) K. Shimoda (ed.), *High Resolution Laser Spectroscopy*, Springer-Verlag, Berlin, 1976.

  (c) R. C. Thompson, 'High-resolution Laser Spectroscopy of Atomic Systems', *Rep. Prog. Phys.*, **48**, 531–578, 1985.

5

Industrial, Medical and Military Applications

In this chapter we consider the laser primarily as a source of thermal energy, although the high spatial coherence which allows the laser beam to be focused to a very small spot is also of importance (see Sections 3.4 and 3.6). Perhaps more than any other, the application of the laser to cutting through materials, especially metals, has captured the public imagination right from the start (no doubt helped by the science fiction idea of a laser 'death ray'!). Although in the early days such ideas were rather fanciful, fact has now gone some way toward catching up with fiction. Quite a number of laser types are now sufficiently powerful to enable a wide variety of materials to be heat treated, melted (e.g. in welding) and even vaporized (e.g. in cutting and drilling).

It is of course perfectly possible to weld, cut and drill without having to resort to such a technically advanced (and expensive!) solution as the laser. Lasers do offer a number of advantages, however, when compared to more conventional techniques. For example:

(1) Laser radiation is a very 'clean' form of energy, in that no contaminating materials need come into contact with the workpiece. In fact, the working atmosphere can often be controlled to suit a particular task.
(2) Laser beams, because of their high spatial coherence, may be focused onto very small areas. This intense local heating can take place without neighboring areas being affected.
(3) It is comparatively easy to control the beam irradiance.
(4) The beam is readily directed into relatively inaccessible places; it can pass through transparent windows and be directed round sharp corners.
(5) As we shall see shortly, most of the laser energy is deposited very near the surface of the target, thus enabling shallow surface regions to be treated without necessarily affecting the bulk.

The two most commonly used lasers for materials processing are the Nd:YAG and the CO_2 lasers. It is probably fair to say that of these two, the CO_2 laser is the most versatile. It is available with a wide range of output powers and at reasonable cost. There are, however, some areas in which the Nd : YAG has a number of advantages because of its shorter operating wavelength. The ruby laser, being one of the first to be developed, was at one time widely used for materials processing but it is not now very common. Another possibility is the alexandrite laser which would appear to have some advantages over Nd : YAG (it has a shorter wavelength for example) but it has not been available for long enough for many commercial applications in this area to emerge.

Of course the laser is a very delicate optical instrument and considerable thought needs to be put into making the final package sufficiently rugged for it to be used in heavy industrial environments when considerable vibration and dust may be present. Another problem is that of designing a beam transport system to 'carry' the beam from the laser to the workpiece. This is usually done using steerable mirrors, although flexible fiber-optical waveguides can also be used for relatively low-power beams. Careful consideration must be given to the safety aspect. Often the radiation is invisible and, particularly with very high-power lasers, even a very small amount of scattered radiation can be potentially hazardous. In addition great care needs to be taken to ensure that the beam is focused onto the right spot and at the right time, otherwise irreparable damage may be done to the workpiece or the surrounding hardware.

A detailed theoretical analysis of the interaction between a laser beam and a material surface is almost impossibly complicated to carry out, especially when the material melts or vaporizes. Here we can only make the very simplest of assumptions and adopt rather crude models. Nevertheless, such calculations as we are able to make enable the important parameters to be identified and orders of magnitude estimates of such quantities as temperature rise and rate of material removal to be made.

5.1   THEORETICAL ANALYSIS

We assume first of all that a beam of laser radiation of constant irradiance is incident normally onto a smooth material surface. For simplicity initially we take the beam to be of infinite lateral extent and the material to be in the form of a semi-infinite slab. The first process we need to examine is the amount of the incident radiation that actually penetrates into the material. We may write this as $I(1 - R_s)$, where I is the beam irradiance and R_s the surface reflectance. Curves of reflectance versus wavelength for various metals are shown in Fig. 5.1. Generally we see that reflectance decreases with decreasing wavelength, so that it would seem advantageous to use lasers with as short a wavelength as possible. However, the values of R_s

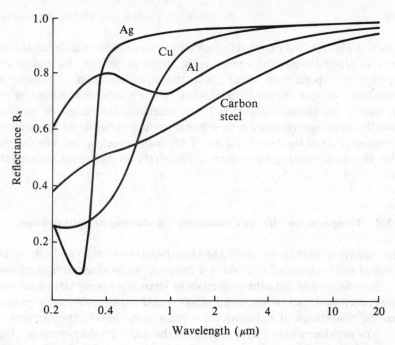

Fig. 5.1 Reflectance versus wavelength for various polished metal surfaces.

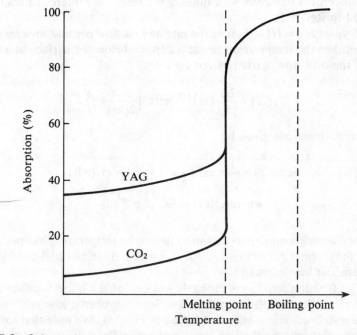

Fig. 5.2 Schematic variation of absorption with temperature for a typical metal surface for both the YAG and CO_2 laser wavelengths.

shown in Fig. 5.1. only apply at room temperature. The reflectance of most surfaces drops during a laser pulse as the temperature rises. As soon as any melting or vaporization takes place the situation changes even more drastically, so that the initial advantage of the shorter wavelength is not necessarily maintained. Figure 5.2 is a schematic indication of how the overall percentage absorption by a metal surface varies as its temperature increases at both the Nd:YAG and CO_2 laser wavelengths. We see that once above the melting point there is effectively no difference between the two.

5.1.1 Temperature changes assuming no melting or vaporization

The radiation that is not reflected then penetrates into the bulk of the material and is absorbed at a rate that depends on the absorption coefficient α. For most metals and other materials of interest α is very large (there are some exceptions such as glass and plastics) and a reasonable assumption is that the absorption of radiation takes place very close to the surface.

The problem we then have to tackle is the relatively simple one in which heat energy is incident at a constant rate onto the surface of a semi-infinite slab. Even this problem, however, would take too long to solve here and we must content ourselves with quoting the result; the interested reader is referred to Ref. 5.1.

If we let $H\, (= I(1 - R_s))$ be the rate of heat flow per unit area into the surface, then the temperature rise at a depth z below the surface at a time t after the heat flow starts is given by

$$T(z, t) = \frac{2H}{K}\, (\varkappa t)^{1/2}\, \text{ierfc}\, \left(\frac{z}{2(\varkappa t)^{1/2}}\right). \tag{5.1}$$

The function ierfc is given by

$$\text{ierfc}(x) = \frac{1}{\sqrt{\pi}}\, \{\exp(-x^2) - x(1 - \text{erf}(x))\}$$
$$\text{where } \text{erf}(x) = \frac{2}{\sqrt{\pi}} \int_0^x e^{-\xi^2}\, d\xi \tag{5.2}$$

K is the thermal conductivity (assumed here to be temperature independent) and $\varkappa$ the thermal diffusivity (i.e. $K/\rho C$, where ρ is the material density and C its specific heat capacity).

The function ierfc(x) is probably not one of the more familiar functions (erf(x), the so-called error function, is perhaps better known). To help a little with familiarization it is sketched in Fig. 5.3. We note that ierfc(x) becomes relatively small when $x > 1$ and hence Eq. 5.1 indicates that the

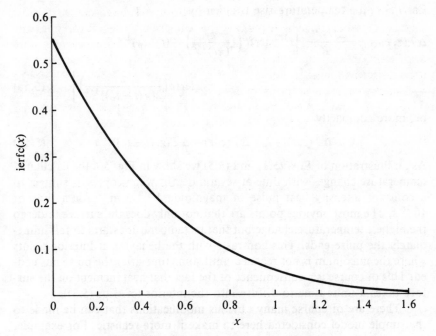

Fig. 5.3 Graph of the function ierfc(x).

temperature rise will be correspondingly small when

$$\frac{z}{2(xt)^{1/2}} > 1,$$

that is when $z^2 > 4xt$. Thus we can say that heat will diffuse a distance L in a time of the order of τ, where

$$\tau = L^2/4x. \tag{5.3}$$

The variation of the surface temperature with time is easily obtained from Eq. (5.1) by putting $z = 0$, and since Eq. (5.2) gives ierfc $(0) = 1/\sqrt{\pi}$, we have

$$\Delta T(0, t) = \frac{2H}{K} \left(\frac{xt}{\pi}\right)^{1/2}. \tag{5.4}$$

We see that the surface temperature will increase indefinitely provided heat is constantly supplied. A more realistic situation, however, is that heat is supplied for a finite time (t_p) and then switched off. In this case the temperature rise for $0 < t < t_p$ will be identical to that given by Eq. (5.1).

For $t > t_p$ the temperature rise is given by

$$\Delta T(z, t)_{t > t_p} = \frac{2H\varkappa^{1/2}}{K} \left[t^{1/2} \, \mathrm{ierfc}\left(\frac{z}{2(\varkappa t)^{1/2}}\right) - (t - t_p)^{1/2} \right.$$

$$\left. \mathrm{ierfc}\left(\frac{z}{2(\varkappa(t - t_p))^{1/2}}\right)\right] \quad (5.5a)$$

or, more compactly

$$\Delta T(z, t)_{t > t_p} = \Delta T(z, t) - \Delta T(z, (t - t_p)). \quad (5.5b)$$

As an illustration of Eqs. (5.1) and (5.5) we show in Fig. 5.4 the calculated temperature changes with time at several depths when copper is subject to a constant intensity heat pulse of magnitude $10^{10} \, \mathrm{W \, m^{-2}}$ for a time of $10^{-6} \, \mathrm{s}$. The most obvious points are that not only does the surface undergo the highest temperature change but that its temperature starts to fall immediately the pulse ends. This contrasts with the behavior at interior points where the maximum is not reached until some time after the pulse has ended. This of course is a consequence of the fact that heat incident on the surface takes a finite time to diffuse into the interior (cf. Eq. (5.3)).

There are of course many obvious modifications that can be made to the simple model considered here to make it more realistic. For example,

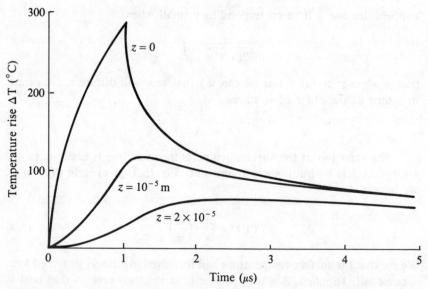

Fig. 5.4 Calculated temperature increases at various depths (z) below the surface of a semi-infinite copper block when irradiated with a constant heat pulse of $10^{10} \, \mathrm{Wm^{-2}}$ for a time of 1 μs.

to mimic the effect of a focused laser beam more accurately we should consider the non-uniform distribution of heat energy over the material surface. As a first approximation we may take the heat energy as being uniformly distributed over a circular area of radius a. For the same value of the incident heat energy per unit area we would expect smaller temperature rises than those given by the uniform heating model, since now heat energy can diffuse sideways as well as into the material. A detailed analysis [5.2] confirms this. The temperature rise at a depth z below the center of the heated area at a time t after the heating starts is given by

$$\Delta T(z, t) = \frac{2H(\varkappa t)^{1/2}}{K} \left[\text{ierfc}\left(\frac{z}{2(\varkappa t)^{1/2}}\right) - \text{ierfc}\left(\frac{(z^2 + a^2)^{1/2}}{2(\varkappa t)^{1/2}}\right) \right]. \qquad (5.6)$$

It is evident that the second term on the r.h.s of this expression must account for the sideways diffusion of heat. The surface temperature at the center of the spot is obtained by putting $z = 0$, i.e.

$$T(0, t) = \frac{2H(\varkappa t)^{1/2}}{K} \left[\frac{1}{\pi^{1/2}} - \text{ierfc}\left(\frac{a}{2(\varkappa t)^{1/2}}\right) \right].$$

This expression in fact gives almost identical results to those of the uniform heating (i.e. Eq. (5.4)) provided that

$$\text{ierfc}\left(\frac{a}{2(\varkappa t)^{1/2}}\right) \ll 1 \qquad \text{or} \qquad t \ll a^2/4\varkappa.$$

The quantity $a^2/4\varkappa$ thus represents the time taken for any significant radial heat conduction to occur. This result should not be altogether unexpected since from Eq. (5.3) it also represents the time for heat to diffuse a distance a. Typical values of $a^2/4\varkappa$ are of the order of a millisecond or so. For example, taking $a = 1$ mm and $\varkappa = 10^{-4}$ m^{2}s^{-1} (i.e. copper) gives a value of 2.5×10^{-3} s.

For very long heating times (i.e. taking $t \to \infty$) it may be shown (see Problem 5.4) that Eq. (5.6) reduces to

$$\Delta T(z, \infty) = \frac{H}{K} [(z^2 + a^2)^{1/2} - z].$$

Thus for long heating times the temperature no longer increases indefinitely as in the uniform heating model but tends towards a limit. The highest surface temperature rise than can be achieved is given by

$$\Delta T(0, \infty) = Ha/K.$$

The effects of other non-uniform surface heating distributions (for example Gaussian or rectangular distributions) may also be calculated; however, in general the results are not too different from those given by Eq. (5.6).

As well as spatial non-uniformities in the surface heating more realistic temporal variations may be considered. For example, laser pulse shapes are

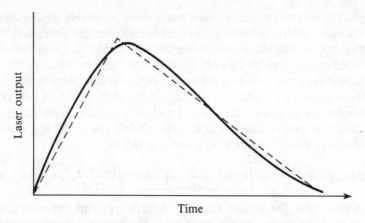

Fig. 5.5 Typical variation of laser output with time over a laser pulse. It may be approximated by a triangle.

Example 5.1   Estimated temperature rise during a heat pulse

Suppose a heat pulse of duration t_p falls onto a metal surface. We may estimate the depth (L_p) to which the heat will diffuse in a time t_p by using Eq. (5.3); thus

$$L_p = 2\sqrt{(\varkappa t_p)}$$

Considering a unit cross-sectional area of the material, the heated volume is $L_p \times 1$ and the total amount of heat deposited during the pulse is Ht_p, where H is the (constant) heat flow per unit area during the pulse. Assuming that the heat is uniformly deposited throughout the heated volume, the average temperature rise is Ht_p/mC, where m is the mass of the heated volume. Now $m = L_p\rho$, where ρ is the material density, and we may replace ρC by $K/\varkappa$. Thus the final result for the average temperature rise is

$$\Delta T = \frac{Ht_p \varkappa}{L_p K} = \frac{H}{2K}\sqrt{(t_p \varkappa)}.$$

We may apply this to the situation dealt with in Fig. 5.4. Substituting $H = 10^{10}\ \mathrm{W\,m^{-2}}$, $t_p = 10^{-6}\ \mathrm{s}$, $K = 385\ \mathrm{W\,m^{-1}\,K^{-1}}$, $\varkappa = 10^{-4}\ \mathrm{m^2\,s^{-1}}$ gives

$$\Delta T = 135\,^{\circ}\mathrm{C}.$$

We see that this result is in reasonable agreement with the more exact analysis illustrated in Fig. 5.4.

---

closer to a triangle than they are to a rectangle (Fig. 5.5). Another problem concerns the effects of a finite material thickness, where, in general, temperature rises turn out to be larger because of the 'reflection' of heat from the rear surface.

However, all these refinements add considerably to the mathematical complexity of the model, often making it impossible to obtain an analytical solution. To make matters worse most of the relevant material properties such as reflectance, absorption coefficient, thermal conductivity and thermal diffusivity are themselves temperature dependent.

We therefore concentrate wherever possible on the use of comparatively simple formulae which, whilst not being strictly accurate, readily allow at least rough estimates to be made. An illustration of this is given in Example 5.1. Table 5.1 contains the values of several thermal parameters such as K and $\varkappa$ for various materials of importance.

5.1.2 Melting depths

We have seen that Eq. (5.4) predicts that so long as heat is continuously supplied to a surface, the temperature of that surface will continue to increase indefinitely. In practice the surface temperature will rise until the material melting point is reached and then the liquid/solid interface will move into the material. Continued heating may even bring the surface temperature to the material vaporization point. The main practical application of melting is of course laser welding, and here the main point of interest is the depth of penetration of the liquid zone that can be achieved before surface evaporation begins.

As in the previous section we are obliged to make some fairly drastic assumptions in the interests of simplicity. We suppose that, even when melting has taken place, we can still treat the material as if it were a single (solid) phase. From Eqs. (5.1) and (5.4) we see that at time t the ratio of interior to surface temperature is

$$\frac{\Delta T(z, t)}{\Delta T(0, t)} = \pi^{1/2} \, \text{ierfc}\left(\frac{z}{2(\varkappa t)^{1/2}}\right).$$

We wish to calculate the depth at which the temperature has just reached the material melting point when the surface has just reached the boiling point. Hence putting $\Delta T(z, t) = T_m$ (the melting point) and $\Delta T(0, t) = T_b$ (the boiling point)† the maximum depth of penetration of the melting

---

† We are assuming that we are using °C temperature units rather than K (Kelvin) since then the temperature rise is approximately equal to the final temperature.

Table 5.1

Material	Thermal conductivity† (K) ($W\,m^{-1}\,K^{-1}$)	Thermal diffusivity ($\varkappa$) ($m^2\,s^{-1}$)(10^{-6})	Specific heat capacity (C) ($J\,kg^{-1}\,K^{-1}$)	Density(ρ) ($kg\,m^{-3}$)	Melting point(T_m) (K)	Boiling point(T_v) (K)	Latent heat of vaporization(L_v) ($J\,kg^{-1}$)(10^6)
Aluminum	238	97.3	903	2710	932	2720	10.90
Copper	400	116.3	385	8960	1356	2855	4.75
Iron	82	23.2	449	7870	1810	3160	6.80
Mild steel	45	13.6	420	7860	1700		
Stainless steel (304)	16	4.45	460	7818	1700		
Nickel	90	22.8	444	8900	1726	3110	6.47
Silver	418	169	235	10500	1234	2466	2.31
Alumina (ceramic)	29	9.54	800	3800	2300		
Perspex	0.2	0.11	1500	1190	350		
Silicon	170	103	707	2330	1680	2628	10.6

†Measured at 300 K, values fairly strongly temperature dependent.

surface (z_m) is found by solving

$$T_m/T_b = \pi^{1/2} \, \text{ierfc}\left(\frac{z_m}{2(\varkappa t)^{1/2}}\right).$$

From Eq. (5.4) we have

$$(\varkappa t)^{1/2} = \frac{T_b K \pi^{1/2}}{2H}.$$

Thus z_m is given by solving

$$\text{ierfc}\left(\frac{Hz_m}{KT_b\pi^{1/2}}\right) = \frac{T_m}{\pi^{1/2}T_b}. \tag{5.7}$$

It is at once apparent that, since the only variables are H and z_m, for a given situation the product Hz_m is fixed, thus large welding depths will be given by low heat intensities applied for a long time. A numerical calculation based on Eq. (5.7) is given in Example 5.2.

Example 5.2 Welding depth in copper

As an example of solving Eq. (5.7) we estimate the heat flow per unit area required to give a weld depth of 0.1 mm. The melting and boiling points of copper are 1060°C and 2570°C respectively and hence $T_m/T_b = 0.413$. To solve Eq. (5.7) we first of all determine the number X where $\text{ierfc}(X) = \pi^{-1/2} \times 0.413$. or 0.232. From Fig. 5.3 we see that $X = 0.44$, and since

$$H = \frac{KT_b\pi^{1/2}X}{z_m}$$

we finally obtain $H = 8 \times 10^9 \, \text{W m}^{-2}$.

5.1.3 Vaporization depth

If the laser-beam irradiance is such that the temperature of the material reaches its boiling point, then significant amounts of the surface material may be removed. The rate of removal may be estimated by employing a simple energy balance arrangement. As before we consider a semi-infinite solid with a rate of heat flow H into unit area of surface. We suppose that because of vaporization the material surface is moving inwards at a velocity v_s. Thus in unit time a mass of material equal to $v_s\rho$ will be removed. Now the total amount of energy required to convert a mass m of material at an initial temperature T into a vapor can be written

$$E_v = m(C_s(T_m - T) + C_L(T_v - T_m) + L_f + L_v),$$

where

C_s = solid specific heat capacity

C_L = liquid specific heat capacity

T_m = melting point

T_v = boiling point

L_f = latent heat of fusion

L_v = latent heat of vaporization.

Usually $L_f \ll L_v$ and $T \ll T_v$ (if temperatures are in $°C$) and we assume we can put $C_s \approx C_L = C$.

Thus the heat flow required to support a surface velocity of v_s is given by

$$H = v_s \rho (CT_v + L_v) \qquad (5.8)$$

Obviously this represents the absolute *minimum* heat flow required, since we have ignored the fact that some of the material in front of the moving surface will have to be heated up as well. However, provided the normal rate of diffusion of heat into the material (as given by Eq. (5.3)) is less than v_s, then Eq. (5.8) should hold reasonably well. Equation (5.8) may be used to estimate both hole depth (see Example 5.3 and Section 5.3) and cutting rates (Sections 5.6 and 5.8).

Example 5.3   Calculation of hole depth

Suppose a heat pulse with $H = 10^{11} \, \mathrm{W\,m^{-2}}$ and with duration 500 μs is incident onto a copper surface. The hole depth will be given by $v_s t_p$ and hence from Eq. (5.8) we have

$$d = \frac{Ht_p}{\rho(CT_v + L_v)}.$$

Taking the values for L_v, ρ and C from Table 5.1 we obtain $d = 0.95$ mm.

5.2   BEAM TRANSPORT AND FOCUSING

We turn now to some of the more practical aspects of laser materials processing. A schematic diagram of the layout often used to direct the laser

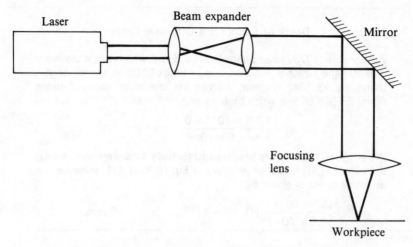

Fig. 5.6   Schematic layout of a laser beam delivery system.

beam onto the workpiece is shown in Fig. 5.6. Basically the beam is passed through a beam expander and then focused to a small spot on the workpiece using a lens. The reason for incorporating a beam expander into the optical system is that it enables a smaller final spot to be obtained. We recall from Eq. (3.19a) that the focused spot size (r_s) is given by

$$r_s = \lambda f / \pi w_L.$$

Here w_L is the beam radius at the final focusing lens, and so r_s is inversely proportional to the beam diameter at the final lens. We can also see from this equation that r_s is directly proportional to λ, so that, all other factors being equal, the focused power density varies as λ^{-2}. In this respect Nd : YAG lasers have an inherent advantage over CO_2 lasers; for identical powers and beam diameters the former can give power densities which are a factor $(10.6/1.06)^2$, i.e. some 100 times, greater.

Another aspect of interest is the so-called *depth of focus* of the beam, that is the distance we can move the workpiece away from the minimum beam radius and still have an acceptably small spot. We know from Eq. (3.11a) that the beam radius varies with distance in a parabolic manner. In fact rearranging this equation yields

$$z = \frac{\pi w_0^2}{\lambda} \left[\left(\frac{w(z)}{w_0} \right)^2 - 1 \right]^{1/2}. \tag{5.9}$$

Thus if we know the maximum value of $w(z)/w_0$ that is acceptable, then Eq. (5.9) enables the maximum tolerable variation in z to be calculated. We may note that the smaller we make the minimum beam radius the smaller also is the depth of focus.

Example 5.4   Depth of focus for a CO_2 laser beam

We consider a CO_2 laser beam ($\lambda = 10.6\ \mu m$) which has a diameter of 5 mm and which is focused using a lens of 100 mm focal length. Using Eq. (3.19a) we may obtain the minimum focused beam diameter (which we write here as w_0):

$$w_0 = \frac{10.6 \times 10^{-6} \times 0.1}{\pi \times 5 \times 10^{-3}} = 67\ \mu m.$$

We suppose that we are prepared to tolerate 10% variation in $w(z)$ then the largest value of $w(z)/w_0$ in Eq. (5.9) is 1.1, whence the depth of focus is given by

$$\frac{\pi (67 \times 10^{-6})^2}{10.6 \times 10^{-6}}\ [(1.1)^2 - 1]^{1/2} \quad \text{or} \quad 0.6\ \text{mm}.$$

Another technique that may be used for transporting laser beams from the laser to the point where the beam is required is to send the beam down a flexible fiber-optical waveguide. These will be described in more detail in Chapter 7, but basically they consist of a small diameter (~ few hundred microns) glass or quartz fiber containing a core region where the refractive index is higher than the surrounding 'cladding' (Fig. 5.7). A ray is able to travel down the core in a zig-zag fashion, undergoing total internal reflection at the core–cladding interface provided the angle it makes with the normal to the interface is greater than the critical angle. By using very high purity materials, beam losses can be made very small (as low as 0.5 dB per kilometer of fiber is possible). Because of the flexibility of such fibers, targets that are not easily accessible can be illuminated. Unfortunately such fibers can be used only up to a wavelength of some 1.6 μm, where very heavy optical absorption sets in. Thus it is not possible to use CO_2 lasers with these fibers, although the Nd:YAG laser wavelength can be readily used. CW powers of several hundred watts and pulsed powers of several

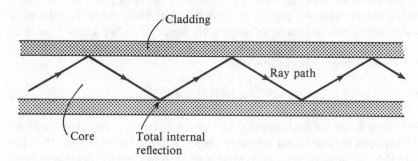

Fig. 5.7 Beam transport down an optical fiber utilizing total internal reflection.

hundred kilowatts can be transmitted. It may be possible to develop materials other than glass and silica for use as optical fiber materials which will allow transmission at 10.6 μm, but as yet nothing really satisfactory has emerged.

Having discussed some of the basic theory and hardware employed, we now consider some of the more common materials-processing applications.

5.3 MATERIALS-PROCESSING APPLICATIONS

5.3.1 Surface hardening

Surface hardening was one of the first successful applications of high-power lasers in industry. Surface hardening of ferrous materials involves heating to above a critical temperature followed by a rapid cooling (termed *quenching*). Physically what happens is that the initial heating causes a phase change to austenite. In 4% carbon steel under slow heating the austenite phase starts to form at 723 °C (called the A_1 temperature) and the phase transformation is complete by 800 °C (the A_3 temperature). In addition to the formation of austenite another important process which takes place on heating is the redistribution of the carbon that is present to form a homogeneous solid solution. Then when the austenite phase is quenched rapidly (i.e. in less than about 1 s) it is converted into martensite. It is the presence of martensite that gives the increased hardness.

There are two main problems that arise when lasers are used for heating. Firstly the heating usually takes place comparatively rapidly and this may cause the temperature required for complete austenitization to be higher than the generally accepted value. Secondly the quenching action is dependent on the rapid conduction of heat into the interior of the material, which may not be rapid enough over the range 800–250 °C to ensure the complete transformation of austenite to martensite. This latter difficulty can be overcome by employing additional cooling, usually at the surface.

Surface hardening may be carried out by scanning a laser beam over the surface to be treated. The slower the scan the higher is the maximum surface temperature that will be reached, the maximum allowable temperature being the melting point of the material. We may readily estimate the depth to which we expect to obtain martensite (this is known as the *case depth*). Suppose a laser beam of CW power W is focused onto a circular spot of diameter d which is scanned across the surface at a velocity v_b. Any particular spot will be receiving heat for a time d/v_b and during that time the rate of heat input per unit area is $4W/d^2\pi$. In terms of heat energy actually entering the material we must multiply this by $(1 - R_s)$, the average absorbance of the surface during the beam traverse. To determine the extent of the formation of austenite (and hence martensite) we need to determine the maximum temperatures that are reached at various depths within the material. This can be done by plotting curves of temperature versus time at fixed distances, such as illustrated in Fig. 5.4, and determining the maximum point on the curve. The maximum surface temperature is of course

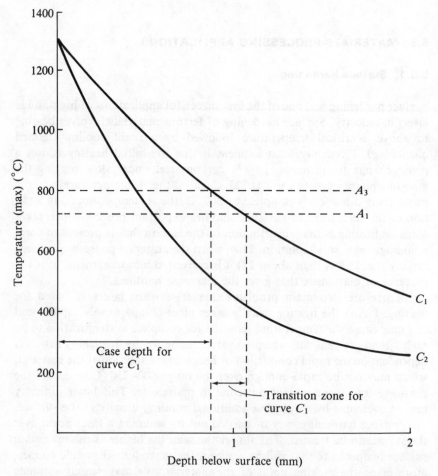

Fig. 5.8 Curves showing the maximum temperatures reached as a function of depth in 1045 steel. Curve C_1 corresponds to a heat input of $2.5 \times 10^7 \, \mathrm{W\,m^{-2}}$ applied for 0.4 s, while C_2 corresponds to $5 \times 10^7 \, \mathrm{W\,m^{-2}}$ applied for 0.1 s. The intersection of these curves with the horizontal lines corresponding to the temperatures A_3 and A_1 enables the appropriate case-hardening depths and transition zones to be determined.

easily determined from Eq. (5.4). Two such maximum temperature–distance curves determined in this way are shown in Fig. 5.8. These curves are calculated for 1045 steel which is heated by (a) a beam of irradiance $2.5 \times 10^7 \, W \, m^{-2}$ for a time of 0.4 s (curve C_1), and (b) a beam of irradiance $5 \times 10^7 \, W \, m^{-2}$ for a time of 0.1 s (curve C_2). Both of these situations give rise to the same maximum surface temperature but we see that the less intense but longer duration heating pulse results in higher temperatures in the interior. If we draw horizontal lines through the A_1 and A_3 temperatures we can see to what depth the steel has been hardened. All the material heated to above A_3 is fully hardened, whereas that material which was heated to less than A_3 shows progressively less hardening until the A_1 temperature is reached. No hardening occurs below this temperature because no austenite is formed. From Fig. 5.8 we may readily determine the depth to which full hardening is expected and also the width of the transition zone. For example, for the lower-irradiance longer-heating-time situation (curve C_1) the full hardening zone is 0.9 mm deep and the transition zone some 0.2 mm deep. It is evident from Fig. 5.8 that for the same surface temperature rise a deeper case depth is obtained by reducing the laser power density while simultaneously increasing the heating times. From Eq. (5.4) the surface temperature is proportional to $Ht^{1/2}$. Thus if the power density is reduced by a factor 2 the heating time must be increased by a factor 4 to maintain the same surface temperature. Of course the case depth may also be increased by increasing the surface temperature, but care must be taken not to exceed the material melting point or the workpiece may become damaged.

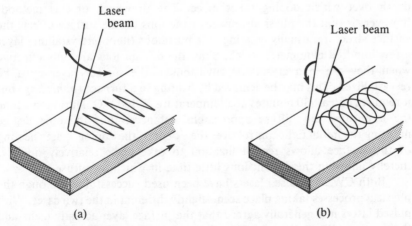

Fig. 5.9 Two methods of generating uniform heat distribution acrosss a surface by dithering the beam producing either (a) a zig-zag or (b) a spiral trace.

Often, and especially when a laser is operating in a low-order mode, the irradiance across the focused beam varies too much to give a sufficiently uniform heat treated zone across the beam diameter. Several techniques can be used to obtain a more uniform heat distribution. For example, the beam may be dithered about the mean direction of travel either in a zig-zag or a spiral fashion (Fig. 5.9). Another method involves sending the beam down the inside of a highly polished copper tube. Special multifaceted mirrors are also commercially available for the same purpose.

The efficiency of the process can be improved by coating the metal surface with an absorptive surface such as black spray paint, manganese phosphate or zinc phosphate, although the thickness used is fairly critical. If it is too thick a significant amount of energy can be wasted in burning off the coating, while if it is too thin it may be all burnt off before the beam has completely passed by.

5.3.2   Semiconductor processing

One of the main areas of semiconductor processing is the annealing of ion implant damage in silicon. Ion implantation is an important technique for the precision doping of semiconductors (that is, for the controlled introduction into pure silicon of relatively small concentrations of impurity ions which affect the electrical properties). One alternative doping technique is to use gaseous diffusion where the semiconductor surface is exposed to a gas containing the impurity which is then deposited on the surface and diffuses in. With ion implantation the surface is physically bombarded with the impurity ions, and the kinetic energy of the ions controls very precisely the depth over which doping takes place. The drawback of this method, however, is that the physical impact of the ions on the surface affects the surface structure, usually creating an amorphous (i.e. noncrystalline) layer a few hundred nanometers thick. Since the dopant ions are only effective when they are in a crystalline environment the surface layer must be recrystallized. This may be achieved by heating in a furnace (*annealing*) but it requires at least 30 minutes at a temperature of 1000 °C. During this time the impurities can diffuse appreciable distances, thus to some degree negating the initial tight control over the extent of the doping. Laser heating of the surface allows recrystallization to take place relatively quickly, thereby allowing the dopant ions little time in which to diffuse.

Both CW and pulsed lasers have been used successfully, although the physical processes taking place seem slightly different in the two cases. With pulsed lasers it is generally agreed that the surface layer actually melts and then re-crystallizes. Provide the melt depth is such that there is a liquid–crystalline structure interface, then when the surface layer re-solidifies it takes on the crystal structure of the underlying material (a process called *liquid phase epitaxy*). Typical melt times are of the order of 10^{-6} s, during which time the dopant ions can only diffuse to the order of 0.1 μm. With CW lasers, on the other hand, no melting need take place, but nevertheless the surface structure is again restored (a process called *solid phase epitaxy*).

Athough laser annealing has the advantage of giving rise to relatively small dopant diffusion it can also be used to modify the profile of the implanted ions. Figure 5.10 shows the different profiles obtained in arsenic doped silicon for two different values of the energy density.

It must be said, however, that although laser annealing offers a much better control over the doping profile, devices made from laser-annealed material are often inferior to those made from furnace-annealed material. The problems seem to arise from the presence of point and cluster defects,

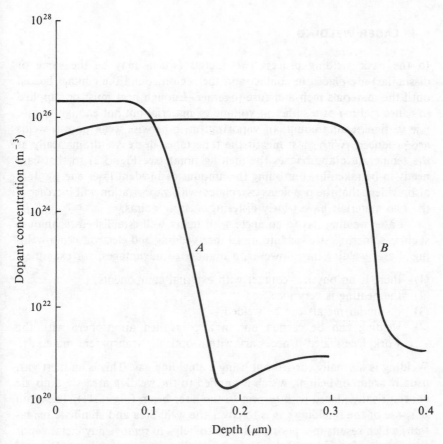

Fig. 5.10 Doping profiles of laser-annealed arsenic-implanted silicon. Curve A corresponds to a laser heat input of 1.2×10^{-4} J m^{-2}, and curve B to 2×10^{-2} J m^{-2}.

and although these can be removed by further treatment, this does make the manufacturing technique rather more involved.

Laser annealing of polycrystalline silicon is another area of interest. Polycrystalline silicon is being used increasingly by semiconductor device manufacturers as a replacement for aluminum in interconnections and gate materials for MOS devices. It has the advantage of being able to withstand higher temperatures. In addition, since oxide layers can be grown on it, polycrystalline silicon allows multilayer connections to be made. Its main disadvantage lies in its relatively high resistivity. The main reasons for this are small grain size and the inability of dopant ions to release free electrons or holes; laser annealing can improve both these and hence give rise to much improved conductivities.

5.4 LASER WELDING

In the basic welding process two metals (which may be the same or dissimilar) are placed in contact and the region round the contact heated until the materials melt and fuse together. Enough heat must be supplied to cause melting of a sufficient volume of material but not enough to give rise to significant amounts of vaporization, otherwise weak porous welds are produced. With most metals the reflectance decreases dramatically as the temperature approaches the melting point (see Fig. 5.2) so that care needs to be taken in controlling the amount of incident laser energy. It is also evident that the problems associated with vaporization will increase if the two materials have widely differing melting points.

Laser welding has to compete with many well-established techniques such as soldering, arc welding, resistance welding and electron beam welding. Laser welding has, however, a number of advantages, for example:

(1) there is no physical contact with external components;
(2) the heating is very localized
(3) dissimilar metals can be welded;
(4) welding can be carried out in a controlled atmosphere with the workpiece sealed if necessary within optically transparent materials.

Welding is normally carried out using a shielding gas. This is an inert gas, usually argon or helium, which is applied to the welding area via a nozzle concentrically placed with respect to the laser beam (Fig. 5.11). The main purpose of the shielding gas is to cover the weld area and eliminate oxidation, which results in a poor weld. It also helps to remove any metal vapor that may be formed (and that may deposit on the focusing lens). If metal vapor is produced it may be hot enough for ionization to take place and thus form a plasma above the metal surface. This is often highly absorbent

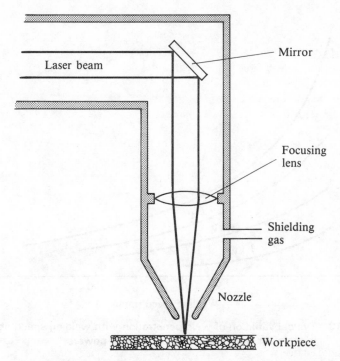

Laser beam

Mirror

Focusing
lens

Shielding
gas

Nozzle

Workpiece

Fig. 5.11 Schematic beam focusing head design for laser welding when using
a shielding gas.

at the laser wavelength and can prevent some, or in extreme cases all, of the
laser energy reaching the surface. For medium- to low-power lasers argon
is often used as the shield gas, as it is less expensive than helium but can
itself ionize in the presence of high-power pulsed beams. In such cases
helium or a mixture of helium and argon may be used.

Both CW and pulsed lasers can be used in welding. For situations
where only a small spot weld is required a single pulse from a pulsed laser
may be sufficient. If a continuous weld is required, however, the beam is
moved across the workpiece. The CW laser produces a continuous weld,
while the pulsed laser produces a train of spot welds, which may overlap
(and hence produce effectively a continuous weld) or be separated, depending on the scanning speed. We have already demonstrated how the basic
heat flow equations may be applied to a determination of the melting depth,
although such calculations yield only order-of-magnitude estimates. Figure
5.12 shows how weld pentration depends on beam scanning speed at various
power levels in 304-type stainless steel. The actual joint geometry itself can
exert a strong influence on the thickness of material that can be welded.
Close-fitting joints are desirable since there is usually little time for the

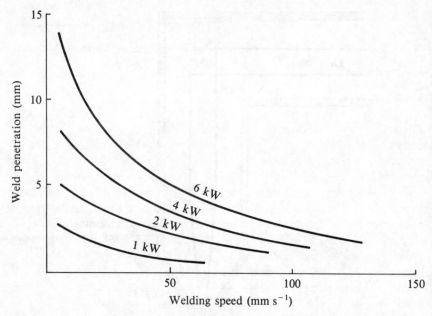

Fig. 5.12 Typical variation of weld penetration with welding speed observed in stainless steel for various CO_2 laser powers.

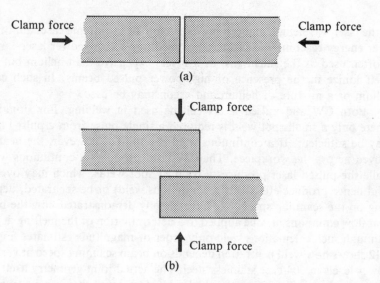

Fig. 5.13 Two geometries suitable for laser welding: (a) the butt join; (b) the lap join.

molten metal to flow to any extent. In any case only small amounts of liquid are present, mainly because the heating is usually very local. Figure 5.13 shows some typical joint designs suitable for laser welding.

5.4.1 Microwelding

The ability to focus a laser beam down to an area only a few microns across and the ease with which it can be directed and controlled has naturally led to the use of lasers in welding and soldering minute metal contacts such as are found in electronic circuits. A typical example is the precision attachment of a thermocouple to an object whose temperature is to be measured. Using a laser it is possible to create the junction, weld the thermocouple in position and even rough cut the wires to the exact length required, all in one continuous process. Thermocouple welds produced in this way have been used to attach measuring probes to such objects as transistors, turbine blades and nuclear fuel elements. Such applications rely heavily on the ability to weld dissimilar metals and to avoid thermal damage to adjacent materials.

In the realm of soldering in microcircuitry the primary advantage is again the ability to deposit exactly the required amount of heat on precisely the area to be processed. Many hybrid circuits cannot tolerate the high temperatures to which they would be subject during conventional soldering

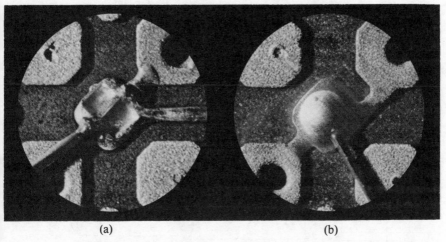

(a)   (b)

Fig. 5.14   A comparison between (a) a conventionally made microweld and (b) one made with a laser (CO_2). The connecting wires in fact link chips in a microcomputer. According to Amdahl the laser-made welds are cleaner, some 20% stronger and, because of increased precision, enable the components to be some 90% closer together (Courtesy Amdahl Corporation).

and lasers are an obvious advantage here. The increased accuracy also allows components to be more closely packed and the bond strengths are usually improved. Figure 5.14 shows a comparison between a conventional and a laser bond.

In this area the Nd:YAG laser can offer some advantages compared to the CO_2 laser. The 1.06 μm wavelength radiation of the former is much more readily absorbed by metals than by insulator materials. Consequently the beam can be scanned across multipin connectors, for example without needing to be switched off between each soldering event. The CO_2 laser wavelength on the other hand is more readily absorbed initially by insulating materials than by metals. Reflected energy from the metallic components may be sufficient to cause damage to nearby heat-sensitive objects.

5.4.2 Deep penetrating welding

When using a multikilowatt CW or pulsed-mode laser the welding process becomes somewhat more complicated than just the simple diffusion of heat away from the surface considered hitherto. When a high-power beam initially strikes the surface a significant amount of material may be vaporized,

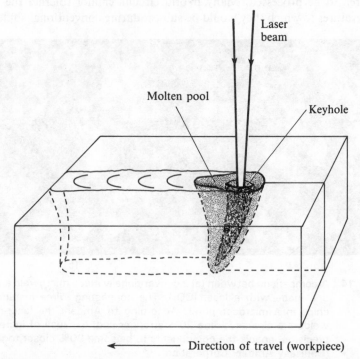

Fig. 5.15 Formation of a 'keyhole' during high-power laser welding.

forming a small hole known as a *keyhole*. Laser energy that subsequently enters the hole is trapped and carried deeper into the material than would otherwise be the case. Figure 5.15 illustrates this process when a CW laser is being used. Pulsed CO_2 lasers can also make efficient use of this process by employing a pulse consisting of a very high-power initial spike of duration about 100 μs followed by a much lower irradiance for the remainder of the pulse (Fig. 5.16). Such a pulse shape can be obtained by controlling the discharge current in the laser. The peak power during the spike is sufficient to create the inital keyhole but during the rest of the pulse there is insufficient power to cause further vaporization. The material round the keyhole melts, however, and fills in the hole. Since the absorption of energy within the keyhole is not very dependent on the condition and type of metal surface this type of action enables materials with high melting points to be welded.

CO₂ lasers are now available with CW powers of tens of hundreds of kilowatts and consequently it is possible to weld steel plates of up to several tens of millimeters thick at rates of some meters/minute. It has thus become possible to contemplate the use of laser welding in heavy industrial situations such as shipbuilding.

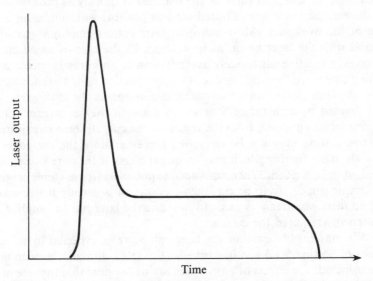

Fig. 5.16 Idealized laser pulse shape for efficient keyhole welding.

5.5 LASER-ASSISTED MACHINING

One of the problems associated with conventional approaches to the cutting of especially tough materials such as titanium alloy is that at high cutting speeds the life of the cutting tool is very short. Since these materials are used extensively in the aerospace industry there is much interest in techniques that enable the cutting rates to be speeded up. One possibility is laser-assisted machining. During cutting a high-power laser beam is focused onto the work surface just ahead of the cutting tool. The material is softened and hence more readily removed. Because only a small area is heated the cutting tool remains relatively cool. Thus higher cutting rates become possible or alternatively longer tool life can be achieved for a given cutting speed. To reduce the natural reflectance of the metal surface an absorptive coating may be sprayed on just ahead of the laser beam. When used with Iconel 718 (a nickel-based 'super alloy'), laser-assisted machining using a 10 kW CO_2 laser and an absorptive spray has achieved a 33% increase in the metal removal rate, while at the same time reducing the wear on the cutting tool by some 40%. However, as yet laser-assisted machining is in its infancy and a good deal more research needs to be done to demonstrate its economic viability.

5.6   LASER CUTTING

In cutting, the aim is to vaporize the material as quickly as possible and to produce as narrow a heat-affected zone as possible with minimum distortion of the workpiece. Most industrial laser cutters employ a gas stream coaxial with the laser beam, as in welding. In the case of metal cutting, however, a reactive gas (usually oxygen) is used. This greatly speeds up the cutting rate since the heat produced by the reaction adds to that absorbed from the laser beam. Under favorable circumstances the cutting rate may be increased by a factor of 5 or so. In addition the gas stream helps to remove molten material from the region of the cut. In some circumstances reactive cutting may not be desirable, however, since the cut edges will have an oxide coating which may cause problems if they are subsequently required to be welded. When non-metallic materials (for example ceramics, plastics or wood) are to be cut, then oxidization is usually better avoided and an inert gas stream is used. In this case the laser has to supply all the heat energy required for cutting.

We may readily estimate the laser cutting rates expected by using the results of Section 5.1.3 and in particular Eq. (5.8), although they do not of course include the effects of any oxygen assist. Suppose that the rate of surface removal is v_s (as given by Eq. (5.8)). If the focused beam has a diameter d and the laser beam is being scanned at a velocity v_b, then the beam will traverse a distance equal to its diameter in a time d/v_b. During this time a depth of material equal to dv_s/v_b will have been removed. Hence if the required cutting depth is z, then we have

$$v_b = dv_s/z. \tag{5.10}$$

Example 5.5 Cutting rates in metals

As an example of a metal for which we have the required thermal constants we consider pure iron. From Table 5.1 we have C (specific heat capacity) = 435 $J\,kg^{-1}K^{-1}$, L_v (Latent heat of vaporization) = $6.8 \times 10^6\,J\,kg^{-1}$, ρ (density) = 7870 $kg\,m^{-3}$ and T_v (boiling point) = 3160 K (or 2887 $^{\circ}$C). We suppose the laser beam to have a power of 1 kW and to be focused down to a spot of diameter 0.25 mm. Taking Eq. (5.8) and assuming for simplicity that we may neglect the surface reflectance R_s, that is that $H = I$, we obtain

$$v_s = \frac{I}{\rho(CT_v + L_v)} = \left(\frac{10^3}{\pi(0.125 \times 10^{-3})^2}\right)\left(\frac{1}{7870(435.2887 + 6.8 \times 10^6)}\right)$$

v_s = 323 $mm\,s^{-1}$.

If the iron has a thickness of 2.5 mm, then from Eq. (5.10) we have

$$v_b = 32.3\ mm\,s^{-1}.$$

Table 5.2 shows some typical cutting rates that may be obtained in various materials, while Fig. 5.17 shows a 1200 W CO_2 laser used for cutting 6 mm steel sheet.

As well as cutting rate other important factors in cutting include the width of the material removed (the *kerf*) and the width of the heat affected zone about the cut (the *HAZ*). The kerf width is approximately equal to the

Table 5.2

	Thickness (mm)	Cutting Speed(mm/s)	Power(kW)
Aluminum	1.3	97	2
Aluminum	13	14	3
410 stainless steel	6.4	25	1.2
410 stainless steel	0.3	38	0.2†
Carbon steel	3.2	9	0.2†
Titanium alloy	6.4	47	0.25†
Invar	0.76	69	2
Glass	3.2	76	5
Ceramic tile	6.4	8	0.85
Plywood	6.4	90	0.85
Hardboard	4.8	76	0.85
Polyethylene	0.5	152	0.38

†Oxygen assist

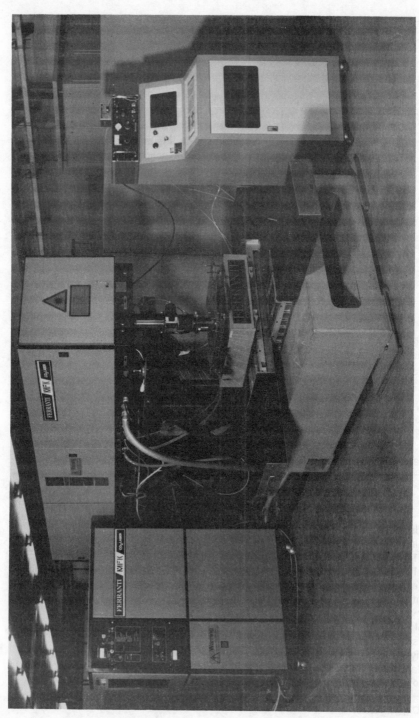

Fig. 5.17 A 1200 W CO₂ laser cutting 6 mm sheet steel. (Photo courtesy Ferranti PLC).

focused beam diameter and hence is usually relatively narrow compared to those produced by other techniques. Similarly the HAZ width is also narrow. For example, a CO_2 laser with power up to 1 kW can give a kerf of about 0.2 mm with a HAZ of 0.02 mm. These properties of laser cuts have been useful when dealing with titanium. The only other techniques available for cutting this material (plasma arc and oxyacetylene cutting) both give rise to a large kerf and to a wide HAZ. Since the HAZ must be machined away before use, laser cutting is more efficient in its use of material and also reduces the post-cutting treatment costs.

Most materials can be readily cut using a CO_2 laser with the exception of those such as brass, copper and aluminum which have high reflectances at 10.6 μm and also high thermal conductivities. In these materials little heat penetrates into the material initially and what does is rapidly conducted away into the bulk. Consequently it is difficult to raise the temperature rapidly to the melting point unless very high powers or very slow scanning speeds are used. However, since the reflectances are much lower at 1.06 μm Nd : YAG lasers can be used instead.

For non-metals, lasers have several advantages. In the slitting of paper, for example, the debris problem normally associated with mechanical techniques is eliminated. Nylon seat belt material may be cut cleanly – the cut edges are sealed and there is no burning. Foam rubber may also be cut cleanly and with no discoloration.

5.7 MICROMACHINING

There are several areas in which the ability of lasers to selectively vaporize small areas of material is useful. One such example is in the laser trimming of resistors. Resistors are made by a wide variety of techniques but often consist of a thin film of conductive material (for example nichrome, tin oxide or tantalum nitride) deposited on an insulating substrate (generally alumina, Al_2O_3) between two electrodes (Fig. 5.18(a)). As manufactured the films may not have exactly the required resistance or range of resistances and so require some kind of trimming. With a laser this may be achieved in several ways. For example, the resistance may be increased by selectively removing material from the film either by drilling holes or by cutting slots in the film (Fig. 5.18(b), (c)). A somewhat different technique is to use the laser to effect a thermally induced change in the film material. This latter technique has the advantage that in some instances it results in a reduction of the resistance. The film resistance can be monitored at all times during the trimming process (provided the material does not exhibit appreciable photoconductivity), thus ensuring very precise adjustment. The resistor can

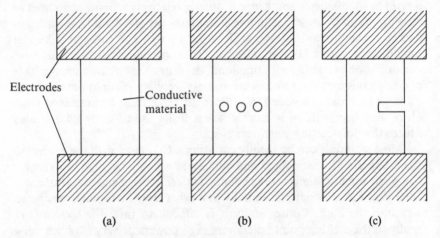

Electrodes   Conductive
                                  material

(a)   (b)   (c)

Fig. 5.18   Use of lasers for resistor trimming: (a) shows the basic resistor
structure; (b) the resistance is increased by drilling holes in the conductive material; (c) a slot is cut.

even be adjusted once it is in place in a circuit to ensure optimal performance of the circuit.

In addition to resistor trimming, lasers have also been used to form
capacitors and to process components on a silicon substrate.

5.8   DRILLING, SCRIBING AND MARKING

One of the very first industrial uses of the laser was reported in 1965 when
a diamond die for wire drawing was drilled using a pulsed ruby laser. A hole
4.7 mm in diameter and 2 mm deep was made in about 15 minutes; using
a mechanical process this had previously taken 24 hours. Figure 5.19 shows
a more recent example where cooling holes have been drilled in an aircraft
engine turbine blade using a pulsed Nd:YAG laser.

Efficient hole drilling requires that we raise as much surface target
material as possible to above its boiling point. From Eq. (5.4) we have that
$\Delta T(0, t) \propto (Ht)t^{-1/2}$. This shows that for the same total amount of heat
deposited (that is Ht) the surface temperature rise is higher the shorter the
pulse length. (A little thought shows that this is entirely reasonable. During
a long pulse the heat deposited has more time to diffuse into the material,
resulting in a relatively large volume of material being heated to a relatively
low temperature). We therefore expect pulsed lasers to be more effective
than CW ones (assuming comparable average powers). As far as hole
drilling in metals is concerned the CO_2 laser suffers from the problem of

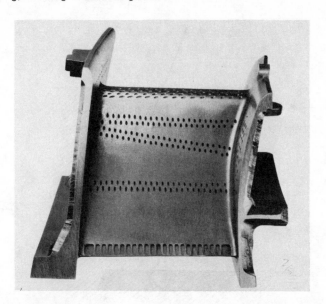

Fig. 5.19   Holes drilled in an aircraft engine turbine blade using a pulsed
Nd : YAG laser. The holes are drilled at various angles to the surface
and are 0.3–0.8 mm in diameter. Drilling time per hole varies from
0.5 to 3 s depending on the thickness of material and the hole
diameter (Photo courtesy Lasag AG).

poor initial energy absorption, and generally the Nd : YAG laser is to be
preferred. For nonmetals, however, the situation is reversed.

Hole dimensions are often described in terms of the 'aspect ratio' (the
ratio of hole depth to hole diameter) and 'taper' (the ratio of the entrance
diameter to the midsection diameter). It is found that using several pulses
rather than a single one results in holes with larger aspect ratios and smaller
tapers. As soon as a hole starts to form the radiation is striking the material
at non-normal incidence and thus may be channeled to the bottom of the
hole by an 'optical waveguide' type mechanism in which the radiation
undergoes large-angle multiple reflections at the sides of the hole (Fig.
5.20). This effect is more apparent in glass-like materials, which exhibit
large variations in reflectance with incidence angle, rather than in metals,
which have an essentially constant reflectance. As might be expected it is
found that large aspect ratios are favored by slowly converging laser beams.
One problem with holes with a large aspect ratio is that material evaporated
from the bottom of the hole may redeposit itself higher up; in severe cases
this can result in the hole being completely sealed off. In ceramic-type
materials aspect ratios of about 25 may be attained, whereas in metals this
figure is only about 12.

Holes are readily drilled in nonmetallic materials such as rubber and

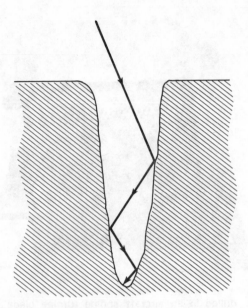

Fig. 5.20 Efficient transport of a laser beam energy to the bottom of a hole by multiple reflections at the walls.

paper. Here lasers have the advantage over conventional mechanical techniques that no distortion is introduced during the hole formation. For example lasers are used to drill holes in cigarette paper. If mechanical techniques are used the paper is so deformed that the holes can close up after they have been formed. Lasers have also been used successfully to drill holes in baby bottle nipples and in aerosol propellant valves.

Another application of lasers is in scribing. This is a process whereby a line of weakness is deliberately created along the surface of a material prior to breaking that material along the line.

Lasers have proved particularly useful in scribing silicon wafers upon which discrete elements or integrated circuits have been fabricated. Usually a large number of identical circuit elements are formed on a single substrate, which may be several tens of millimeters in diameter. Conventional separation techniques consist of traversing a diamond point along the surface under mechanical pressure. However, wear of the diamond can result in ill-defined scribing and the consequent loss of some of the circuit elements when the wafer is broken up. The use of lasers ensures a consistent and uniform scribe line as a direct result of the much more precise control that is involved.

In laser marking the beam irradiance is such as to allow only a small amount of material removal from the surface. In this way a visible mark may be produced, which provides a convenient way of engraving identification numbers or logos etc. on particular objects. Both Nd : YAG (pulsed) and CO_2 (pulsed or CW) lasers can be used. Materials that are transparent to the laser wavelength may still be marked if they are coated with a material that is absorbent.

There are basically two methods of obtaining the required pattern. One is to scan the beam across the surface using computer-controlled mirrors so that the pattern is traced out directly on the surface. This technique is very versatile but it does require a relatively high capital outlay. The other approach is to use a reflective mask with the required pattern cut out of it. This is placed over the surface, which is then irradiated with the laser beam. If a fairly high-powered pulsed CO_2 laser is used, then all that may be required is to expand the beam to the size of the mask and expose the surface to a single pulse. Alternatively the laser beam may be scanned in a raster across the mask. Use of a mask in either of these two ways is a comparatively economical technique, but is not so versatile as the other approach.

5.9 LASERS IN MEDICINE

In medicine there are three main areas in which lasers have successfully established themselves. These are in surgery as a cutting tool, in ophthalmology and in dermatology. As far as surgery is concerned, the CO_2 laser has proved the most successful all-rounder, although Nd : YAG lasers can also be used. The 10.6 μm output of the CO_2 laser is strongly absorbed by the water molecules present in tissue and the subsequent evaporation of the water leads to the physical removal of the tissue. There are several advantages over mechanical cutting: the laser beam can be positioned and controlled with a high accuracy, relatively inaccessible regions can be reached, limited damage is caused to adjacent tissue and the laser beam has a cauterizing effect on nearby blood vessels, which reduces bleeding. Obviously an essential requirement is an easily maneuverable beam delivery system. The ideal solution to this would seem to be some type of optical fiber. For the Nd : YAG laser this is no problem; however, suitable fibers do not as yet exist for 10.6 μm radiation and in CO_2 systems the beam is usually passed down the center of a series of articulated metal tubes with a mirror at each junction (Fig. 5.21).

In ophthalmology detached retinas have been successfully treated by lasers for many years now. Although ruby lasers were used initially in such operations, the green output from argon ion lasers is now more popular. The radiation is strongly absorbed by red blood cells and the resulting thermal effects lead to a re-attachment of the retina. Ophthalmology is one area where treatment is sometimes needed at some point within a uniform

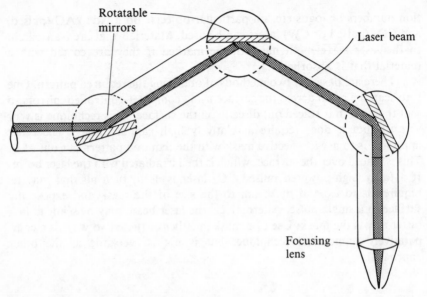

Rotatable mirrors

Laser beam

Focusing lens

Fig. 5.21   Schematic diagram of articulated arm beam delivery system for use with CO_2 lasers in surgery.

transparent optical medium. Normal 'thermal' techniques rely on the absorption of laser radiation and are not suitable here, since areas other than those needing treatment will also suffer heating effects. However, it is possible to use a laser beam to break down a medium which is transparent to the beam by using the phenomenon of dielectric breakdown. This only occurs at very high light irradiances when the electric field exceeds a critical value (in the region of $10^8 \, V \, m^{-1}$). Thus it can easily be arranged that the critical electric fields are exceeded only within a small volume surrounding, say, the focal point of a lens. In the breakdown region the high electric fields cause electrons to be stripped from the atoms present and a plasma is formed. This in turn generates a local high-pressure shock wave which expands outwards like a miniature explosion and vaporizes the surrounding medium.

Some disfiguring skin conditions can be successfully treated with lasers. Portwine marks, for example, are often difficult to treat using conventional surgery because of the extensive areas that can be involved. Uniform exposure of such areas to an argon ion laser beam can cause a bleaching of the affected areas which appears to be permanent. Similar treatment can be used in the removal of tattoos.

A method of cancer treatment called photoradiation therapy can also be used in conjunction with lasers. Patients are injected with a dye substance called HpD. After a few days the dye accumulates in the cancerous tissue (normal tissue excretes the dye). When exposed to light of

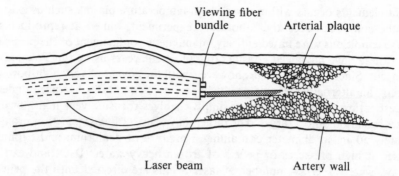

Fig. 5.22   Removal of arterial plaque using laser radiation carried down an optical fiber inserted into the artery. A viewing fiber bundle is also incorporated.

about 630 nm wavelength HpD undergoes a series of photochemical reactions resulting in the formation of a chemical that kills the cancer tissue. The radiation needed may be obtained from a dye laser pumped with an argon ion laser.

Finally in this section we may mention one possible future application. Since laser beams are readily sent down optical fibers and since fibers can be introduced into arteries using catheters, it becomes possible to contemplate the treatment of coronary artery blockages using lasers. The coronary arteries becomes blocked when deposits of plaque, a fatty material, build up on the arterial wall and reduce the space available for blood flow. Provided the optical fibers transmitting the laser beam could be accurately positioned then the plaque could, in theory, be removed by being vaporized with the laser beam (Fig. 5.22). The main danger is of accidentally burning a hole in the arterial wall. However, since plaque and arterial wall differ in a number of their optical properties it may be possible to sense the type of tissue being aimed at or being vaporized by using an auxiliary sensing fiber. Similar techniques could also possibly be used to remove other types of obstruction from veins and arteries such as blood clots.

5.10   VERY HIGH-POWER LASER USES

We conclude this chapter by describing two possible future uses of very high-power lasers.

5.10.1   Laser-induced nuclear fusion

For many years research has been directed towards a system for producing controlled thermonuclear reactions to generate energy. Nuclear fusion of light elements occurs within a very high-temperature plasma such as exists in the sun. Until recently, laboratory experiments aimed at reproducing these conditions were based entirely on magnetic confinement of the plasma and these have advanced considerably in recent years using the Tokamak concept. Since the early 1970s, however, with the advent of very high-power lasers, an alternative way of producing suitable conditions has been under investigation. The basic concept simply involves focusing very high-power laser radiation onto a target. The target may consist of glass pellets approximately 50 μm in diameter containing a mixture of deuterium and tritium gases at high pressures or pellets of frozen heavy water (D_2O) and extra heavy water (T_2O). A number of laser beams are directed onto the pellet simultaneously from symmetrically arrayed directions. Absorption of the laser radiation at the surface of the pellect causes ablation (burning off) of the outer material and an implosion of the contents. The implosion is caused by a compressional wave driving radially into the material from the periphery, thereby squeezing the pellet into a very dense core. Very high temperatures, in excess of 10^8K, are produced within this core and at these temperatures the velocities of the deuterium and tritium atoms are so great that the electrostatic repulsion of the positive nuclei is overcome and the atoms undergo fusion. A typical fusion reaction is

$$^3_1H + ^2_1H \rightarrow ^4_2He + ^1_0n \quad (14 \text{ MeV}). \quad (5.11)$$

The reaction yields a helium atom and an energetic neutron. For many such reactions to take place within the compressed pellet the high temperature must be maintained for about 1 ps and the compression must be in the region of $10^4 : 1$. These conditions require enormous laser pulse energies.

Neutron numbers in excess of 10^9 per pulse have been observed but this is considerably lower than that required to reach 'scientific breakeven', which is defined as the level at which the thermonuclear energy generated equals the laser energy input. Calculations indicate that a laser input pulse of perhaps 10^{14} W with a subnanosecond duration may be necessary to achieve breakeven and also that laser-induced fusion may be most efficient in the wavelength range 300–600 nm. A series of lasers with steadily increasing capability has been built over the last few years for this research. Between 1977 and 1981 the Shiva Nd : glass laser at the Lawrence Livermore Laboratory, California was one of the world's most powerful lasers and provided much valuable information on problems associated with ablatively compressed targets. It had 20 amplifier chains each delivering about 1 TW in a 100 ps pulse. The energy supplied to each amplifier chain was derived from a single Nd : glass master laser. Because each amplifier chain had to deliver its energy to the target at precisely the same instant the optical path lengths had all to be equal. This led to some quite contorted geometries for each chain. Fuel compressions of some 100 times that of the density of liquid deuterium–tritium were obtained. It was concluded that a laser some

10 times more powerful should create conditions close to energy breakeven, and this led to the construction of a laser called Nova, which was completed in 1985. Nova can produce 3 ns long pulses at 1.05 μm with energies up to 100 kJ; if necessary the pulsewidth can be shortened to 300 ps. In addition frequency doubling can provide 80 kJ pulses at 525 nm and 70 kJ at 350 nm (for further details see Ref. 5.3). It is hoped to be able to achieve target compressions of some 1000 times that of the liquid values.

5.10.2 Laser weapons

The outputs of the highest power lasers are now such that their use as weapons can be contemplated. To be at all effective, average output powers of at least 20 kW or single pulse energies of at least 30 kJ are called for. The laser system must be reasonably compact, light and robust and in addition the peripheral control systems require a very high level of sophistication. In a typical sequence during use the target must first of all be found and a decision taken as to which is its most vulnerable spot. The laser beam must then be aimed at the target, fired and finally a decision made as to whether the target has been destroyed. The United States of America has carried out several evaluation trials of such weapons. One possible scheme is to have such weapons situated in space and able to shoot down intercontinental nuclear missiles. Obviously for space use, size, weight and reliability are key factors. The first lasers to be tested for weaponry purposes were gasdynamic carbon dioxide lasers; however, these produced insufficient power per unit of fuel consumption to be viable. DF and HF chemical lasers emitting at 3.8 μm and 2.7 μm respectively have also been considered and may be possible candidates. Ideally, however, the output should be at shorter wavelengths than these. For example, a high-power laser operating at 0.5 μm could provide an order of magnitude increase in beam irradiance for a given laser-beam diameter. Three short-wavelength lasers are currently being examined; these are the eximer (XeF), free electron and iodine lasers. It is too early as yet to decide whether any of these will prove to be superior to the chemical laser.

PROBLEMS (Use data from Table 5.1 as required.)

5.1 A beam from a 10 W CO_2 laser is focused into a spot of area 5 mm^2 on a sheet of perspex. Estimate how how long it will take before the surface reaches its melting point.

5.2 Plot temperature–time curves at depths of 0 m and 1 mm for a semi-infinite sample of nickel when irradiated with a constant irradiance heat pulse of magnitude $7 \times 10^7 \, \text{W m}^{-2}$ and duration 0.1 s. You may find it convenient to write a short computer program to evaluate the results. A useful series expansion is:

$$\text{erf}(x) = 1 - (t(a_1 + t(a_2 + ta_3)))\exp(-x^2)$$

where $t = 1/(1 + px)$

$\qquad p = 0.47047$

$\qquad a_1 = 0.348\,024\,2$

$\qquad a_2 = -0.095\,879\,8$

$\qquad a_3 = 0.747\,855\,6.$

5.3   A heat pulse of $7 \times 10^7 \, \text{W m}^{-2}$ is incident onto a semi-infinite slab of nickel. The energy is uniformly distributed over a circle of radius 1 mm. Plot a graph of the temperature variation directly below the center of the spot at distances of 0 m and 1 mm below the surface for times up to 0.1 s. Compare your results with those of the previous problem and comment. Again, you may find it a help to write a computer program.

5.4   Show that for small x:

$\text{ierfc}(x) \sim 1/\sqrt{\pi} - x + x^2/\sqrt{\pi}.$
Hence show that in the limit $t \to \infty$, Eq. (5.6) reduces to

$$T(z, \infty) = \frac{2H}{K} \left((z^2 + a^2)^{1/2} - z \right).$$

5.5   By using an 'energy balance' argument for laser welding similar to that used in the calculation of hole depths in Example 5.3, show that the welding depth d may be written

$$d = \frac{2W}{\pi r v \rho (CT_m + L_m)}$$

Where W is the laser power (CW) actually absorbed by the surface, r is the focused beam diameter, v the welding speed and L_m is the latent heat of melting.

     Use this model to estimate the welding speed possible when welding two 1 mm thick iron plates together using a 2 kW laser. Assume that the laser output is focused down to a spot of 0.5 mm diameter. Take $L = 2.7 \times 10^5 \, \text{J kg}^{-1}$ and assume a surface reflectance of 0.5.

5.6   Examine the example in the previous problem using the technique employed in Section 5.1.2, and show that surface vaporization is expected to take place before the melting surface has penetrated to the required depth. Why in fact is this not necessarily a problem? (*Hint:* see Section 5.4.3).

5.7   It is required to drill 0.5 mm diameter holes in a nickel sheet 1 mm thick using a pulsed Nd : YAG laser with a 5 kW peak power output. Estimate the pulse length required.

5.8   Estimate the size of the focused spot required to achieve the cutting rates quoted for aluminum in Table 5.2.

5.9   It is required to focus the output of an Nd : YAG laser ($\lambda = 1.06 \, \mu\text{m}$) down to a spot of 50 μm radius. Given that the beam has an initial diameter of 1 mm, calculate the focal length of the lens required. What will be the resulting depth of focus?

5.10 Calculate the total energy released in the typical nuclear fusion reaction quoted in Eq. (5.11). Explain why this differs from the value given in the text for the energy of the neutron. (You will need a table of nuclear masses.)

5.11 Estimate the total volume of Nd : Glass laser amplifier material required to produce pulses at 1.06 μm with energy of 100 kJ. Assume that the Nd ion concentration is 3×10^{26} ions m^{-3}.

REFERENCES

5.1 H. S. Carslaw and J. C. Jaeger, *Conduction of Heat in Solids*, Oxford University Press, 1959 (2nd Ed.), Section 2.9

5.2 H. S. Carslaw and J. C. Jaeger, *Conduction of Heat in Solids*, Oxford University Press, 1959 (2nd Ed.), Section 10.5

5.3 (a) R. O. Goodwin et al., "Livermore builds a giant", *Laser Focus*, **17**, 1981, pp 58–64.

    (b) R. O. Goodwin and W. W. Simmons, "How industry helped build Nova, the world's largest high precision optical project", *Laser Focus*, **21**, 1985, pp 78–88.

More detailed information on the industrial and medical uses of lasers may be obtained from the following:

M. Bertolotti and G. Vitali, 'Laser Annealing of Semiconductors', *Current Topics in Materials Science,* **8**, 1982.

S. S. Charschan (ed.), *Lasers in Industry,* Van Nostrand Reinhold, New York, 1972.

W. W. Duley, *CO₂ Lasers, Effects and Applications,* Academic Press, New York, 1976.

A. F. Gibson, 'Lasers for Compression and Fusion', *Contemp. Phys.,* **23**, 285–97, 1982.

L. Goldman, *Lasers in Medicine and Surgery,* Vol. 37 of SPIE Proceedings, SPIE – The International Society for Optical Engineers, Bellingham, 1982.

H. Koebner, *Industrial Applications of Lasers,* Wiley, Chichester, 1984.

J. T. Luxton and D. E. Parker, *Industrial Lasers and their Applications,* Prentice-Hall, Englewood Cliffs, N.J., 1985.

J. F. Ready, *Industrial Applications of Lasers,* Academic Press, New York, 1978.

J. F. Ready and R. K. Erf (eds.), *Laser Applications,* Vol. 5, Academic Press, Orlando, 1984, Chapter on, 'Laser Processing of Integrated Circuits and Microelectronic Materials'.

6

Holography

6.1 INTRODUCTION

Holography is a technique which, in some respects, is similar to photography. It can lead to the formation of optical images and often uses photographic materials. In other respects, however, it is fundamentally different. The two techniques should be seen as complementary rather than competing processes.

In conventional photography we record the two-dimensional irradiance distribution of the image of an 'object scene', which may be regarded as consisting of a large number of reflecting or radiating points. The waves from these points all contribute to a complex resultant wave, which we call the object wave. This wave is then transformed by a lens into an image of the object which is recorded in photographic emulsion.

In holography, on the other hand, we record the object wave itself rather than the image of the object. The object wave is recorded in such a way that on subsequently illuminating the record the original object wavefront is reconstructed, even in the absence of the original object. Holography, in fact, is often referred to as *wavefront reconstruction*. Visual observation of the reconstructed wavefront gives a view of the object which is indistinguishable from the original object. That is, the image generated in holography possesses the depth and parallax properties normally associated with real objects.

The fundamental difference between photography and holography is that in photography we record only the amplitude of the resultant wave from the object (strictly speaking the photographic plate records irradiance, which is proportional to the square of the amplitude), while in holography we record both the amplitude *and* phase of the wave. We may see, in simple terms, how this is achieved, as follows.

To record the phase of the object wave we use a beam of monochromatic light originating from a small source so that the light is coherent (see Section 3.4). By this we mean that the temporal and spatial variations of the phase of the light beam are regular and predictable. If light beams are coherent then interference effects which are stable in time can be obtained. The monochromatic beam is split into two parts, as illustrated in

Fig. 6.1(a), one of which is used to illuminate the object, while the other, which we call the *reference* wave, is directed towards a photographic plate. The light directed towards the object is scattered and some of it, the object wave, also falls on the photographic plate. If the original monochromatic light has a sufficiently high degree of coherence, then the reference and object waves will be mutually coherent and will form a stable interference pattern in the photographic emulsion. The interference pattern, in general, is a complicated system of interference fringes due to the range of amplitudes and phases of the various components of the light scattered from the object. This interference pattern, which is unique to a particular object, is stored in the photographic emulsion when the plate is developed. This record is called a *hologram*.

The hologram consists of a complicated distribution of clear and opaque areas corresponding to dark and bright interference fringes. When it is illuminated with a beam of light similar to the original reference wave, as shown in Fig. 6.1(b), light is transmitted only through the clear areas, resulting in a complex transmitted wave. The hologram behaves rather like a diffraction grating. Because of the action of the recorded interference fringes the transmitted wave divides into three separate components, one of which duplicates the original object wave. In viewing this reconstructed wavefront we see an exact replica of the original object even though the object is no longer present. Holography then is a two-step process. Firstly, an interference pattern is recorded to form the hologram. Secondly, the hologram is illuminated in such a way that part of the light transmitted by it is a replica of the original object wave.

Holography was in fact invented before lasers became available. It will be appreciated, however, that as light with a high degree of coherence is required its development has proceeded most rapidly since the advent of the laser.

The science of holography was initiated by Gabor in 1948 [6.1] when trying to improve the performance of transmission electron microscopes. He realized that if a hologram were formed by light of one wavelength and then viewed by a similar beam of another wavelength then the reconstructed object would be magnified by the ratio of the wavelengths of the reconstructing and forming waves. Thus if the hologram could be created using electron waves and viewed using visible light waves, then a magnification of about 10^5 should be expected. For a number of technical reasons the method did not succeed. The most serious of these, however, was that the three components transmitted by the hologram mentioned above were coincident. These three components, the undiffracted transmitted beam, the virtual image, and the real image, will be discussed in more detail presently.

The optical arrangement depicted in Fig. 6.1(a), the so-called off-axis geometry developed by Leith and Upatnieks [6.2], avoids this problem by physically separating the two images which may be regarded as the two first

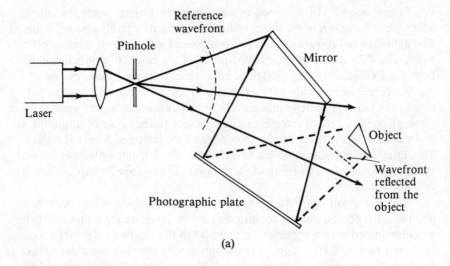

(a)

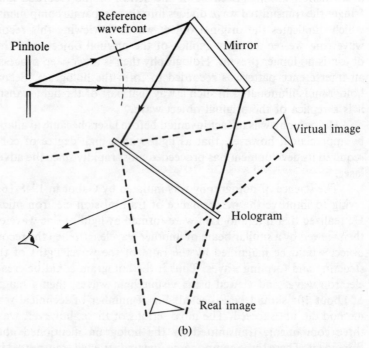

(b)

Fig. 6.1   A typical holographic arrangement: (a) making the hologram by recording the interference pattern produced by the interference of the reference and object wavefronts; (b) reconstruction of the object wavefront. The reconstruction produces two images, a virtual (orthoscopic) image and a real (pseudoscopic) image.

orders of the diffraction pattern produced by the hologram. At about the same time that Leith and Upatnieks introduced the off-axis method lasers became more widely available. The intense, coherent and monochromatic nature of laser radiation makes it ideal for holography and enables high-resolution holograms of much larger objects to be made than was previously possible.

During the last 20 years many additional geometrical arrangements and methods for producing holograms have been introduced. These include plane (or thin) and volume (or thick) holograms. In turn plane and volume holograms can be either of the absorption or phase type. These various types of hologram are described in Section 6.2, but for a more detailed discussion of them see, for example, the texts cited in Ref. 6.3. All these techniques have the unifying principle that a record of the *phase* as well as the amplitude of the object wavefront is made. Some of these different arrangements and their applications will be described later.

In parallel with the advances in the optical arrangements for holography improved photosensitive materials for recording the hologram have been introduced. These need to have a high resolution with the grain size less than about 50 nm as the interference fringes are typically one wavelength apart. In addition, for some purposes, the photosensitivity should be high to reduce exposure times, though the high irradiance available from lasers often compensates for this. Thus, while the high sensitivity of silver-halide emulsion makes it attractive in some applications, the greater resolution obtainable in other materials, such as dichromated gelatin films, is an advantage in others (see Refs. 6.4†).

6.2 CLASSIFICATION OF HOLOGRAMS

As we mentioned above, holograms can be divided into a number of different types. There are plane and volume (or thin and thick respectively) holograms depending on the interference fringe spacing relative to the thickness of the recording medium. While plane holograms are of the transmission type, volume holograms can be formed as either transmission or reflection holograms. Then, depending on the detailed nature of the recording medium, each of the above types may be an absorption or phase hologram. We shall now briefly enlarge on this classification.

Let us initially consider a hologram formed by the interference of a plane object wave such as might be produced by an infinitely distant point object and a similar plane reference wave as shown in Fig. 6.2. Such

---

† In the rest of this chapter we often refer to photographic plate or film but it should be appreciated that other recording media may be used with better effect.

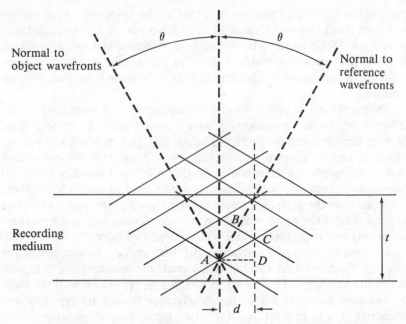

Fig. 6.2 A hologram formed by the interference of plane object and reference wavefronts in a medium of thickness t. Bright fringes which occur where the wavefronts interfere constructively are separated by distance d.

holograms are often called Fraunhofer or Fourier transform holograms, while those formed with a nearby object are called Fresnel holograms. For simplicity we let the normals for each set of wavefronts make an angle θ with the normal the recording medium, while λ is the wavelength of the light waves and t the thickness of the recording medium. The hologram produced consists of a set of equally spaced plane interference fringes which bisect the angle between the wave normals. The spatial period, d, of the fringe spacing can be derived from the geometry of Fig. 6.3.

The angle ACB is 2θ and as $AB = \lambda$; we have $AC = \lambda/\sin 2\theta$. The angle CAD is θ, so that

$$d = AC \cos \theta \qquad \text{or} \qquad d = \frac{\lambda \cos \theta}{\sin 2\theta}.$$

Expanding $\sin 2\theta$, we have

$$d = \frac{\lambda}{2 \sin \theta}. \tag{6.1}$$

Equation (6.1) is, of course, identical to the well-known Bragg condition associated with the diffraction of X-rays by the planes of atoms in crystals

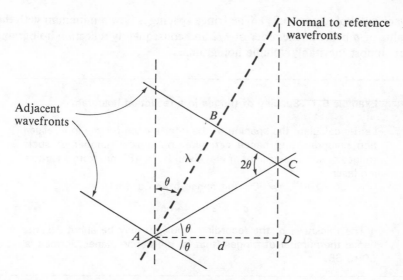

Fig. 6.3   An enlargement of region *ABCD* of Fig. 6.2 to enable the spatial period *d* of the fringes to be evaluated.

[6.5]. To record the fringe pattern the recording medium should be able to resolve approximately $1/d$ fringes per unit distance. If the angle between the object and reference waves is quite small (of the order of a few degrees), then the fringe separation d is relatively large and may be greater than the thickness of the recording medium. In this case the hologram acts as a *plane* diffraction grating as after development it consists of alternate clear and opaque strips. Thus when the hologram is illuminated with a plane wave the transmitted light comprises a zero-order wave traveling in the direction of the illuminating wave and two first-order waves. The higher diffracted orders are generally missing or very weak since the irradiance distribution of a two-beam interference pattern varies sinusoidally and rapidly drops to zero as we move away from the straight-through direction [6.6].

As the angle 2θ between the object and reference waves becomes larger the spacing d between the interference planes becomes smaller. Eventually, providing the thickness, t, of the recording medium is greater than the fringe spacing, the hologram must be considered as a *volume* or three-dimensional diffraction grating. The hologram may be regarded as a series of partly reflecting planes which respond to incident light according to Bragg's law (Eq. (6.1)). The similarity to the case of planes of atoms in a crystal selectively interacting with X-rays of certain wavelengths incident at certain angles of incidence is fairly obvious [6.5].

When the reference and object waves enter the recording medium from opposite sides, as illustrated in Fig. 6.4, that is 2θ approaches $180°$, a *reflection* hologram is formed (often referred to as a Bragg–Lippmann or a

Denisyuk hologram [6.7]). The fringe spacing is now a minimum with the value of d being of the order of $\lambda/2$ and consequently reflection holograms are almost inevitably volume holograms.

Example 6.1   Spacing of fringes in a reflection hologram

Let us calculate the spacing of the interference fringes in a reflection hologram and hence estimate the typical number of such fringes created using light of wavelength $\lambda = 488$ nm from an argon ion laser.

As $2\theta \simeq 180°$, $\theta \simeq 90°$ and hence from Eq. (6.1)

$$d \simeq \lambda/2 \simeq 244 \text{ nm}.$$

The thickness of the recording emulsion may be about 15 μm, hence the number of fringes (that is, diffraction planes) formed is 60 to 65.

The diffraction planes lie nearly parallel to the surface of the hologram plate as shown in Fig. 6.4 (if $2\theta = 180°$ then of course the planes are parallel to the surface). They act as a resonant wavelength filter, that is, because of the need to satisfy the Bragg condition only certain wavelengths will be reflected, for a given angle of incidence of the reconstructing light. Accordingly reflection holograms may be viewed in white light providing it is spatially coherent. The reconstructing beam enters the hologram from the same side as the viewer and is reflected to produce a monochromatic, three-dimensional virtual image behind the hologram. The color of the image is determined by the small range of wavelengths in the white light beam that satisfy the Bragg condition. If the angle between the reconstructing beam and the viewer is changed, then a new wavelength range satisfies the Bragg condition and the holographic image changes color. This is the principle behind the holograms incorporated into credit cards and the like. Though in these cases the original hologram is partly masked with a screen containing a horizontal slit and a second, or rainbow, hologram is constructed with the light which passes through this slit. The slit limits the angles providing vertical information so that the rainbow hologram only has horizontal parallax. Thus as the observer's head is moved from side to side a three-dimensional view is obtained but many colored identical images can be seen as the viewer's head moves vertically up and down [6.8].

Color holograms may be made using this effect. A colored object is illuminated using red, green and blue light and the reflected light is allowed to interfere with a similarly composed reference beam. Each color then forms its own set of interference planes in the recording medium, each with different spacing. On illuminating the resultant hologram with white light

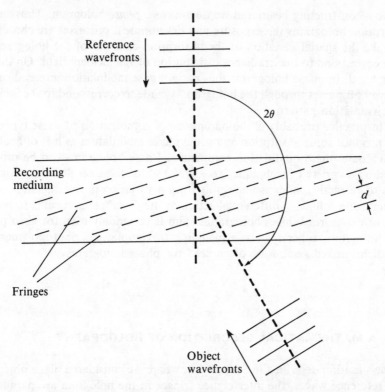

Fig. 6.4 Formation of a reflection hologram; the object and reference wavefronts are incident in nearly opposite directions. To view a reflection hologram the observer is situated on the same side of the hologram as the reference beam.

each set of planes filters out the appropriate color with which it was made and a colored reconstruction is produced.

Finally, the various holograms can be produced as absorption or phase holograms. If the recording medium is, for example, a silver halide photographic emulsion, then exposure and development of the medium converts some of the silver halide to silver atoms which form opaque regions. The transmission properties of the hologram (see Section 6.3) thus depend on the fact that some of the light of the reconstructing beam is absorbed by the opaque regions. Such holograms are called *absorption* (or amplitude) holograms.

If the hologram is now bleached so as to convert the silver to a transparent compound whose refractive index differs from that of the gelatin matrix, then the holographic record is preserved in variations in refractive index of the recording emulsion. These variations affect the phase of the reconstructing beam and we now have a *phase* hologram. Thus, in absorption holograms the exposure and development processes are chosen to make the spatial variation of the absorption constant of the hologram plate correspond to the irradiance distribution of the incident light. On the other hand, in phase holograms the spatial phase modulation imposed on a wave as it passes through the hologram is made to correspond to the incident irradiation pattern.

In practice probably all holograms are a combination of these types; they produce some absorption and some phase modulation as it is difficult to eliminate phase modulation completely. Phase holograms can be produced by a variety of techniques [6.9]. Not all of these result from variations of refractive index; some result from a variation in the thickness of the emulsion following differential action of the developer according to the level of exposure. While photographic film is commonly used for absorption holograms other materials including thermoplastics, photopolymers and dichromated gelatin are often used for phase holograms.

6.3   A MATHEMATICAL DESCRIPTION OF HOLOGRAPHY

In the situation described in Section 6.2, where we considered plane object and reference waves, the interference fringes in the hologram are parallel planes. As we mentioned in the introduction, however, the object usually consists of a very large number of reflecting points so that the object wave is complicated. The recorded interference pattern is a correspondingly complicated fringe pattern.

Let us consider the interference of two plane waves, initially traveling in the x direction and which have a phase difference between them, being brought together to interfere. The waves may be represented by equations of the form

$$\mathscr{E}_1 = \mathscr{E}_{01} \cos(\omega t - kx + \phi_1)$$

and   (6.2)

$$\mathscr{E}_2 = \mathscr{E}_{02} \cos(\omega t - kx + \phi_2)$$

The resultant of superposing these waves is

$$\mathscr{E} = \mathscr{E}_1 + \mathscr{E}_2.$$

On expanding Eqs. (6.2) and collecting terms we obtain

$$\mathscr{E} = (\mathscr{E}_{01} \cos \phi_1 + \mathscr{E}_{02} \cos \phi_2)\sin(\omega t - kx) -$$
$$(\mathscr{E}_{01} \sin \phi_1 + \mathscr{E}_{02} \sin \phi_2)\cos(\omega t - kx). \quad (6.3)$$

Equation (6.3) can be written as

$$\mathcal{E} = \mathcal{E}_0 \cos(\omega t - kx + \phi)$$

where $\mathcal{E}_0^2 = (\mathcal{E}_{01} \cos \phi_1 + \mathcal{E}_{02} \cos \phi_2)^2 + (\mathcal{E}_{01} \sin \phi_1 + \mathcal{E}_{02} \sin \phi_2)^2$

or

$$\mathcal{E}_0^2 = \mathcal{E}_{01}^2 + \mathcal{E}_{02}^2 + 2\mathcal{E}_{01}\mathcal{E}_{02} \cos(\phi_2 - \phi_1) \tag{6.4a}$$

and

$$\tan \phi = \frac{\mathcal{E}_{01} \sin \phi_1 + \mathcal{E}_{02} \sin \phi_2}{\mathcal{E}_{01} \cos \phi_1 + \mathcal{E}_{02} \cos \phi_2}. \tag{6.4b}$$

If the two waves are coherent then the term $\cos(\phi_2 - \phi_1)$ in Eq. (6.4a) varies periodically as we move across a plane on which the two waves are falling. Consequently the irradiance on this plane, given by $\mathcal{E}_0^2$, also varies periodically between maximum and minimum values given by

$$I_{max} = \mathcal{E}_{01}^2 + \mathcal{E}_{02}^2 + 2\mathcal{E}_{01}\mathcal{E}_{02}$$

or

$$I_{max} = (\mathcal{E}_{01} + \mathcal{E}_{02})^2 \tag{6.5a}$$

and

$$I_{min} = \mathcal{E}_{01}^2 + \mathcal{E}_{02}^2 - 2\mathcal{E}_{01}\mathcal{E}_{02}$$

or

$$I_{min} = (\mathcal{E}_{01} - \mathcal{E}_{02})^2 \tag{6.5b}$$

according to whether the waves are completely in phase, that is, $(\phi_2 - \phi_1) = 2n\pi$, or completely out of phase, that is, $(\phi_2 - \phi_1) = (2n + 1)\pi/2$, where n is an integer. The interference pattern thus consists of alternate bright and dark fringes.

If the object wave is from an irregular object, then the phase difference varies in a complicated way as we move across the interference plane and the interference fringes are irregular. In this case the object wavefront may be represented in the (y, z) plane, the plane of the recording medium, by

$$\mathcal{E}_{ob}(y, z) = U_0(y, z)\cos(\omega t - kx + \phi(y, z)), \tag{6.6a}$$

where x is the direction of propagation and $U_0(y, z)$ is the amplitude of the object wave, which is generally complex.† Similarly, assuming that the

---

†In general, equations such as Eq. (6.2) and (6.6) can be written in the form

$$\mathcal{E} = \mathcal{E}_0 \cos(\omega t - kx + \phi),$$

where ϕ gives the displacement of the electric vector at some point such as $x = 0$, when $t = 0$, ϕ is sometimes called the epoch angle. If we are considering only one wave, then the origin of t can be chosen so that $\phi = 0$. If we are considering many waves such as

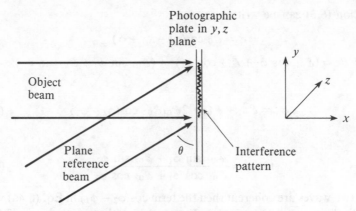

Fig. 6.5 Recording a hologram.

direction of propagation of the reference beam is inclined at an angle θ to the y direction, as shown in Fig. 6.5, then the electric field of the reference beam in the (y, z) plane may be written as

$$\mathscr{E}_r(y, z) = U_r \cos(\omega t - kx \sin \theta + ky \cos \theta), \tag{6.7a}$$

where the amplitude U_r is constant as the reference beam is a plane wave. The term $ky \cos \theta$ is a phase factor introduced because of the relative direction of travel of the two beams.

The wave equations contain the term ωt (where $\nu = \omega/2\pi$ is the frequency of the light) and the recording process will involve an average over many cycles of the light wave, so the term in ωt will simply introduce a constant multiplying factor which we may ignore. Hence the object and reference waves (Eqs. (6.6a) and (6.7a)) may be written, using complex notation, as

$$\mathscr{E}_{ob}(y, z) = U_o(y, z) e^{i(\phi(y, z) - kx)} \tag{6.6b}$$

and

$$\mathscr{E}_r(y, z) = U_r e^{i(\psi y - \beta x)}, \tag{6.7b}$$

---

we might expect in the light reflected from an object, then in general they have different epoch angles and the appropriate value of ϕ must be included in each constituent wave.

Using complex quantities the above equation can be represented by

$$\mathscr{E} = \mathscr{E}_0 \exp i(\omega t - kx + \phi),$$

if it is understood that only the real part has physical significance. Rearranging this equation, we have

$$\mathscr{E} = \mathscr{E}_0 e^{i\phi} e^{i(\omega t - kx)}$$

that is, $\mathscr{E} = U e^{i(\omega t - kx)}$, where $U = \mathscr{E}_0 e^{i\phi}$ is often called the complex amplitude and it represents both the constants $\mathscr{E}_0$ and ϕ. It follows that $UU^* = \mathscr{E}_0^2$ is proportional to the irradiance, where U^* is the complex conjugate of U.

where $\psi = k \cos \theta$ and $\beta = k \sin \theta$ are introduced to simplify the notation.

The irradiance distribution across the recording medium is the resultant of the object and reference waves and can be expressed by

$$I(y, z) = |\mathscr{E}_{ob} + \mathscr{E}_r|^2 = (\mathscr{E}_{ob} + \mathscr{E}_r)(\mathscr{E}_{ob} + \mathscr{E}_r)^* \tag{6.8}$$

$$= |\mathscr{E}_{ob}|^2 + |\mathscr{E}_r|^2 + \mathscr{E}_{ob}^* \mathscr{E}_r + \mathscr{E}_{ob} \mathscr{E}_r^* \tag{6.9}$$

where we have, for the time being, omitted the dependence of the various terms on y and z.

Substituting Eq. (6.6b) and Eq. (6.7b) into Eq. (6.9), we have

$$
\begin{aligned}
I(y, z) &= U_o^2 + U_r^2 + U_o U_r (e^{-i(\phi - kx)} e^{i(\psi y - \beta x)} + e^{i(\phi - kx)} e^{-i(\psi y - \beta x)}) \\
&= U_o^2 + U_r^2 + U_o U_r (\cos(kx - \phi + \psi y - \beta x) \\
&\quad + i \sin(kx - \phi + \psi y - \beta x) + \cos(kx - \phi + \psi y - \beta x) \\
&\quad - i \sin(kx - \phi + \psi y - \beta x)) \\
&= U_o^2 + U_r^2 + 2 U_o U_r \cos(\psi y - \phi + x(k - \beta)) \tag{6.10}
\end{aligned}
$$

or

$$
I(y, z) = U_o^2 + U_r^2 + 2 U_o U_r (\cos(\psi y - \phi) \cos(x(k - \beta)) \\
- \sin(\psi y - \phi) \sin(x(k - \beta))). \tag{6.11}
$$

Equation (6.10) indicates that the recording medium will record the sum of the squares of the amplitudes of the constituent waves together with an oscillating cosine function. This describes a pattern of fringes similar to those depicted by Eq. (6.4a).

Now if the thickness of the recording medium is small, that is, of the order of the fringe spacing, the value of x does not change very much through the film. Accordingly we may take x to be constant and for convenience set $x = 0$. In this case Eq. (6.10) becomes

$$I(y, z) = U_o^2 + U_r^2 + 2 U_o U_r \cos(\psi y - \phi). \tag{6.12}$$

The photographic film is now developed. This process results in the optical density, D, of the developed film having a dependence on the exposure, E (optical energy per unit area, that is, irradiance multiplied by exposure time), of the form shown in Fig. 6.6 (the Hurter and Driffield, or H & D, curve). The optical density is defined by

$$D = -\log_{10} T, \tag{6.13}$$

where T is the transmittance of the developed film. According to this equation the result of exposure and development will be a decrease in the transmission of the film where the light irradiance was high. That is, bright fringes in the holographic interference pattern will be recorded as absorption (or low transmittance) fringes for light transmitted through the hologram.

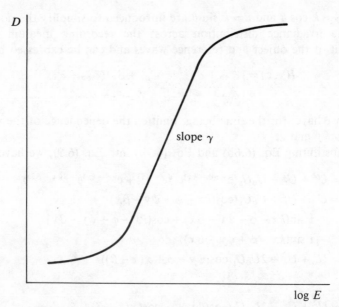

Fig. 6.6 The Hurter and Driffield (H and D) curve of optical density, D as a function of the logarithm of the exposure, E for the response of photographic emulsion.

The variation of D with $\log_{10} E$ (Fig. 6.6) shows a linear region of slope γ, which is where we attempt to work in holography. The value of γ varies with the type of film and developer used, but in many situations $\gamma \simeq 2$. Thus from Eq. (6.13) the transmittance, T, of the film is proportional to $E^{-\gamma}$.

The amplitude transmittance, t, is given by $t = T^{1/2}$, and therefore

$$t \propto E^{-\gamma/2},$$

or

$$t \propto I^{-\gamma/2}. \tag{6.14}$$

Hence for $\gamma \simeq -2$ (where the minus sign arises if the hologram is printed as a photographic positive) we may write Eq. (6.14) as

$$t = KI, \tag{6.15}$$

where K is a constant of proportionality for the given conditions of the development process. The result then of development is a photographic film which has an amplitude transmittance given, with the aid of Eq. (6.12), by

$$t = K[U_o^2 + U_r^2 + 2U_oU_r \cos(\psi y - \phi)].$$

Using Eq. (6.10) with $x = 0$, this equation may be written in the form of Eq.

(6.9), that is,

$$t = K[\mathscr{E}_{ob}^2 + \mathscr{E}_r^2 + \mathscr{E}_{ob}^*\mathscr{E}_r + \mathscr{E}_{ob}\mathscr{E}_r^*]. \tag{6.16}$$

If this film is now reilluminated with the reference beam only, as illustrated in Fig. 6.7, the light transmitted will be given by the reference beam multiplied by the film amplitude transmittance. Therefore, using Eq. (6.16) we have

$$\mathscr{E}_r(y, z)t(y, z) = K\mathscr{E}_r[\mathscr{E}_{ob}^2 + \mathscr{E}_r^2 + \mathscr{E}_{ob}^*\mathscr{E}_r + \mathscr{E}_{ob}\mathscr{E}_r^*]$$

or

$$\mathscr{E}_r(y, z)t(y, z) = K\mathscr{E}_r[U_o^2 + U_r^2] + K\mathscr{E}_r^2\mathscr{E}_{ob}^* + KU_r^2\mathscr{E}_{ob}. \tag{6.17}$$

The first two terms of Eq. (6.17) taken together are equivalent to the reconstructing beam multiplied by the slowly varying factor $K(U_o^2 + U_r^2)$. This represents the undiffracted light (or direct beam) traveling in the same direction as the reconstructing beam. The last term of Eq. (6.17) can be written using Eq. (6.6b) (with $x = 0$) as

$$KU_r^2\mathscr{E}_{ob} = KU_r^2 U_o(y, z)e^{i\phi(y, z)}. \tag{6.18}$$

This is seen to be the light distribution from the object multiplied by the constant factor KU_r^2. This factor does not affect any of the essential features of this light but simply alters the brightness of the image it forms; it is otherwise identical to the light distribution from the original object. An observer then sees the original object including its three-dimensional nature as all of the information on the phase and amplitude function of the light from the original object have been retained. The light forms a virtual image

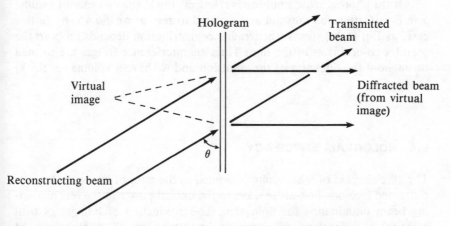

Fig. 6.7 Reconstruction of a hologram. The reconstructing beam is identical to the reference beam of Fig. 6.5. (The real image is excluded for clarity.)

and diverges from the position where the object was originally located relative to the film during the recording process. To view the image one must use a lens to collect and focus the light; alternatively by relaxing the eye and looking through the hologram the image can be seen directly.

The hologram behaves like a window through which one may observe the original object scene. By moving one's head transversely relative to the hologram different views of the object can be seen.

The remaining term in Eq. (6.17), using Eqs. (6.6b) and (6.7b) (again with $x = 0$) is

$$K\mathscr{E}_r^2 \mathscr{E}_{ob}^* = KU_r^2 U_0 \; e^{i(2\psi y - \phi(y, z))}. \tag{6.19}$$

This equation represents light which also has the phase and amplitude functions of the object wave preserved, but the negative sign of the phase $\phi(y, z)$ indicates that the light is converging rather than diverging. This light then forms a real image on an appropriately placed surface but on the opposite side of the undiffracted beam to that of the virtual image.

In fact the real image can best be seen by illuminating the hologram with a beam which is the complex conjugate of the reference beam, as the real image equation (Eq. (6.19)) also contains a term which is the complex conjugate of the object wave. One wave is conjugate with another when its amplitude is the complex conjugate of the other and its rays are oppositely directed. Thus, as in this discussion the reference beam was plane, the real image is best viewed by a plane wave oppositely directed to the original. Because of the conjugate nature of the wave the real image shows peculiar inverted depth and parallax properties – it is often said to be *pseudo-scopic* [6.10], in contrast to the virtual image which shows normal depth properties and is *orthoscopic*.

If the photographic emulsion is relatively thick, then we cannot assume x in Eq. (6.10) to be constant and equated to zero as we did above. In this case, as Eq. (6.10) shows, the irradiance distribution depends on both the y and x co-ordinates of the film. Thus the interference fringes are formed throughout the thickness of the emulsion and we have a volume (or thick) hologram.

6.4 HOLOGRAM EFFICIENCY

The efficiency, η, of a hologram is defined as the ratio of the optical power diffracted into one first-order wave to the optical power in the reconstructing beam illuminating the hologram. The production of holograms with reasonable diffraction efficiency is important in all applications of holography as efficient use of the available illuminating light enables us to use simple and more economical systems for forming and viewing the hologram. The achievement of high efficiency is not the only consideration as it is important that the image does not become 'noisy'.

Noise in holography arises from effects which cause (a) non-image forming light to be diffracted or scattered in the general direction of the reconstructed image, (b) nonlinearity of the amplitude transmittance – exposure characteristic of the recording medium, and (c) noise resulting from the granular nature of the recording medium.

A full discussion of the calculation of the efficiencies of various types of holograms and of noise is beyond the scope of this text. The maximum theoretical diffraction efficiencies for each type of hologram can be calculated and are shown in Table 6.1.

We see that the efficiency of volume, phase holograms in particular, is very high, though unfortunately this type of hologram is inherently noisy. On the other hand the efficiency of amplitude holograms is low. This is hardly surprising as these depend on the absorption of light and thus waste much of the optical energy used for reconstruction.

Apart from the case of the volume phase reflection hologram, these theoretical efficiencies have almost been achieved in practice.

Table 6.1

Type of hologram Modulation	Plane transmission		Volume transmission		Volume reflection	
	Amplitude	Phase	Amplitude	Phase	Amplitude	Phase
η_{max}	0.0625	0.339	0.037	1.00	0.072	1.00

6.5 APPLICATIONS OF HOLOGRAPHY

As with the laser itself the initial growth in the applications of holography was rather slow. Now, however, these are many and varied and their range is increasing at a more rapid pace, as the field continues to develop. Many of these applications, however, require the skillful combination of holography and other techniques.

Some of the more important applications are particle size analysis, high-resolution imaging, holographic optical elements, information storage and processing, displays and holographic interferometry as applied to the measurement and analysis of vibrations, stress and strain and small movements of a wide range of objects. A full understanding of several of these is beyond the scope of this text and the reader is referred to the texts cited in Ref. 6.11. We shall restrict ourselves to a general outline of some of them, sufficient to illustrate the varied nature of holographic techniques.

6.5.1 Holographic interferometry

Holographic interferometry is an extension of the interferometric techniques described in Chapter 4 [6.12]. The unique advantage of holographic interferometry is that the hologram stores the object wavefront for reconstruction at a later time. Thus it enables wavefronts which are separated in time or space, or even wavefronts formed by light of different wavelengths to be compared. Hence changes in the shape or small displacements of objects with rough, diffuse reflecting surfaces can be studied by this method in contrast to the methods described in Chapter 4. Holographic interferometry is commonly divided into a number of classes which we shall now describe.

6.5.1.1 Double exposure holographic interferometry

This technique, which is widely used in industry, enables very small displacements or distortions of an object to be measured. First of all the object under investigation is recorded as a hologram. Then, before the photographic plate is developed, the object is subjected to stress, moved slightly or whatever and a second exposure is made on the same plate. When the processed plate is illuminated with the original reference beam two

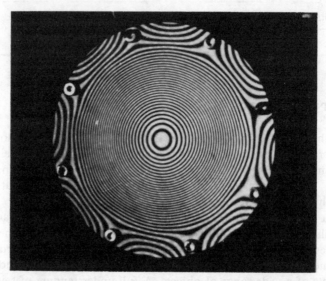

Fig. 6.8 A double exposure holographic interferogram showing the deformation of a circular membrane which has been deformed by uniform pressure. (Photograph courtesy of W. Braga and C. M. Vest, The University of Michigan)

images are reconstructed, one corresponding to the unstressed object, the other to the object in its stressed or displaced state. Thus two sets of light waves reach the observer. These can interfere in the normal way so that the observer sees (an image of) the object covered with a pattern of interference fringes. This pattern is essentially a contour map of the change in shape of the object. A photograph of the fringe pattern produced by a typical double-exposure hologram is shown in Fig. 6.8.

A limitation of the technique is that information on intermediate states of the object as it is stressed is not recorded, rather only the stressed state at the time of the second exposure. This limitation can be overcome by producing either sandwich holograms or by using real-time holography.

6.5.1.2 Sandwich holograms

In sandwich holography [6.13], as shown in Fig. 6.9(a), pairs of photographic plates NF are exposed simultaneously. N_1F_1 are exposed to the unstressed object, while N_2F_2, N_3F_3, ... are exposed with the object increasingly stressed. After all of the plates have been processed, F_1 is combined with, for example, N_2 in the original plate holder and illuminated with the original reference beam to produce an interference pattern corresponding to the deformation resulting from the loading at the time of exposure of N_2. Various combinations F_1N_2, F_2N_3, F_3N_4, ... will enable incremental deformations to be analyzed.

Other advantages of this technique are that (a) ambiguities of directional movement can be eliminated and (b) the effects of large rigid-body motion or tilt of an optical component can be compensated for by slight, relative motions of the holographic images during reconstruction, as illustrated in Fig. 6.9(b) and (c).

6.5.1.3 Real-time holography

In this technique the interference fringes are viewed in real time. A hologram of the object is recorded as before, but in this case it is processed and then replaced exactly in its original position. When the hologram is reconstructed by the reference beam used during the original exposure a virtual image is seen in exactly the same position as the object. To see this image the laser light is blocked off so that it does not reach the object. If the laser beam is now allowed to illuminate the object and the object is stressed the observer will see a system of interference fringes as described above. In this case, however, the fringe pattern changes as the distortion of the object actually takes place. An example of real-time holography is given in Fig. 6.10.

Although real-time holographic interferometry provides a very sen-

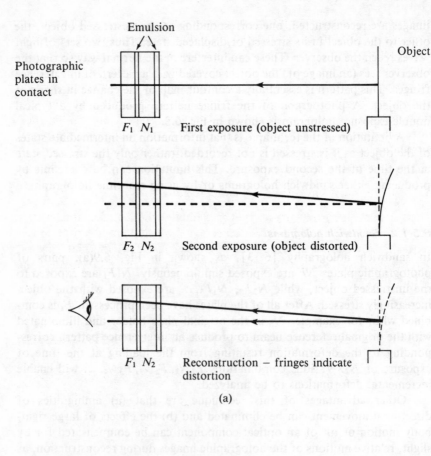

First exposure (object unstressed)

Second exposure (object distorted)

Reconstruction – fringes indicate distortion

(a)

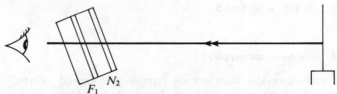

Compensation of whole object tilt between exposure – no fringes are seen in reconstruction

(b)

Fig. 6.9 (a) Diagram showing the principles of sandwich holograph: (a) illustrates how the deformation of an object may be determined from the fringe patterns produced by a simultaneous reconstruction of holograms produced at different stages in the deformation of the object; (b) illustrates how a movement of the whole of the object can be compensated for by manipulation of the holograms relative to the reconstructing beam so that no fringes are produced. The identical

sitive tool for measuring distortions in objects, perhaps several meters in size, as they actually occur there are a number of difficulties. In particular the holographic plate after processing must be replaced in *precisely* the same position as for the original exposure, otherwise spurious fringes may be introduced. In fact if the error in repositioning the plate is too great no fringes are observed at all. Another problem is that shrinkage and local deformations of the photographic emulsion during processing also introduce spurious fringes. These problems can be minimized by the use of alternative photosensitive materials such as thermoplastics.

6.5.1.4 Time-average holographic interferometry

This technique is particularly useful for examining the spatial characteristics of low-amplitude vibrations of an object. In most holographic situations a general rule is that the object should remain perfectly stationary during the period of exposure. In the present case this rule is dramatically violated, for during the exposure the object is moving continuously.

(c)

reference and reconstruction beams have been omitted for clarity). (c) These photographs illustrate, on the left, how a motion of the total object has hidden information concerning the deformation of three central bars held in a rigid frame, while, on the right, a small tilt of the hologram has eliminated the fringes on the frame leaving only the fringes on the bars, which correlate with the expected deform-ation (From an article by Nils Abramson in E. R. Robertson (ed) *The Engineering Uses of Coherent Optics*, 1976, Courtesy Cambridge University Press)

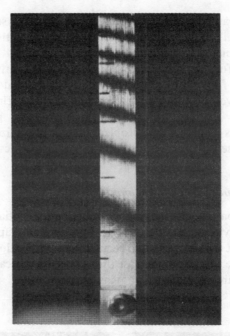

Fig. 6.10 An illustration of real time or single exposure holographic interferometry. Interference of the actual object wave with the reconstructed object wave shows the deformation of the bar. The fact that the fringes are not horizontal indicates that the bar suffers a twist in addition to bending. (From O'Shea/Callen/Rhodes *Introduction to Lasers and their Applications* © 1977 Addison-Wesley, Reading, MA. Fig. 7.14. Reprinted with permission.)

In time-average holographic interferometry one long exposure is made encompassing many vibrations of the vibrating object. As the phase of the object wave changes very slowly with time relative to that of the light the holographic recording process may be envisaged as comprising a very large number of superposed holograms – each successive hologram for a slightly different displaced position of the vibrating object. Accordingly the resulting hologram is the time-average irradiance distribution at the hologram plate.

The amount of light flux diffracted from any region of the hologram depends on the fringe contrast. Thus any motion of the object that causes the fringes to move during the exposure causes a loss of contrast and results in less diffracted flux from that region of the hologram. The greater the motion the less will be the diffracted flux and vice versa.

If the object is vibrating in a normal mode there will be standing waves of vibration across its surface. At the nodes the motion of the surface is almost zero and the hologram produces a bright image of these regions. As the vibration amplitude varies across the surface from the nodes to the antinodes, fringes, which are contours of equal vibration amplitude, cover the reconstructed image. Although the mathematical description of this is rather complicated, a conceptual notion of the result can be obtained from the following simplified model.

The exposure of a continuously vibrating surface may be considered to be similar to a double-exposure hologram in which the two different exposures represent the two positions where the surface is momentarily stationary. This, of course, occurs twice in each vibration when the surface is at the two positions of maximum displacement. In between these positions no interference fringe pattern is formed since the fringes are washed out due to the continuously changing phase of the wavefronts.

When the hologram is illuminated with the reconstructing beam the light diffracted from one set of fringes interferes with the light diffracted from the other to form a secondary set of fringes. These fringes are similar to the Moiré fringes produced when two transparencies of interference patterns are placed on top of one another. The aim is now to relate the secondary interference pattern to the movement of the vibrating surface.

Consider Fig. 6.11, in which the hologram is viewed by reflected light. Two beams are reflected from the fringes formed when the surface is stationary, that is, the two beams correspond to the peak-to-peak displacement of the surface at the point in question. If the optical path difference is λ, then the distance between the two stationary points of the vibrating surface is $\lambda/2$ and the amplitude of vibration, that is the maximum displacement of the surface from its rest position, is $\lambda/4$. Thus each secondary bright fringe represents an amplitude of $\lambda/4$ of the vibrating surface. This situation is illustrated in Fig. 6.12, in which it can be seen that the amplitude

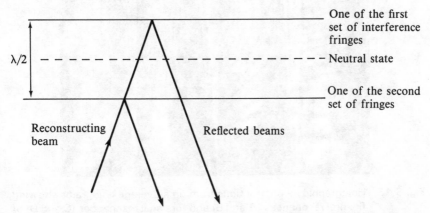

Fig. 6.11 The light reflected from the two sets of fringes formed where a vibrating surface is momentarily stationary interferes to form a secondary fringe system.

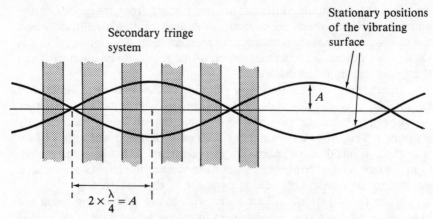

Fig. 6.12 A simplified diagram to show the relationship between the secondary fringe number and the amplitude of the displacement of the vibrating surface.

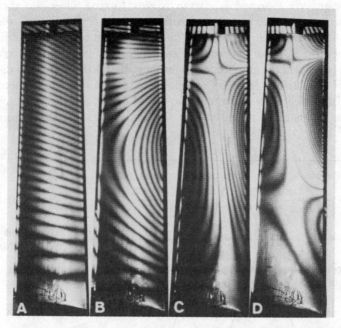

Fig. 6.13 Holographic reconstructions from time-average holograms showing flexural resonances (A and B) and torsional resonances (C and D) of a turbine blade. (From an article by Robert K. Erf in Robert K. Erf (Ed), *Holographic Non-Destructive Testing*, 1974; Courtesy Academic Press.)

of vibration at the antinodes is $\lambda/2$, half the wavelength of the reconstructing light beam. (The contrast is greatest for the zero-order fringes formed at the nodes and falls off at the higher-order fringes, so that it is usually possible to identify the nodes and hence estimate the displacement of the surface at other points.) An example of the application of time-average holographic interferometry to the analysis of the vibrations of a turbine blade is shown in Fig. 6.13.

6.5.2   Holographic optical components

We have seen that a hologram is essentially a pattern of interference fringes which diffract the light transmitted by or reflected from it. Thus a suitable pattern of fringes can perform a variety of tasks which are normally performed by conventional optical components. An obvious example of this is the production of diffraction gratings by holography. Plane object and reference beams will interfere to give a series of straight-line parallel fringes which, if the beams are of equal irradiance, will have a cosine squared irradiance distribution (see Eq. (6.4a)). Although the first transmission gratings were produced some twenty-five years ago [6.14] the most successful gratings are formed in photoresist layers coated onto optical blanks. Photoresists are light-sensitive organic films which yield a relief image after exposure to light. The relief image is coated with an evaporated metal film to form a reflection grating of high quality for spectrographic applications [6.14a].

Holographic gratings have several advantages over diamond ruled gratings. For example, they are simpler and therefore cheaper to produce, they are free from the periodic and random errors in line spacing of ruled gratings, and they produce less scattered light. In addition it is possible to produce larger gratings with narrower line spacing than by conventional ruling techniques, which are limited by wear of the diamond cutter. On the other hand, to produce high-quality gratings the hologram optics must produce wavefronts which are plane to about $\lambda/10$ and the fringe pattern must be kept very stable as photoresists are photographically 'slow' and require long exposures.

Another holographic optical component which is being increasingly used in such applications as point-of-sale bar-chart readers and laser printers (see Section 7.2) is the holographic scanner. A simple disk holographic scanner is illustrated in Fig. 6.14. The disk has up to 20 or so separate holograms recorded on it. Each hologram is recorded with a point source as the object and a collimated reference beam. When the hologram is re-illuminated with the conjugate of the reference beam (see Section 6.3) a point image is formed. If now the disk is rotated about an axis perpendicular to its plane, the reconstructed image point scans out a fine line.

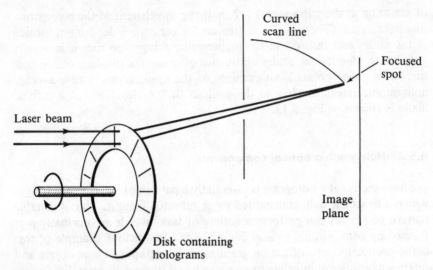

Fig. 6.14 Schematic diagrams of holographic beam scanner, which produces a curved scan line.

The main problem is that the scanning line is curved and thus not suitable for many applications such as printing. A straight-line scan can quite easily be produced, however, by the use of subsidiary optics [6.15].

Holographic scanners are replacing multifacet mirror (or polygon) scanners not only because they are cheaper but also because the optical system can be made simpler in virtue of the holographic element being able to combine multiple functions as mentioned above. In this case the hologram can combine diffraction, focusing and spectral filtering functions, in which case it may be referred to as a holographic optical element.

6.5.2.1 Holographic Optical Elements (HOE)

Holographic optical elements [6.16] have a grating structure which may be used to transform optical wavefronts in the same way as do lenses. The unique characteristics and capabilities of HOEs include the following. HOEs can serve several functions, for example an HOE may act as a combined lens, beam splitter and spectral filter. Also several HOEs may be formed in the same area of the emulsion so that several lenses can exist simultaneously. Another very important point is that the fabrication and replication of HOEs are essentially photographic and are therefore much simpler than for conventional optical components which require laborious grinding and polishing processes. Finally as they can be produced on quite thin substrates HOEs can be very light in weight even for large-aperture devices.

In principle HOEs are able to duplicate most of the functions of conventional optical elments, ranging from simple beam splitters (or combiners) to complex instruments. It seems, however, that apart from applications where their unique features are important, HOEs will not in general replace conventional optics. A typical example of an application which requires the unique features of HOEs is in providing beam combiners for display purposes such as head-up displays.

Head-up displays (HUD) are essentially reflectors arranged so that cathode ray tube (CRT) information displays may be viewed at infinity superimposed over an air pilot's normal field of view. The need for such displays originated from problems of piloting high-performance aircraft. If the pilot were to look down at the CRT display or move his head whilst executing a tight turn it would be all too easy for him to lose equilibrium and control of the aircraft. The HUD allows the pilot to have a complete and continuous view of the CRT information without the need for him to move his head.

A typical HUD is shown in Fig. 6.15. Obviously the beam combiner must not restrict the pilot's forward vision by significantly attenuating the light passing through it. Hence its reflectance must be low. If this is the case, however, the CRT display must be very bright, significantly shortening its life time.

Holographic beam combiners can be very efficient reflectors over a narrow spectral range and have a very low reflectance outside of this range. They can also be made to be physically large. Thus, by matching the

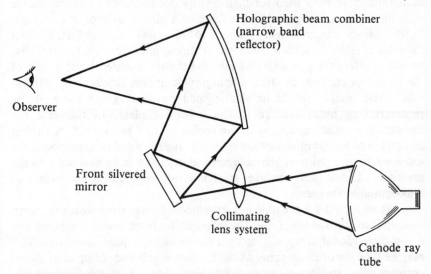

Fig. 6.15 Schematic diagram of the optical system of a head-up display. The observer can view the scene to the right of the beam combiner with information from the CRT superimposed upon it.

spectral range to that of the CRT phosphor output, we can produce an HUD with a large unimpeded field of view with the CRT information brightly superimposed upon it. Using dichromated gelatin holographic beam combiners a bandwidth of about 25 nm can be achieved matched to the phosphor peak output at a wavelength of about 525 nm. Furthermore, if the display requires a very large field of view, then curved-beam combiners, which incorporate magnification, can be produced.

Other applications of HOEs include special lenses for imaging or Fourier transformation, optical data processing elements such as matched filters, grating interferometers and information storage and display (see references cited in Ref. 6.16).

6.5.3 Information storage and display

The use of holograms as information storage devices has long been recognized as potentially a very useful application of holography [6.17]. Although a great deal of effort has been expended in their development, the applications of holographic stores are still somewhat limited. This is perhaps not too surprising when we consider the rapid development of more conventional magnetic data stores. Although access to a holographic store can be much more rapid than for other types of data store, facilities for fast-write and erasability are not so readily achieved.

The potential storage capacity of a hologram is enormous and holograms have been used for high-density document and picture storage with the information stored in the form of a binary code or microimage. In this case the storage density is about 10^4 bits mm^{-2} and, in fact, is about the same as could be achieved with conventional photography. Holography, however, offers the possibility of utilizing the three-dimensional nature of the recording medium by storing holographic images throughout its thickness; these images would be interrogated by altering the angle of the reconstructing beam relative to the hologram plate. In this case the theoretical storage capacity is in the region of 10^{10} bits mm^{-3}. A further advantage of holographic storage is that, as the recorded information is not localized but spread over the hologram plate, there is an immunity to the presence of dust and surface scratches not enjoyed by conventional photographic storage.

Let us consider a possible holographic computer store which is shown in simplified form in Fig. 6.16. The information to be stored is formed into a two-dimensional array of bits by a device called a page composer. This may be thought of as an array of light valves which may be open or closed corresponding to ones or zeros respectively. The array, containing of the order of 10^4 bits, is then stored at a particular location of the holographic memory. During recording the light modulators allow maximum irra-

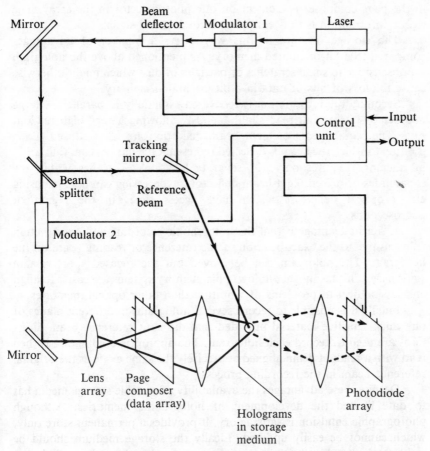

Fig. 6.16 Schematic diagram of a possible holographic memory store. The data array formed by the page composer is stored as one of many holograms in the store. These can then be accessed using the reference beam; the resulting image is projected onto the diode arrays (dotted lines).

diance in both the signal and reference beams. The beam deflectors, which may be acousto-optic or electro-optic modulators, then move the laser beam so that other holograms may be stored in appropriate positions.

Readout of the data occurs when the hologram is addressed only by the reference beam. The first modulator is partly closed to reduce the irradiance of the light reaching the holographic storage medium, while the second modulator is closed to cut off the signal beam. The deflector directs the beam to the hologram to be read via the tracking mirror and an image representing the arrays of ones and zeros is produced. This image is focused by a lens and projected onto the detector array. Each bit originally stored in the page composer is incident on one photodetector in the array. The stored information is thus converted into electrical signals.

The storage of data in this way offers a number of advantages compared to a bit-orientated memory. As mentioned above the hologram is not sensitive to small scratches or particles of dust which might otherwise cause the loss of bits of data in a bit-orientated memory.

Secondly the information is recovered essentially in parallel. A large number of bits are all read simultaneously allowing a very high readout rate. The requirements on light beam deflection are also reduced. Each position to which the beam is deflected represents 10^4 bits of data; thus a 10^8 bit memory requires only 10^4 separate locations. This lies within the capabilities of present light beam deflectors. Addressing can be done using electro-optical deflectors which have access times in the region of microseconds.

A third advantage is that the holographic recording and construction is insensitive to the exact position of the reference or reading beam on the hologram. The hologram can be moved but the focused spots remain stationary. This means that holographic memory systems are easier to align and less subject to problems of vibration than other optical memories.

Finally it is possible to record several holograms in different planes of one thick sensitive material provided that different reference beam directions are used to record each hologram. The appropriate hologram is then read with a readout beam aligned at precisely the same angle as the original reference beam in the recording process.

Despite these advantages the availability of suitable storage media has to date limited the development of holographic memories. Although photographic emulsion is satisfactory, it provides a permanent store only, which cannot be easily updated. Ideally the storage medium should be stable and alterable, have low write energy and high readout efficiency. Potentially useful read/write/erase optically sensitive materials include thermoplastic photoconductor layers, magneto-optic MnBi and electro-photochromic KCl.

Further applications of the storage capability of holograms include examination of moving or potentially dangerous objects. Thus, for example, the microscopic examination of moving particles or objects distributed throughout an appreciable volume is not possible using conventional techniques. A hologram of the whole field at any instant can be made, however, and then the reconstructed image may be viewed at leisure using a conventional microscope [6.18]. Obviously the exposure time used in making the hologram must be very short, depending on the velocity of the particles. Typically, a 10 μm particle moving with a velocity of 1 m s^{-1} requires an exposure time of about 1 μs. Suitable laser sources for this are either a pulsed ruby laser or, if a high repetition rate is required, a frequency-doubled Nd:YAG laser.

Similarly holograms have been made of discharged fuel elements from atomic reactors, enabling them to be examined in a remote situation free from nuclear radiation [6.19].

6.5.4 Character recognition

Objects can be identified by comparing them with an image of a similar object stored in a hologram. This facility finds applications in such areas as machine vision systems and the identification of aircraft and tanks for the armed forces.

In principle a hologram is made of a transparency of the set of objects to be identified using a point reference source. When the hologram is processed it is replaced in precisely the same position in which it was recorded. Whenever an object from the original set is illuminated and the scattered light allowed to fall on the hologram the transmitted light produces a bright spot. This is the reconstructed image of the reference source. Light scattered from any other object does not produce such a spot. The appearance of a spot of light is thus an indication that an object has been 'recognized'. This basic technique has been extended to permit the simultaneous recognition of many objects such as the characters on a page [6.20].

A full appreciation of holographic character recognition and many other applications of holography requires an understanding of the mathematical description of the object and reference beams and the ways in which these form the particular hologram. In turn, the way in which the hologram transforms the reconstructing beam to produce an image can also be described mathematically. While these descriptions are based on the sort of equations developed in Section 6.3, the details are far beyond the scope of this text.

In conclusion it should be pointed out that holograms can be generated by means of computers. This permits the generation of wavefronts with any prescribed amplitude and phase distribution. Thus 'ideal' three-dimensional models of objects can be produced. A typical example of the use of computer-generated holograms is in optical testing. In conventional optical testing, see Section 4.2.2, the test component is compared with a 'perfect' reference component. Such perfect components are difficult to produce in practice and they are thus replaced by a computer-generated hologram representing a perfect component [6.21].

REFERENCES

6.1   D. Gabor, 'A New Microscopic Principle', *Nature*, **161**, 777–778, 1948.
6.2   E. N. Leith and J. Upatnieks, 'Reconstructed Wavefronts and Communications Theory', *J. Opt. Soc. Am.*, **52**, 1123–1130, 1962.

6.3   (a)   H. M. Smith, *Principles of Holography* (2nd edn), Wiley-Interscience, New York, 1975, Chapters 2–5.

(b)   P. Hariharan, *Optical Holography – Principles, Techniques and Applications*, Cambridge University Press, Cambridge 1984, Chapter 4.

(c)   R. J. Collier *et al.*, *Optical Holography*, Academic Press, New York, 1971, Chapters 8–9.

6.4   See Ref. 6.3(a), Chapter 11; Ref. 6.3(b), Chapters 6 and 7; Ref. 6.3(c), Chapter 10.

6.5   W. L. Bragg, 'The Diffraction of Short Electromagnetic Waves by a Crystal', *Proc. Cambridge Phil. Soc.*, **17**, 43, 1912.

6.6   R. S. Longhurst, *Geometrical and Physical Optics* (3rd edn), Longman, London, 1973, Chapters 7, 11 and 12.

6.7   (a)   Yu N. Denisyuk 'Photographic Reconstruction of the Optical Properties of an Object in its own Scattered Radiation Field', *Soviet Physics – Doklady*, **7**, 543–545, 1962.

(b)   Yu N. Denisyuk, 'On the Reproduction of the Optical Properties of an Object by the Wave Field of its Scattered Radiation', Part I *Optics and Spectroscopy*, **15**, 279–284, 1963; Part II *Optics and Spectroscopy*, **18**, 152–157, 1965.

6.8   S. A. Benton, 'Hologram Reconstructions with Extended Incoherent Sources', *J. Opt. Soc. Am.*, **59**, 1545–1546, 1969.

6.9   See for example Ref. 6.3(a), Chapter 5.

6.10   (a)   E. N. Leith and J. Upatnieks, 'Wavefront Reconstruction with Diffused Illumination and Three-dimensional Objects', *J. Opt. Soc. Am.*, **54**, 1295–1301, 1964.

(b)   R. W. Meier, Magnification and Third Order Aberrations in Holography', *J. Opt. Soc. Am.*, **56** 219, 1966.

6.11   In addition to the texts cited in Ref. 6.3, see E. R. Robertson, 'The Engineering Uses of Coherent Optics', *Proceedings of a conference held at the University of Strathclyde, 1975*, Cambridge University Press, 1976.

6.12   C. M. Vest, *Holographic Interferometry*, John Wiley, New York, 1979.

6.13   N. Abramson, 'Sandwich Hologram Interferometry: a New Dimension in Holographic Comparison', *Applied Optics*, **13**, 2019–2025, 1974.

6.14   (a)   J. M. Burch and D. A. Palmer, 'Interferometric Methods for the Photographic Production of Large Gratings', *Optica Acta*, **8**, 73, 1961.

(b)   A. Labeyrie and J. Flamand, 'Spectrographic Performance of Holographically Made Diffraction Gratings, *Optics communications*, **1**, 5, 1969.

6.15   C. J. Kramer, 'Holographic Laser Scanners for Non Impact Printing', *Laser Focus*, **17**(6), 70, 1981.

6.16   (a)   R. Rallison, 'Applications of Holographic Optical Elements', *Lasers and Applications*, 61, 1984.

(b)   B. J. Chang, 'Dichromated Gelatin Holograms and Their Applications', *Opt. Eng.*, **19**(5), 642, 1980.

6.17   (a)   G. R. Knight, Holographic Memories', *Opt. Eng.*, **14**, 453, 1975.

(b)   L. K. Anderson, 'Holographic Optical Memory for Bulk Data Storage', *Bell Labs Record*, 46, 313, 1968.

6.18   J. D. Trolinger, 'Particle field holography', *Opt. Eng.*, **14**, 383–392, 1975.

6.19   B. A. Tozer and J. M. Webster, 'Holography as a Measuring Tool', *CEGB Research*, January, 3–30, 1981.

6.20   A. Vander Lugt, F. B. Rotz and A. Klooster, Jr., 'Character Reading by

Optical Spatial Filtering', In J. T. Tipper *et al.* (eds.), *Optical and Electro-optical Information Processing*, MIT Press, Cambridge, Mass., 1965.

6.21 (a) W. J. Dallas, 'Computer Generated Holograms', In B. R. Frieden (ed.), *The Computer in Optical Research*, in the series Topics in Applied Physics, Springer-Verlag Berlin, Vol. 41, pp. 291–336.

(b) A. J. MacGovern and J. C. Wyant, 'Computer-generated Holograms for Testing Optical Components', *Applied Optics*, **10**, 619–624, 1971.

7

Optical Information Transmission and Storage

7.1 OPTICAL COMMUNICATION

The use of light as the basis of a communication system is of great antiquity, the earliest recorded example being by the Greeks in the eighth century BC which relied on fire signals. Although intermediate relay stations enabled long distances to be covered, the transmission of complex messages proved to be very slow and the system was easily disrupted by adverse weather conditions. It was generally more reliable to send messages by courier using the road system. Little further progress in optical communications was made until 1880 when Alexander Graham Bell devised the *photophone*. This used a diaphragm to modulate sunlight and was capable of speech transmission over 200 m. Unfortunately it could not compete with the electrical telegraph invented by Morse in 1838, and it remained little more than a laboratory curiosity.

In 1895 Marconi demonstrated free space communication using long radio waves. Since then an ever-increasing part of the electromagnetic spectrum has been utilized for communication purposes. As the amount of information that can be transmitted increases with the frequency of the electromagnetic wave used, the interest has always been in utilizing higher and higher frequencies. Light, with a frequency of about 10^{14} Hz, has therefore a correspondingly higher potential signal capacity than either radio or microwaves (with frequencies of about 10^7 Hz and 10^{10} Hz respectively – see Fig. 1.7). Although the advantages of using light have been apparent for a long time the problem has always been to devise a transmission path that was secure and not subject to the vagaries of the weather. In 1966 Kao and Hockham, who were working at the Standard Telecommunication Laboratories in Harlow, England, realized that a glass fiber was a possible candidate [7.1]. At that time the attenuation in such fibers was very high (about 1000 dB/km†) but Kao and Hockham proposed that if this could be reduced to 20 dB/km or less then the use of optical fibers for communica-

---

† For a formal definition of the fiber attenuation, see p. 241.

tion purposes could become viable. Since then the attenuation in fibers has fallen dramatically; at present the best fibers exhibit attenuations of less than 0.2 dB/km, which in fact is very close to the theoretical limit. This has meant that information can now be sent over links some tens of kilometers long at data rates of up to several gigabits/sec (Gb/s). A number of such links has been installed (many of them for telecommunication purposes) and all have performed at or better than expectations. In the future more and more high capacity trunk links are expected to become based on optical fibers. Recent interest has also been shown in shorter links (that is a few tens or hundreds of meters long), which may, for example, be between computers at different sites or between offices at the same site. Such 'Local Area Networks' or LANs as they are called, present their own problems particularly in terms of fiber coupling and switching and, as yet, they have not met with such a ready acceptance as have telephone links.

The role of lasers in optical communication systems is to provide the source of radiation. They are not the only possibility and light emitting diodes (LEDs) can provide a much cheaper alternative. However, lasers do have several advantages over LEDs. They are able to couple much more radiation into fibers and in addition enable a higher data rate to be achieved. As we have seen in Chapter 3, the laser is a coherent source and so in principle it should be possible to employ 'homodyne' and 'heterodyne' detection systems as in radio communications. This would enable a higher detection sensitivity to be achieved and indeed experiments have shown that this is the case. However, at present the complexity of the equipment required has restricted such techniques to the laboratory.

It was mentioned at the start of this section that because of its relatively high frequency, a light-based communication system offers the possibility of very high data rates. At present, however, the highest practicable data rates are some 10^5 times smaller than is theoretically possible. The main advantages so far over say coaxial cable or twisted-wire pairs are an increased maximum distance between emitter and receiver, a smaller cable for the same data rates and an almost total immunity from electromagnetic interference. A fiber-based communication link consists of three main elements: the emitter which converts the original electrical signal to an optical signal, the fiber itself and the detector which re-converts the optical signal back into an electrical one. Before discussing these in more detail, however, we must look briefly at the form of the signal that is to be transmitted.

7.1.1 Light modulation schemes

Light is an electromagnetic wave whose electric (and magnetic) field components oscillate at a frequency of some 10^{14} Hz. The term modulation describes the process of varying one of the parameters associated with the

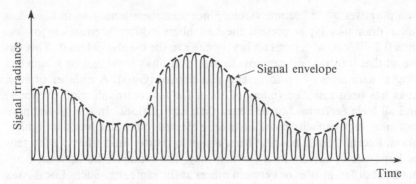

Fig. 7.1 Amplitude modulation of an optical light beam. The signal is defined by the envelope of the waveform.

carrier wave to enable information to be carried. Variations in the amplitude, irradiance, frequency, phase and polarization can all in principle be used for this purpose. Since, however, most optical detectors respond to the irradiance of the light falling on them, irradiance modulation is by far the most popular technique and is the only one we shall consider further. There are two main modulation methods commonly used to convey information via irradiance variations, namely *analog* and *digital*.

In analog modulation, the primary information signal, which we take to be a time-varying electrical voltage, continuously varies the light irradiance (Fig. 7.1). In digital modulation on the other hand, the signal amplitude is 'sampled' at regular time intervals and this information is then conveyed by means of a series of pulses. The timing and widths of the pulses are fixed but their amplitudes are restricted to certain quantized values. In the simplest such scheme, two-level binary, the pulse amplitude can take only one of two levels which are referred to as 'zero' and 'one'. The 'one' state may be represented by the presence of a pulse with a greater amplitude than some predetermined value and the 'zero' by the absence of such a pulse. The pulses are taken to occur within predetermined time slots. If the pulse width is less than the time slot it occupies, then we refer to a *return to zero* (RZ) signal. Conversely, if the pulse width fills the time slot we refer to a *non-return to zero* (NRZ) signal. Figure 7.2 illustrates these ideas. The complete process whereby an analogue signal is converted into a digital pulse-coded one is shown in Fig. 7.3. The amplitude of the incoming signal is measured at discrete intervals and the result converted into a binary number. For example, in Fig. 7.3 the signal height at $t = 2$ ms is 3 V. The number 3 in binary notation is 011 (for simplicity we use a three-digit binary number, in practice eight or more are usually required). During the interval between this sampling event and the next, the information is transmitted as a series of pulses. Thus the signal heights at the five times indicated on

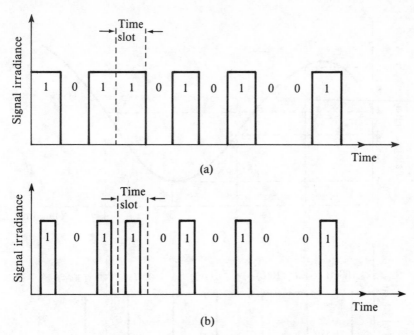

Fig. 7.2 (a) In a *non-return to zero* (NRZ) signal, each pulse exactly fills the time slot. (b) In a *return to zero* (RZ) signal, the pulse width is less than the time slot.

Fig. 7.3(a) become converted into the digital pulse train shown in Fig. 7.3(b).

To reproduce a given signal the *sampling theorem* [7.2] tells us that we must sample the signal at a rate that is at least twice that of the highest frequency component in the signal. Thus when using an 8-bit number the bit rate must be at least 16 times the highest signal frequency. In telephone communication systems, for example, the highest signal frequency is usually 4 kHz; a digital system would therefore require a bit rate of some 4×16 kb s^{-1} or 64 kb s^{-1}. The frequency bandwidth would then have to be approximately 64 kHz to enable the pulse shapes to be reasonably accurately reproduced. In fact for most practical purposes the frequency bandwidth Δf required to transmit a bit rate B is given by $\Delta f = B/2$. We thus have to use a system bandwidth that is several times larger than the corresponding analogue one, and digital systems would hardly be worth considering were it not for their relative freedom from noise and distortion. Inevitably in any communication system the transmitted and received signals will not be identical. Noise may be introduced and non-linearities in component response will distort the signal. In analog systems there is no means of countering this, but a digital signal can suffer severe distortion and still be capable of

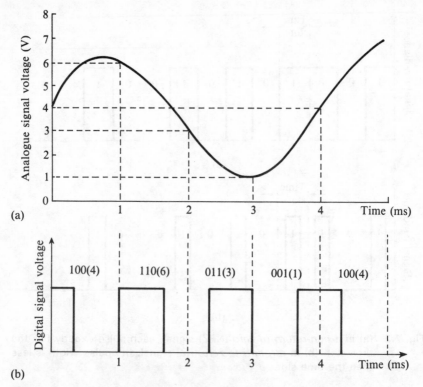

(a)

(b)

Fig. 7.3   The transformation of an analog signal into a digital one. The analog
voltage (a) is sampled every millisecond and each measurement converted into a three-bit two-level binary NRZ signal (b).

accurately imparting the original information. In Fig. 7.4 we show a severely
degraded signal but, provided that during each time slot we can always
make the correct decision as to whether it contains a 'one' pulse or a 'zero',
the original signal can be exactly reproduced. The way in which this is
usually done is to set up a *decision level*. If the signal exceeds this level at
a particular time (the *decision time*) within each time slot then a 'one' is
recorded, if it does not then a 'zero' is recorded. We shall assume in what
follows (unless it is stated otherwise) that we are dealing with a digital
system and so the information-carrying capacity of the system will be determined by the *bit rate*. For example in Europe one standard digital rate is
$139.364 \, \mathrm{Mb \, s^{-1}}$, which corresponds to a capacity of about 1920
simultaneous telephone conversations (assuming $64 \, \mathrm{kb \, s^{-1}}$ are required for
each one). After this brief overview we now move on to consider the main
components of a fiber-optical-based communication system.

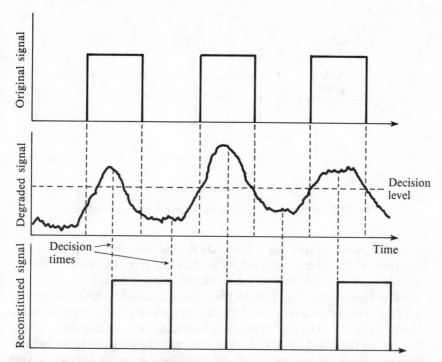

Fig. 7.4 Showing how a severely degraded digital signal can still be restored to its original condition.

7.1.2 The optical fiber

The idea that a light beam could be carried down a dielectric cylinder is not new. In 1870 Tyndall [7.3] demonstrated the guiding of light within a jet of water. However, the idea was not pursued very far since it was known that the light penetrates a little way into the medium surrounding the cylinder. This causes losses to be high and makes handling the cylinder difficult. In 1954, however [7.4], the idea of a cladded optical waveguide was put forward and the optical fiber as we know it today was born. One of the initial difficulties was that the fiber showed very high attenuation, typically 1000 dB km^{-1}. The units used here for attenuation require a little explanation. Suppose a beam of power P_i is launched into one end of an optical fiber and that the power remaining after a length L km is P_f. The attenuation (dB km^{-1}) is then given by

$$\text{Attenuation} = \frac{10 \log_{10}(P_i/P_f)}{L} \text{ dB km}^{-1}. \quad (7.1)$$

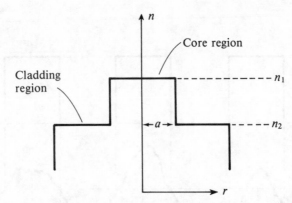

Fig. 7.5 Refractive index profile for a step-index fiber.

Originally most of the high attenuation was due to the presence of impurities in the fiber. Improved manufacturing techniques have made it possible to reduce the attenuation to values below $1 \, \mathrm{dB \, km^{-1}}$.

The simplest type of optical fiber is the step-index fiber, where the variation with refractive index with distance away from the center is as shown in Fig. 7.5. The central region is known as the core and the surrounding region the cladding. Usually the core and cladding refractive indices differ by only a few percent. Typical dimensions for such a fiber are a core diameter of 200 μm with a combined core and cladding diameter of 250 μm. When made from glass or silica the fiber is reasonably flexible and fairly strong. It is common practice though to coat the outside of the fiber with a layer of plastic which protects the fiber from physical damage and helps preserve its strength.

To see how light can be guided down such a structure, consider a beam of light which passes through the center of the fiber core and strikes the normal to the core–cladding interface at an angle θ (Fig. 7.6). Because the

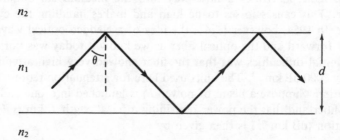

Fig. 7.6 The zig-zag path of a meridonal light ray down an optical fiber: this occurs when the angle of incidence at the interface, θ, is greater than the critical angle, θ_c.

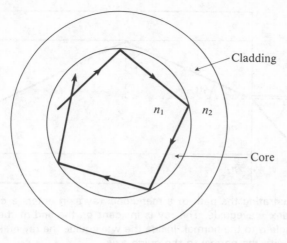

Fig. 7.7 The path of a skew ray in a circular step-index fiber seen in a projection normal to the fiber axis.

cladding has a lower refractive index than the core, total internal reflection can take place provided that the angle θ is greater than the *critical angle* θ_c, where

$$\theta_c = \sin^{-1}(n_2/n_1). \tag{7.2}$$

Total internal reflection implies that the core–cladding interface acts as a 'perfect' mirror. Thus when $\theta > \theta_c$ the ray will travel down the fiber in a zig-zag path. Because such a ray keeps passing through the center of the fiber it is known as a *meridional ray*. Other guided rays are possible which do not pass through the center. These are known as *skew rays*, and they describe angular helices as sketched in Fig. 7.7.

Let us now examine what happens to a meridional ray when it leaves the fiber. Assuming the external medium to have a refractive index of n_0 (usually $n_0 = 1$ of course if the fiber is in air), from Fig. 7.8 we see that, by Snell's law, the angle α that the ray outside the fiber makes with the normal to the fiber end is given by

$$\frac{\sin \alpha}{\sin(90° - \theta)} = \frac{n_1}{n_0}.$$

Hence $\sin \alpha = (n_1/n_0)\cos \theta$.

Since θ must always be greater than θ_c, the maximum value, α_{max}, that α can take is given by

$$\begin{aligned}
n_0 \sin \alpha_{max} &= n_1 \cos \theta_c \\
&= n_1(1 - \sin^2 \theta_c)^{1/2} \\
&= (n_1^2 - n_2^2)^{1/2}
\end{aligned}$$

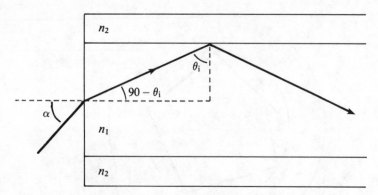

Fig. 7.8 Illustrating the path of a meridional ray as it enters a circular step-index waveguide. The ray is incident on the end of the fiber at an angle α to the normal. Inside the waveguide the ray makes an angle θ_i with the normal to the guide axis.

The quantity $(n_1^2 - n_2^2)^{1/2}$ is known as the *numerical aperture* (*NA*) of the fiber and hence

$$\alpha_{max} = \sin^{-1}(NA/n_0) \tag{7.3}$$

As well as representing the maximum angle at which light can emerge from a fiber α_{max} also represents the largest angle which light can have and still enter the fiber. Consequently α_{max} is known as the fiber acceptance angle (sometimes $2\alpha_{max}$ is used and is called the total acceptance angle). In practice because of the presence of skew rays the fiber acceptance angle is somewhat larger than the value given by Eq. (7.3). Typical values of the fiber parameters introduced so far are derived in Example 7.1.

Example 7.1 Calculation of typical fiber parameters

We consider a step-index fiber in air where $n_1 = 1.53$, $n_2 = 1.50$. The value of θ_c is given by Eq. (7.2) thus $\sin \theta_c = 1.50/1.53$, whence

$$\theta_c = 78.6°.$$

The numerical aperture of the fiber is given by

$$NA = (1.53^2 - 1.50^2)^{1/2} = 0.301.$$

The largest external angle a ray can make with the normal to the fiber end is determined from Eq. (7.3):

$$\alpha_{\mu\alpha\chi} = \sin^{-1}(0.301) = 17.5°.$$

On the simple ray picture described here the only restriction on θ is that $\pi/2 > \theta > \theta_c$. A more detailed analysis shows that between these limits θ is restricted to certain values, each one of which describes what is known as a *mode*. The modes are often referred to as linearly polarized (or LP_{lm}) modes, where the two integers l and m characterize the mode. On a simple ray picture l is a measure of the degree of helical propagation, the larger its value the 'tighter' the helix. The integer m, on the other hand, is related to θ; the larger m the larger is the value of θ involved. Each mode has its own characteristic electric field intensity distribution across the fiber (see Fig. 7.9). It is interesting to note that the electric field extends beyond the core; although it declines exponentially (and usually very rapidly) with distance into the cladding. That part of the mode that is within the cladding is often referred to as the *evanescent* mode.

The number of modes that can propagate in a fiber may be expressed in terms of a parameter V given by:

$$V = \frac{2\pi a}{\lambda_0} (n_1^2 - n_2^2)^{1/2}, \qquad (7.4)$$

where λ_0 is the vacuum wavelength of the radiation and a is the radius of the fiber core. When $V \gg 1$ (i.e. $a \gg \lambda_0$) the number of modes, N, is given by [7.5]

$$N \simeq V^2/2. \qquad (7.5)$$

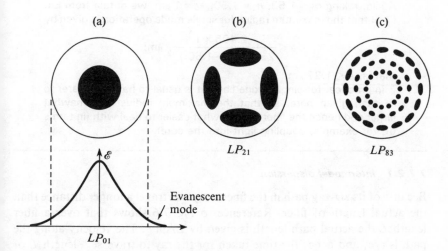

Fig. 7.9 Electric field distributions in three circular waveguide modes.

Example 7.2   Number of modes in a fiber

As in Example 7.1, we consider a fiber where $n_1 = 1.53$, $n_2 = 1.50$ and $\lambda_0 = 1$ μm. If the core radius is 100 μm, then the value of V is given by Eq. (7.4) as

$$V = \frac{2\pi \times 100 \times (1.53^2 - 1.50^2)^{1/2}}{1} = 189.4.$$

Thus the approximate number of modes N able to propagate is given by Eq. (7.5) as

$$N \simeq (189.4)^2/2 \simeq 71\,772.$$

When, however, the parameter V has a value less than 2.405, then only one mode can propagate; such a fiber is called *single-mode* (or *monomode*) fiber. From Eq. (7.4) the radius of a step-index single-mode fiber must therefore obey the condition

$$a \leqslant \frac{2.405\lambda_0}{2\pi(n_1^2 - n_2^2)^{1/2}}. \tag{7.6}$$

As we shall see in Section 7.1.2.3, one of the main advantages of single-mode fibers is that they are capable of transmitting very high-data-rate signals.

Example 7.3   Single-mode fiber radius

Again, taking $n_1 = 1.53$, $n_2 = 1.50$, $\lambda_0 = 1$ μm, we obtain from Eq. (7.6) that the maximum radius for single mode operation is given by

$$a \leqslant \frac{2.405 \times 1}{2\pi(1.53^2 - 1.50^2)^{1/2}} \ \mu\text{m};$$

that is, $a \leqslant 1.27$ μm.

In practice, for single-mode fibers it is usual to have n_1 nearer to n_2 than given here, so that the maximum radius is somewhat larger and hence the fiber is somewhat easier to deal with (in terms of, for example, coupling light into the core).

7.1.2.1   *Intermodal dispersion*

Because of its zig-zag path in the fiber a ray will travel a longer distance than the actual length of fiber. Reference to Fig. 7.6 shows that over a fiber length L the actual path length is given by $L/\sin \theta$. The velocity along the path is c/n_1 and hence the time taken for the ray to traverse a length L of fiber is given by $(L/\sin \theta)/(c/n_1) = Ln_1/c \sin \theta$. Now θ varies between θ_c and $90°$, so that the maximum difference $\Delta\tau$ between the times taken for two rays to travel a length L is given by

$$\Delta\tau = \frac{Ln_1}{c}\left(\frac{1}{\sin\theta_c} - \frac{1}{\sin 90°}\right).$$

Substituting for θ_c from Eq. (7.2) we obtain

$$\Delta\tau = \frac{L(n_1 - n_2)n_1}{n_2 c}. \tag{7.7}$$

Hence if a narrow pulse of radiation is launched into a fiber and all possible modes are excited, then we would expect that, after a given length, the pulse would broaden because of the different velocities (and hence different transit times) of the various modes present. The amount of broadening expected may be estimated from Eq. (7.7). This phenomenon is known as *intermodal* dispersion, and in multimode fibers sets a limit on the maximum bit rate that a fiber can transmit. Thus if the time between adjacent optical pulses is less than the pulse broadening, then at the end of the fiber adjacent pulses will overlap in time and degrade the signal, as illustrated in Fig. 7.10. Interestingly Eq. (7.7) often gives an overestimate of $\Delta\tau$ in the case of long fibers. This is due to mode mixing, that is, because of irregularities in the fiber (bends etc.) energy that is in one particular mode may be transferred to another mode. Thus the energy within the fiber is being continually exchanged between the different modes and hence tends to travel with an 'average' velocity. The information capacity of an optical fiber is often expressed by the *bandwidth–distance* product in MHz km.

Example 7.4 Intermodal dispersion in fibers

If we consider a 1 km length of step-index fiber with $n_1 = 1.53$ and $n_2 = 1.50$, then from Eq. (7.7) the pulse spreading is given by

$$\Delta\tau = \frac{10^3 \times (1.53 - 1.50) \times 1.53}{1.50.3 \times 10^8}\ \text{s};$$

that is, $\Delta\tau = 102$ ns.

Hence the maximum bit rate, B, in such a fiber is $1/\Delta\tau$, or approximately 10 Mb/s. Since the bandwidth required to transmit a bit rate B is $B/2$, the bandwidth–distance product of the fiber is 5 MHz km.

In single-mode fibers intermodal dispersion does not exist and in consequence much higher bit rates are possible. However, there is another type of fiber which has a much larger core diameter than a single-mode fiber and yet has a much smaller intermodal dispersion than step-index fiber; this is graded-index fiber, which we discuss in the next section.

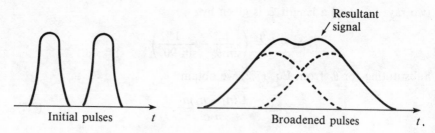

Fig. 7.10   Effect of pulse broadening on digital signal.

7.1.2.2   Graded-index fiber

Graded index fiber, as its name suggests, has a variation in refractive index across its core. This variation is often expressed in the form

$$n(r) = n_1 [1 - 2\,\Delta(r/a)^\gamma]^{1/2} \qquad r \leqslant a$$
$$n(r) = n_1 (1 - 2\,\Delta)^{1/2} \qquad\qquad r > a \qquad\qquad (7.8)$$

where $\Delta = (n_1 - n_2)/n_1$. Thus n_1 is the axial refractive index while n_2 is related to (but does not exactly equal) the cladding index. The parameter γ (the profile parameter) determines the shape of the refractive index profile. A typical refractive index profile is shown in Fig. 7.11. Graded-index fibers have somewhat smaller cores than step-index fibers, usually 50 μm diameter, with a combined core and cladding diameter of 125 μm.

We may distinguish between three different types of ray path in graded-index fibers, as illustrated in Fig. 7.12, namely the *central ray*, the *meridional rays* and the *helical rays*. In the latter two cases the rays follow smooth curves rather than the zig-zags of step-index fibers. These diagrams enable us to appreciate why intermodal dispersion is smaller than in step-index fibers. A helical ray, for example, although traversing a much longer

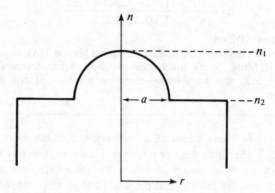

Fig. 7.11   Refractive index profile for a graded-index fiber.

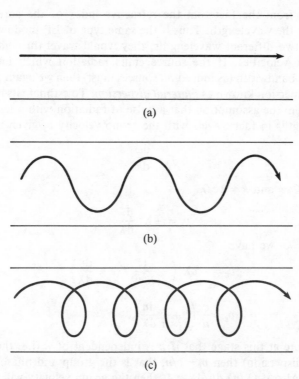

Fig. 7.12 Ray paths in a graded-index fiber. We may distinguish between (a) a *central* ray, (b) a *meridional* ray and (c) a *helical* ray avoiding the center.

path than the central ray, does so in a region where the refractive index is less and hence the velocity greater. To a certain extent the effects of these two factors can be made to cancel out, resulting in very similar propagation velocities down the fibers for the two types of ray. Similar arguments apply to the meridional rays. The amount of intermodal dispersion is dependent on the factor γ in Eq. (7.8); it is smallest when γ is slightly less than 2. Graded-index fibers have been made with bandwidth–distance products as high as 2 GHz km. The number of guided modes within a graded-index fiber with $\gamma = 2$ is one half of that for a comparable step-index fiber, which means that under the same excitation conditions it will only carry half the energy.

7.1.2.3 Low dispersion fibers

As we have seen, one way of eliminating intermodal dispersion is to use single-mode fibers. Such fibers still have bandwidth limitations, however.

This stems from the fact that the refractive index of the core material depends on the wavelength. Thus if the same type of LP mode were to be excited by two different wavelengths, they would travel through the fiber at different velocities. If the source emits radiation which has a finite wavelength bandwidth (as indeed *all* sources must) then we again get a form of pulse dispersion known as *material dispersion*. To estimate its magnitude we start from the assumption that a pulse of radiation with a finite spread of wavelengths in fact travels with the group velocity v_g given by [7.6]

$$v_g = \frac{d\omega}{dk},$$

where $\omega = 2\pi\nu$ and $k = 2\pi/\lambda$.

Hence
$$v_g = -\lambda^2 \frac{d\nu}{d\lambda}.$$

Since $\nu = c/\lambda n$ we have

$$v_g = -c\lambda^2 \left(-\frac{1}{\lambda^2 n} - \frac{1}{\lambda n^2} \frac{dn}{d\lambda} \right)$$

$$v_g = \frac{c}{n} \left(1 + \frac{\lambda}{n} \frac{dn}{d\lambda} \right). \tag{7.9}$$

We may note at this stage that if n is independent of λ (i.e. the material shows no dispersion) then $v_g = c/n$, that is the group and phase velocities are equal. Also if $(\lambda/n)\, dn/d\lambda \ll 1$, then the group velocity will not differ too much from the phase velocity, and this is indeed usually the case. At several places earlier in this chapter it has been tacitly assumed that the velocity of a pulse is that of the phase velocity (c/n). Although not quite correct, in some circumstances (but not in this section!) this does not matter too much.

If the wavelength spread of the source is $\Delta\lambda$ then the spread in group velocity Δv_g is given by

$$\Delta v_g = \frac{dv_g}{d\lambda} \Delta\lambda.$$

Using Eq. (7.9) to evaluate $dv_g/d\lambda$, we have

$$\Delta v_g = \frac{c\lambda}{n^2} \left[\frac{d^2 n}{d\lambda^2} - \frac{2}{n} \left(\frac{dn}{d\lambda} \right)^2 \right] \Delta\lambda.$$

Now the spread in time $(\Delta\tau)$ of an initially very narrow pulse after traveling a distance L is given by

$$\Delta\tau = \frac{L\, \Delta v_g}{v_g^2} = \frac{L\lambda \left(\dfrac{d^2 n}{d\lambda^2} - \dfrac{2}{n} \left(\dfrac{dn}{d\lambda} \right)^2 \right) \Delta\lambda}{c \left(1 + \dfrac{\lambda}{n} \left(\dfrac{dn}{d\lambda} \right) \right)^2}.$$

The relative magnitudes of the quantities n, $dn/d\lambda$ and $d^2n/d\lambda^2$ are such that the expression for $\Delta\tau$ may be simplified to

$$\Delta\tau = \left| \frac{L\lambda}{c} \left(\frac{d^2n}{d\lambda^2} \right) \Delta\lambda \right|. \tag{7.10}$$

The modulus sign is used in Eq. (7.10) since we are only interested in the magnitude of the pulse spreading and not whether the shortest or longest wavelengths arrive first. Figure 7.13 shows the variation of $d^2n/d\lambda^2$ for pure silica; we see that at about 1.3 μm it becomes zero and hence at this wavelength material dispersion should become very small indeed. Although fibers are not actually made from pure silica very similar conclusions may be reached for the doped silica materials (and glasses) that are used (Section 7.1.2.5). As well as material dispersion there are other factors

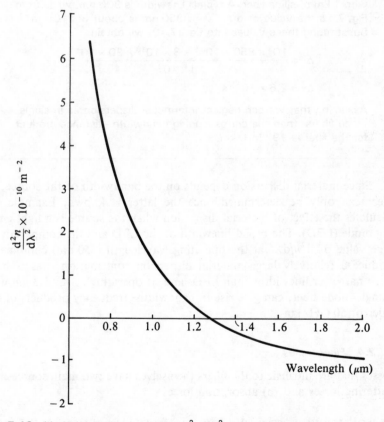

Fig. 7.13 Variation in the quantity $d^2n/d\lambda^2$ with wavelength for pure silica (SiO$_2$). The function becomes zero at about 1.3 μm, which results in very small values for the material dispersion. The addition of dopants displaces the curve slightly.

(such as waveguide dispersion) which contribute to the overall dispersion in a fiber. However, the fact that the material dispersion term changes sign at 1.3 μm while the others do not enables fibers to be constructed which have a zero total dispersion wavelength somewhere between 1.3 and 1.7 μm. As we shall see in the next section, this wavelength region is also of interest from the point of view of low fiber attenuation. Consequently considerable interest has arisen in developing sources (particularly lasers) and detectors which operate in this region.

Example 7.5   Material dispersion using an LED source

We may use Eq. (7.10) to estimate the effects of material dispersion when a GaAs LED operating at 850 nm is used in conjunction with 1 km of silica fiber. A typical linewidth is 300 nm, while from Fig. 7.13 the value of $d^2n/d\lambda^2$ at 850 nm is about 3×10^{10} m^{-2}. Substituting these values into Eq. (7.10) we obtain

$$\Delta\tau = \frac{10^3 \times 850 \times 10^{-9} \times 3 \times 10^{10} \times 30 \times 10^{-9}}{3 \times 10^8}$$

$$\Delta\tau = 2.6 \times 10^{-9}\,\text{s}.$$

Assuming that we can neglect intermodal dispersion as in single-mode fibers, then the corresponding bandwidth–distance product for the fiber is 192 MHz km.

Since material dispersion depends on the bandwidth of the source, its effect can only be determined once the latter is known. Example 7.5 calculates the effect of material dispersion when the source is a light emitting diode (LED). The broad linewidth of the LED and the comparatively large value of $d^2n/d\lambda^2$ at the operating wavelength (850 nm) combine to produce a relatively large material dispersion contribution. Lasers have much narrower linewidths than LEDs and, if operating at say 1.3 μm with a single-mode fiber, can give rise to bandwidth–frequency products of the order of 50 GHz km.

7.1.2.4 Fiber losses

Losses that are intrinsic to the fibers themselves have two main sources: (a) scattering losses and (b) absorption losses.

SCATTERING LOSSES. We have assumed, when discussing light propagation, that the fiber materials are homogeneous. Most fibers are in fact made from glasses which have a 'disordered' structure. This disorder may be either structural or compositional in origin. In structural disorder the same basic molecular units are present throughout the material, but they are connected together in an essentially random way. In compositional disorder, on the other hand, the exact chemical composition varies from place to place. Whichever of these types of disorder is present the net effect is a fluctuation in refractive index through the material. If the scale of these fluctuations is of the order of $\lambda/10$ or less then each irregularity acts as a point-source scattering center. This type of scattering is known as *Rayleigh scattering* and is characterized by an effective absorption coefficient that varies as λ^{-4} [7.7]. Rayleigh scattering is important since it represents the minimum loss that can be attained in a fiber.

ABSORPTION LOSSES. Absorption losses in the visible and near-infra red regions arise mainly from the presence of impurities, particularly traces of transition metal ions (e.g. Fe^{3+}, Cu^{2+}) or hydroxyl $(-OH)$ ions. The latter give rise to strong absorption peaks at 0.95 μm, 1.24 μm and 1.39 μm. Most

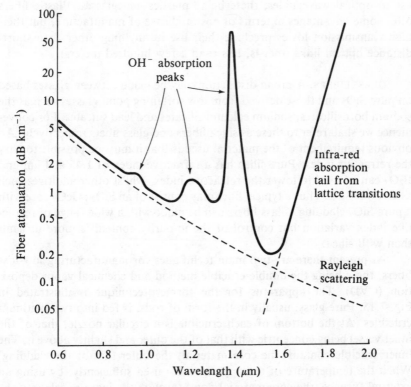

Fig. 7.14 Typical attenuation versus wavelength plot for a silica-based optical fiber. The contribution from Rayleigh scattering is shown, as are the two other main loss mechanisms, namely the infra red absorption tail and the hydroxyl (OH^-) absorption peaks.

of the dramatic successes in reducing fiber losses to date have come about because of better control of impurity concentrations.

At wavelengths greater than about 1.6 μm the fiber attenuation increases rapidly with increasing wavelength. This sudden increase is due to the presence of a lattice absorption band. Although the maximum absorption occurs at wavelengths a good deal higher (e.g. about 9 μm) the bands are very broad and extend down to below 2 μm. A typical attenuation curve is shown in Fig. 7.14. Minimum attenuation occurs at about 1.5 μm; to date some of the lowest attenuations have been obtained with GeO_2-doped SiO_2 fibers [7.8]. These have shown minimum attenuations of about 0.2 dB km^{-1} at 1.55 μm, which is quite close to the limit set by Rayleigh scattering.

7.1.2.5 Fiber materials and manufacture

Only two main types of material have been seriously considered to date for use in optical waveguides, these being plastics and glasses. Plastic fibers offer some advantages in terms of cost and ease of manufacture, but their high transmission losses preclude their use in anything other than short-distance optical links (that is, less than a few hundred meters).

GLASS FIBERS. A broad distinction may be made between glasses based on pure SiO_2 and those derived from low softening point glasses such as the sodium borosilicates, sodium calcium silicates and lead silicates. For convenience we shall refer to these as silica fibers and glass fibers respectively. An obvious requirement of the material used is that it must be possible to vary the refractive index. Pure silica has a refractive index of 1.45 at 1 μm and B_2O_3 can be used to lower the refractive index, whilst other additives such as GeO_2 raise it. Thus a typical fiber may consist of an $SiO_2 : GeO_2$ core with a pure SiO_2 cladding. Glass fibers can be made with a wide range of refractive index variation but control of the impurity content is more difficult than with silica.

At present there are two main techniques for manufacturing low-loss fibers, these being the double crucible method and chemical vapor deposition (CVD). The apparatus for the former technique is illustrated in Fig. 7.15. Pure glass, usually in the form of rods, is fed into two platinum crucibles. At the bottom of each crucible is a circular nozzle, that of the inner vessel being concentric with that of the outer and slightly above it. The inner crucible contains the core material, the outer that of the cladding. When the temperature of the apparatus is raised sufficiently, by using an external furnace, the core material flows through the inner nozzle into the center of the flow stream from the outer crucible. Below the crucibles is a rotating drum and the composite glass in the form of a fiber is wound onto it.

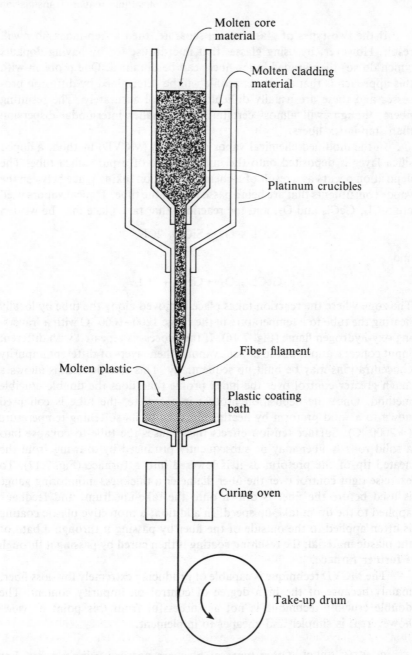

Molten core material

Molten cladding material

Platinum crucibles

Fiber filament

Molten plastic

Plastic coating bath

Curing oven

Take-up drum

Fig. 7.15 Schematic diagram of fiber-drawing apparatus using the double-crucible technique. Omitted for clarity is the furnace surrounding the double crucibles. It is customary, immediately the fiber is formed, to give it a protective coating of plastic by passing it through a bath of molten plastic and a curing oven.

If the two types of glass remain separate, then a step-index fiber will result. However, by using glasses that interdiffuse (or by having dopants which do so) then graded-index fibers can be obtained. One problem with this approach is that the index profile will be determined by diffusion processes and these are usually difficult to control accurately. The resulting fibers, though, will almost certainly have smaller intermodal dispersion than step-index fibers.

In the modified chemical vapor deposition (MCVD) method, a doped silica layer is deposited onto the inner surface of a pure silica tube. The deposition occurs as a result of a chemical reaction taking place between the vapor constituents that are being passed down the tube. Typical vapors used are $SiCl_4$, $GeCl_4$ and O_2, and the reactions that take place may be written

$$SiCl_4 + O_2 \rightarrow SiO_2 + 2Cl_2,$$

and

$$GeCl_4 + O_2 \rightarrow GeO_2 + 2Cl_2.$$

The zone where the reaction takes place is moved along the tube by locally heating the tube to a temperature in the range $1200-1600\,^{\circ}C$ with a traversing oxy-hydrogen flame (Fig. 7.16). If the process is repeated with different input concentrations of the dopant vapors, then layers of different impurity concentrations may be built up sequentially. This technique thus allows a much greater control over the index profile than does the double crucible method. Once the deposition process is complete, the tube is collapsed down to a solid preform by heating the tube to its softening temperature ($\approx 2000\,^{\circ}C$). Surface tension effects then causes the tube to collapse into a solid rod. A fiber may be subsequently produced by drawing from the heated tip of the preform as it is lowered into a furnace (Fig. 7.17). To exercise tight control over the fiber diameter a thickness monitoring gauge is used before the fiber is drawn onto the take-up drum, and feedback applied to the drum take-up speed. In addition, a protective plastic coating is often applied to the outside of the fiber by passing it through a bath of the plastic material; the resulting coating is then cured by passing it through a further furnace.

The MCVD technique is capable of producing extremely low-loss fiber, mainly because of the high degree of control on impurity content. The double crucible technique is not as successful from this point of view, however, it is simpler and cheaper to implement.

PLASTIC FIBERS. Other types of fiber are possible using plastics. For example, fibers can be made with silica cores and plastic claddings. These are easy to manufacture; the fiber core may simply be drawn through a bath of a suitable polymer which is subsequently cured by heating to a higher temperature to provide a solid cladding. This process readily lends

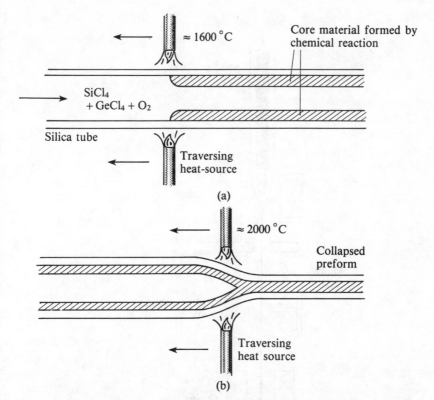

Fig. 7.16 Production of fiber preform by modified chemical vapor deposition. In the first stage, (a), the reactants are introduced into one end of a silica tube and the core material deposited on the inside of the tube in the reaction zone where the temperature is maintained at about 1600°C. Several traverses of the heating assembly may be necessary to build up sufficient thickness of core material. In the second stage, (b), the tube is collapsed into a solid preform rod by heating to the silica-softening temperature (about 2000° C).

itself to the production of step-index fibers with large core diameters where very little of the energy is carried in the cladding. Such fibers are attractive for short-distance, low-bandwidth communication systems, where cost is a major consideration. Typical losses are of the order of $10\ dB\,km^{-1}$.

Fibers can also be made entirely from plastics but these suffer from very high attenuations, mainly because of a large Rayleigh scattering contribution. Such fibers are only of any practical use in the visible region of the spectrum, preferably around 600–700 nm, and then only for short-distance, low-bandwidth systems. Since plastic is an inherently more flexible material than glass, plastic fibers can be made with larger diameters (up to a millimeter or so).

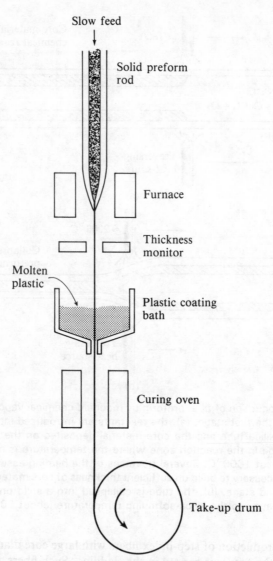

Slow feed

Solid preform
rod

Furnace

Thickness
monitor

Molten
plastic

Plastic coating
bath

Curing oven

Take-up drum

Fig. 7.17   Fiber drawing starting from a solid preform rod. The stages after
and including the plastic coating bath are identical to the
corresponding stages of the double-crucible technique.

7.1.3 Optical detectors

The basis for most detectors used in optical communications is the p–n
junction detector or photodiode. A diagram of such a detector is shown in
Fig. 7.18. Incident radiation is absorbed within the semiconductor regions

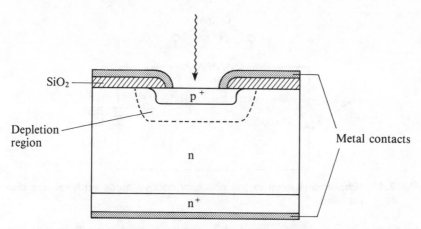

Fig. 7.18 Typical silicon photodiode structure for photoconductive operation. A junction is formed between heavily doped p-type material (p⁺) and fairly lightly doped n-type material so that the depletion region extends well into the n material. The p⁺ layer is made fairly thin. Metallic contacts can be made directly to the p⁺ material but to obtain an ohmic contact to the n material an intermediate n⁺ layer must be formed.

provided that the photon energy is greater than the bandgap energy (that is $\lambda < hc/E_{\mathrm{g}}$). One either side of the physical junction of the p and n regions is the depletion region where there is a high internal electric field (see the discussion in Section 2.2 of the semiconductor laser, which is also based on the p–n junction). When a photon is absorbed it excites an electron from the valence band of the semiconductor to the conduction band, leaving behind a hole in the valence band. If the electron–hole pair so generated is within the depletion region, then the electric field separates the electron and hole. The photodetectors are usually operated in one of two modes. In the *photovoltaic* mode the two sides of the p–n junction are connected externally via a very high resistance. In this case the separated charge gives rise to an external voltage that is proportional to the logarithm of the incident light irradiance [7.9]. More usually the *photoconductive* mode is used, where the two sides of the junction are connected via a relatively low resistance (the *load* resistor). Here the charge separation gives rise to a current flowing in the load resistor that is directly proportional to the light irradiance. This of course gives rise to a voltage across the resistor that is also proportional to the light irradiance. It is often advantageous when using a detector in the photoconductive mode to apply a reverse bias of a few volts to the junction, as shown in Fig. 7.19. The effect of the bias is to increase the width of the depletion layer. This has two consequences; firstly it increases the 'capture volume' for photon absorption, and secondly it reduces the capacitance of the device. This latter effect is useful since it can

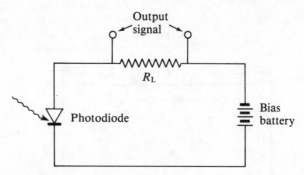

Fig. 7.19 Photodiode used in the photoconductive mode with reverse bias applied.

lead to an increase in the speed of response of the device. To see this we consider the equivalent circuit (somewhat simplified) of the photodiode shown in Fig. 7.20. The device behaves as a current generator (the signal current being i_λ) feeding into a parallel combination of the diode capacitance (C_d) and the external load resistor (R_L). At sufficiently high signal frequencies the capacitance has a very low impedance so that the photogenerated current, instead of flowing mainly through the load resistor, flows through the capacitor. The effect of this is that the signal voltage across the resistor will be reduced and the device will have an output voltage $V(\omega)$ which is given by

$$V(\omega) = \frac{i_\lambda R_L}{(1 + \omega^2 R_L^2 C_d^2)^{1/2}}. \qquad (7.11)$$

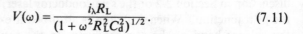

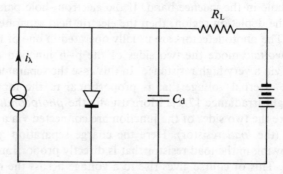

Fig. 7.20 Simplified equivalent circuit of a photodiode in the photoconductive mode. A current generator provides the photogenerated current (i_λ), while the diode itself is simulated by an ideal diode with a capacitance (C_d) in parallel with it. Since the diode is under reverse bias it has a very high impedance. The photogenerated current therefore 'sees' C_d and R in parallel (the battery has a low internal impedance).

The frequency response may be extended by reducing both R_L and C_d. Reducing R_L has the disadvantage that the magnitude of the output voltage is also reduced. C_d may be reduced by decreasing the detector area and, as we have already mentioned, by increasing the reverse bias. However, the detector area cannot be made too small, otherwise it may become difficult to focus all the incident radiation onto the active area. Also increasing the reverse bias too much may cause electrical breakdown at the junction.

Example 7.6   Frequency response of photodiodes

If we examine Eq. (7.11) we see that the voltage output of a photodiode detector will fall to $1/\sqrt{2}$ of its zero-frequency response when $\omega R_L C_d = 1$ (this will be the frequency at which the power output falls to $\frac{1}{2}$ of its zero-frequency value). Therefore the detector will respond up to a frequency f_c given by $f_c = (1/2\pi R_L C_d)$. A typical value of C_d for a photodiode of area 1 mm × 1 mm is about 20 pF. To match the input impedance of fast oscilloscopes etc. the load impedance for high-speed applications is usually 50 Ω. Thus with $R_L = 50$ Ω and $C_d = 20$ pF we obtain

$$f_c = 1/(2\pi \times 50 \times 20 \times 10^{-12}) \text{ Hz}$$
$$f_c = 159 \text{ MHz}.$$

A modification of the basic p–n structure that is often employed is the p–i–n (or PIN) photodiode. In this the p and n regions are separated by a relatively wide intrinsic (or very low doped) region (Fig. 7.21). Now the extent of the depletion region on either side of the junction varies approximately as the factor (doping level)$^{-1/2}$. Thus the depletion regions extend a long way into the intrinsic material and in fact the depletion regions at the p^+–1 and i–n junctions meet at very small reverse-bias levels. This creates a depletion region extending over the whole of the intrinsic region. A large photon collecting volume is formed thereby and the fact that the p and n

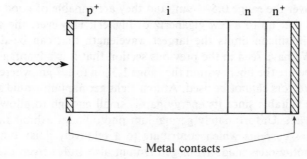

Fig. 7.21   Structure of a p–i–n photodiode.

regions are widely separated means that the device capacitance is relatively low.

In optical communication systems the received signal is often quite small and requires considerable amplification before it can be useful. The problem with this is that amplification invariably degrades the signal, with the introduction of unwanted noise. (We may define noise as an extraneous electrical signal that fluctuates in an unpredictable manner.) One way of combating this difficulty is to employ a detector that features an internal gain mechanism that is relatively noise free. One such device is the avalanche photodiode. In this the basic p—n structure is operated under very high reverse bias of the order of 100 V or so (special precautions must be taken to prevent breakdown at the junction). Carriers traversing the depletion region are then able to gain sufficient energy from the field to enable further carriers to be excited across the energy gap by impact excitation. The process is illustrated in Fig. 7.22. An electron having reached point A on the diagram has enough energy above the conduction band bottom such that it can collide with an electron from the valence band and raise it to the conduction band (C → D). This generates a new electron—hole pair. The initial electron has to lose an equivalent amount of energy, of course, and moves from A to B. The newly generated electron and hole may both subsequently go on to generate further electron—hole pairs by the same process and so on. When all the generated carriers reach the edge of the depletion region they all contribute to the current flowing in the external circuit. Current gains in excess of 100 are readily obtainable, although as might be expected, the gain is very sensitive to the magnitude of the bias voltage, as illustrated in Fig. 7.23. Consequently very stable power supplies are necessary. Another difficulty is that the gain is very sensitive to temperature fluctuations and it is often necessary either to control the temperature of the device or to allow for the effects of temperature changes by altering the bias voltage.

The most readily available PIN and avalanche photodiodes are made from silicon. Such devices exhibit good quantum efficiencies (that is the number of electrons induced to flow in the external circuit for each incident photon) over the range 0.5–1 μm, and they are capable of good frequency responses (i.e. up to a few gigahertz or higher). However, the size of the bandgap in silicon limits the largest wavelength that can be detected to 1.1 μm. We have seen in the previous section that it is advantageous to be able to operate the fibers within the range 1.3 μm to 1.7 μm where of course silicon detectors cannot be used. At first sight germanium would seem to be eminently suitable since its energy gap is small enough to allow detection up to 1.9 μm. Unfortunately germanium photodiodes exhibit rather large reverse-bias currents which contribute to a relatively noisy output. Avalanche photodiodes made from germanium also suffer from excess noise. Other materials with suitable small bandgaps include the ternary and

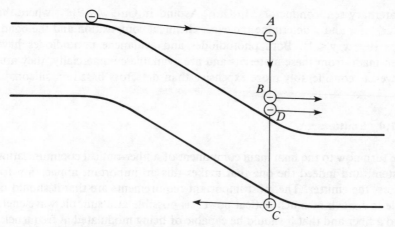

Fig. 7.22 Illustration of the principle of operation of an avalanche photodiode. An electron having reached the point A has sufficient energy above the conduction band bottom to enable it to excite an electron from the valence band into the conduction band ($C \rightarrow D$). In so doing it falls from A to B.

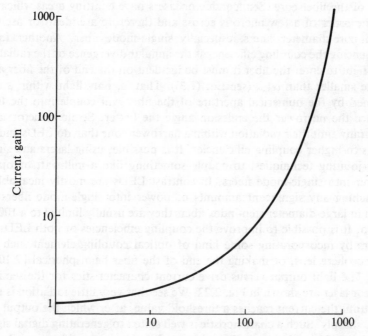

Fig. 7.23 Typical variation of current gain with reverse-bias voltage for an avalanche photodiode.

quaternary semiconductors, $In_xGa_{1-x}As$ and $In_xGa_{1-x}As_yP_{1-y}$, where the values of x and y determine the exact chemical composition and the band-gaps $(0 \leqslant x, y \leqslant 1)$. Both photodiodes and avalanche photodiodes have been made from these materials and are available commercially; they are, however, considerably more expensive than detectors based on silicon.

7.1.4 Emitters

We turn now to the final main component of a fiber-optical communication system, and indeed the one that makes this an important application for lasers, the emitter. The most important requirements are that it should be able to launch as much optical power as possible at a suitable wavelength into a fiber and that it should be capable of being modulated at frequencies up to gigahertz and perhaps beyond. Only two sources are commonly used: these are the LED and the semiconductor laser; both have their advantages and disadvantages. In general semiconductor lasers are superior on most counts but they are considerably more expensive and more difficult to drive.

The simplest way of coupling light into a fiber is to place the fiber end hard up against the surface of the photoemitter. Obviously coupling efficiency can be high only if the emitting area is smaller than or equal to that of the fiber core. Semiconductor lasers have emitting areas which can be the order of a few microns across and therefore are ideal for use with small-core-diameter fibers, especially single-mode fiber. Another factor influencing the coupling efficiency is the angular divergence of the radiation. For light to enter the fiber it must be incident on the end of the fiber at an angle smaller than α_{max} (see Eq. (7.3)). That is, only light within a cone defined by the numerical aperture of the fiber will couple into the fiber. Hence the narrower the emission angle the better. Semiconductor lasers generally emit their radiation within a narrower cone than do LEDs and this leads to higher coupling efficiencies. It is possible, using lasers and simple butt-jointing techniques, to couple something like a milliwatt of optical power into single-mode fibers. In contrast LEDs are mostly incapable of launching any significant amounts of power into single-mode fibers and even in large-diameter step-index fibers they are usually limited to a 100 μW or so. It is possible to improve the coupling efficiencies of both LEDs and lasers by incorporating some kind of optical coupling element such as a microsphere lens, or making the end of the fiber hemispherical [7.10].

The light output versus drive current characteristics for the semiconductor laser are shown in Fig. 2.22. We see that very little radiation is emitted until the current reaches a threshold value, after which the output rises very sharply. Such a characteristic is well suited to generating digital signals since the drive current needs only a small swing to provide a high 'on' to 'off' contrast. Analog signals can also be transmitted since the characteristic is reasonably linear. One problem which severely affects both types of signal is that the threshold current is temperature sensitive and can show long-term drift with age. As with avalanche photodiodes therefore good temperature stabilization or some form of temperature-dependent feedback mechanism is required. One common technique is to mount a photodiode just behind the rear facet of the laser. The average laser drive current is then adjusted until the photodetector indicates some predetermined average power level.

The most commonly available semiconductor lasers are based on GaAs or $Ga_xAl_{1-x}As$ and emit radiation between 800 nm and 950 nm. Although this wavelength range matches well the region over which silicon-based detectors are at their most efficient, it is not of course ideal from the point of view of minimum loss and maximum bandwidth in single-mode fibers. As with detectors, lasers based on InGaAs and InGaAsP are available which operate in the 1.3 μm region.

7.1.5 System design considerations

We now briefly review typical component combinations that may form the basis of practical systems. Three main factors are paramount in influencing the choice of components: bandwidth, maximum transmission distance and, of course, total system cost. For short distances (i.e. up to a few hundred meters) and for bandwidths of up to a few megahertz, a popular combination is that of a red emitting LED, a high NA plastic fiber and a silicon photodiode detector. More exacting distance and bandwidth requirements may be met with a move to silica- (or glass)-based fibers with an LED (or laser) source operating at about 850 nm. The detector may be either a silicon photodiode or avalanche photodiode.

When the required transmission rate exceeds 400 Mb s^{-1} or so then it becomes necessary to move to single-mode fibers, to avoid intermodal dispersion, and to use lasers operating at wavelengths close to the fiber material dispersion minimum (i.e. about 1.3 μm in SiO_2-based fibers). Fiber absorption is also very small in this region and transmission distances of several tens of kilometers are possible.

7.1.6 Future developments

One way of increasing the bandwidth of an existing optical link with no modification to the fiber itself is to employ the technique of *wavelength multiplexing*. In this different signals are transmitted simultaneously down the fiber on carriers of different wavelengths. The scheme is certainly a practical proposition, the main difficulty being in separating the signals at the detector end. Several possible methods have been proposed [7.11]; most involve using a wavelength dispersive element such as a prism or grating to separate the signals spatially so that they can be sent to different detectors. Inevitably both appreciable signal loss and a certain amount of cross-talk between the signals are entailed in any scheme that is used.

The performance of silica-based fibers has been dramatically improved over the last few years to the stage where, over a wide wavelength range, the theoretical attenuation limit given by Rayleigh scattering has been reached. Since Rayleigh scattering gives an attenuation that varies as λ^{-4} it is desirable to work at as high a wavelength as possible. In silica fibres the highest wavelength is limited by the onset of strong lattice absorption bands at 1.6 μm (see Fig. 7.14). Other materials have such absorption bands starting at higher wavelengths. Several materials are being investigated currently, such as the alkali halides and non-oxide glasses [7.12]. These hold out the possibility of attenuations as low as 10^{-3} dB km^{-1} or less at wavelengths between 5 μm and 7 μm. Such low attenuations imply the possibility of links some hundreds or even thousands of kilometers long. The development of these materials for fibers is at a fairly preliminary stage and they are unlikely to be available for a number of years. In addition, of course, new emitters and detectors need to be developed for use at the longer wavelengths. These will probably be based on narrow bandgap semiconductors such as mercury cadmium telluride.

Although lasers are used for sources in optical communications, it is only really because they are able to launch a lot of power into fibers that they are so useful. One of the main characteristics of laser radiation, namely its coherence, has not been a major factor until recently. However, in the same way that radio and microwave links can make use of the coherence of the carrier wave, so can optical links using lasers. One of the advantages is that the receiver sensitivity may be increased by some 10–20 dB. The incoming optical signal is mixed with a signal from a 'local oscillator', that is another laser, before it falls onto the photodetector. In *homodyne detection* the local oscillator has exactly the same frequency as the signal carrier, whereas in *heterodyne detection* the two frequencies are different. It may be shown [7.13] that in both of these cases the resulting detector signal is proportional to the product of the amplitudes of the signal and local oscillator. Thus a comparatively large local oscillator amplitude results in an effective noise-free 'gain'. However, the gain is noise free only if the local oscillator and signal carrier maintain the same phase and frequency relationships. One of the problems with using semiconductor lasers for coherent detection is that they usually possess a comparatively large linewidth (of the order of a few nanometers or in frequency terms about 500 GHz). This is because the output is multimode; hence one of the first priorities for coherent detection is to achieve single-mode operation. This can be done using *distributed feedback* lasers (which are described in the

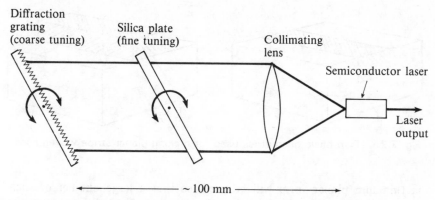

Fig. 7.24 Use of external cavity with a semiconductor laser, enabling much narrower 'tunable' emission lines to be obtained.

next section), resulting in linewidths of between 15 MHz and 50 MHz. For some coherent techniques even this is not enough; yet narrower linewidths are possible using wavelength-selective external cavities as illustrated in Fig. 7.24. Here the laser cavity is deliberately extended outside the laser so that the total cavity length is much increased, resulting in narrower linewidths (see the discussion in Section 3.1). The cavity may be 'tuned' to the desired frequency by rotating a diffracting grating that forms one end of the cavity (fine tuning can also be carried out by rotating a silica plate within the cavity as shown). Such systems are capable of long-term stabilities of some 100 kHz.

Another problem with coherent detection is that of matching the local oscillator polarization to that of the signal. Normal optical fiber is not too good at preserving polarization, and although polarization-maintaining fiber is available, it is more expensive and has higher loss than conventional single-mode fiber. It is apparent that before coherent detection can achieve widespread commercial application a number of engineering problems require solution and the present-day complexity of the coherent receiver will need to be reduced. For a review of current developments, see Ref. 7.14. Some of these problems may be resolved by the application of *integrated optics*, a topic that is discussed in the next section.

7.1.7 Integrated optics

Although optical communication is now well established, if any processing is required the signal usually needs to be converted into an electrical one before this can be carried out. The aim of integrated optics (IO) is to be able to do as much signal processing as possible directly on the optical signal itself. It is envisaged that a family of optical and electro-optical elements

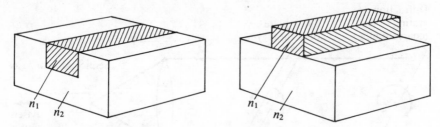

Fig. 7.25   Two basic geometries used for making planar stripe waveguides.

in thin film planar form will be used, so that a large number of such elements can be assembled on a single substrate. Similar advantages are expected to those accruing when the idea of the integrated circuit was adopted in electronics.

The optical signals will probably be carried within planar dielectric waveguides in either slab or stripe form as shown in Fig. 7.25. These can be fabricated by modifying the surface of a suitable substrate. A wide range of different techniques has been proposed, such as sputtering one type of glass onto another, in-diffusion of a deposited layer of titanium onto a substrate of lithium niobate and liquid phase epitaxy. This last technique can be used with semiconducting materials such as GaAs and GaAlAs. It is not possible to discuss here all the different types of device such as switches, active couplers, resonators and detectors etc. which have been constructed in IO form (Ref. 7.15 may be consulted for more details). However, of interest from our point of view is the fact that the most obvious choice for an emitter would seem to be a semiconductor laser, since the radiation is generated within a channel of similar dimensions to those of stripe waveguides. There are problems though in using the conventional structure since cleaved end mirrors cannot be formed. Instead these can be replaced with a corrugated Bragg type reflector. To see how this works, consider the structure shown in Fig. 7.26. This is a waveguide which has a corrugation etched into the surface. Such a structure acts rather like a Bragg type diffraction grating (see Section 6.2). Thus light traveling along the guide will be reflected back (and be in phase with other reflected portions of the wave) provided that the condition $n\lambda = 2D$ is satisfied, where D is the grating period and n is an integer. A reasonable length of such a corrugated waveguide will thus act as a wavelength selective mirror. Rather than just have the mirror outside the laser structure it is possible to have it extend right through the laser itself as illustrated in Fig. 7.27. This constitutes what is known as a *distributed feedback* laser. The corrugated structure is usually in a layer adjacent to the active layer, there being sufficient coupling between the two for the mirror action of the corrugations to be effective. When the laser is not being pumped the active layer will be strongly absorb-

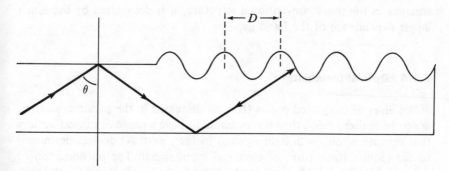

Fig. 7.26 A waveguide with a corrugation etched upon it acts as a one-dimensional Bragg diffraction grating. Light of wavelength λ is reflected back along the waveguide when the grating period, D, and the angle θ of the beam within the waveguide are related by $h\lambda = 2D \sin\theta$. If θ is close to $90°$, this reduces to $h\lambda = 2D$.

ing towards the radiation it emits. Consequently the actual waveguide is usually situated below the active layer; again coupling between adjacent layers causes light to be injected into the guiding layer. Distributed feedback lasers have a very stable emission wavelength with regard to temperature variation. This is because in the DFB structure, the wavelength stability is governed primarily by the temperature dependence of the refractive index

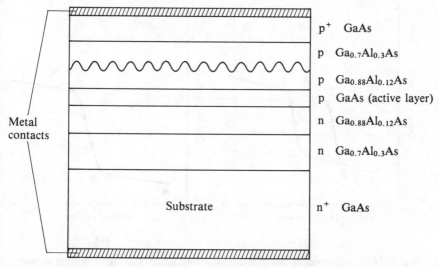

Metal contacts

p^+	GaAs
p	$Ga_{0.7}Al_{0.3}As$
p	$Ga_{0.88}Al_{0.12}As$
p	GaAs (active layer)
n	$Ga_{0.88}Al_{0.12}As$
n	$Ga_{0.7}Al_{0.3}As$
n^+	GaAs

Substrate

Fig. 7.27 Schematic cross-section of a double heterojunction distributed feedback laser structure, based on GaAs/GaAlAs.

whereas in the more conventional structure, it is dominated by the much
larger dependence of the band gap.

7.1.8   Optical bistability

If the aims of integrated optics (IO), as discussed in the previous section,
are to be realized fully, then it is essential to have a range of optical devices
that operate wholly with light signals. In fact, most IO devices developed
so far require some form of electrical input signal. The phenomenon of
optical bistability could, in principle, form the basis of several possible all-
optical devices. As its name implies, optical bistability means the existence
of two stable states in an optical system for a given set of input conditions.
An 'idealized' characteristic of such a system is shown in Fig. 7.28(a). Here
we plot the optical power output of such a device versus the incident power.
Starting at low incident beam powers and increasing the beam power causes
the system to move along the line ABC. On reaching C the system rapidly
switches to a high transmittance state; any further increase in incident
power then moves the system along EF. On reducing the incident power the
high transmission state is maintained down to D when the system makes a
rapid transition back to the low transmittance state.

It is not too difficult to see how several different devices can be built
from a system exhibiting these characteristics. Thus consider two beams of

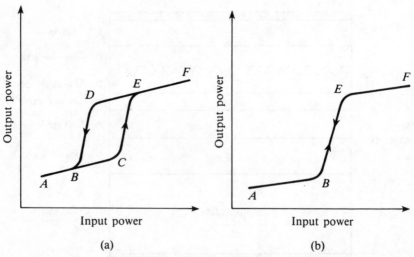

(a)   (b)

Fig. 7.28   (a) Shows an idealized characteristic of a bistable optical element.
Often 'detuning' the element causes the loop to close, resulting in
the characteristic shown in (b).

light incident on the device which we may refer to as the 'main' (strong) and 'control' (weak) beams. Initially let the control beam be off and the main beam power be such that the system is at the point *B*. If the control beam is now switched on and is powerful enough to take the system beyond *C*, then it will switch the system from the low to the high transmittance state. Removing the control beam now causes the system to revert to its starting point. The device acts as an all optical switch with the main beam being switched on and off by the control beam. Also we see that from *A* to *B* and from *E* to *F* the output is relatively independent of the input; the device acts as a 'limiter' and could be used, for example, for pulse shaping.

Often 'detuning' the basic device can lead to the loop closing and giving rise to the characteristic in Fig. 7.28(b). Over the range *BE* the system can behave like an amplifier. Again with two beams present a relatively small power variation on the control beam will cause a much larger power variation in the main beam. We have an all optical amplifier.

The system most commonly used to illustrate optical bistability is shown in 7.29. It consists of a Fabry–Perot etalon containing a medium whose refractive index varies with the irradiance of the radiation in the cavity (I_c). The simplest assumption is that the refractive index (n) is given by

$$n = n_1 + n_2 I_c. \tag{7.12}$$

The transmission T_c of such a cavity can be written [7.16] as

$$T_c = \frac{1}{1 + F^2 \sin^2 \phi} \tag{7.13}$$

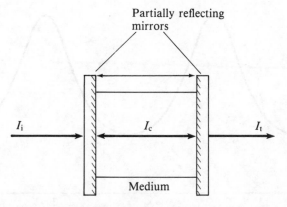

Fig. 7.29 One form of an idealized bistable optical element. A medium, whose refractive index varies with light irradiance, is sandwiched between two plane partially reflecting mirrors (which essentially form a Fabry–Perot cavity).

where F is the *finesse* of the cavity and ϕ is given by $2\pi n L/\lambda$, L being the cavity length.

Equation (7.13) may thus be re-written

$$T_c = \frac{1}{1 + F^2 \sin^2 (\theta + \delta_0)},$$
(7.14)

where $\theta = 2\pi n_2 I_c L/\lambda$ and $\delta_0 = 2\pi n_1 L/\lambda$. A plot of T_c versus I_c when $\delta_0 = \pi/2$ and $F^2 = 2$ is shown in Fig. 7.30. We see that when $\theta + \delta_0$ is an integral multiple of π, then T_c has its maximum value of 1; the cavity is then said to be on 'resonance'.

Now the transmission of the cavity may also be written as

$$T_c = \frac{I_c}{I_i} \frac{(1 - R)}{(1 + R)},$$
(7.15)

where I_i is the incident irradiance and R is the Fabry–Perot mirror reflectance (we assume no absorption in the medium between the mirrors). We see that at resonance we can have $I_c > I_i$, which we may term a *resonant magnification* of I_i.

Equations (7.14) and (7.15) form a pair of simultaneous equations whose solution enables T_c to be obtained as a function of I_i. Unfortunately an explicit solution is not possible, although graphical techniques may be used (see Problem 7.11). We may readily appreciate what happens qualitatively, however, by considering a very low irradiance beam to be incident on the device. The cavity irradiance I_c will be low and hence $\theta \ll \delta_0$ in Eq. (7.14). We may assume for convenience that $\delta_0 = \pi/2$ and hence at low values of I_i the cavity remains in a low transmission state (off resonance).

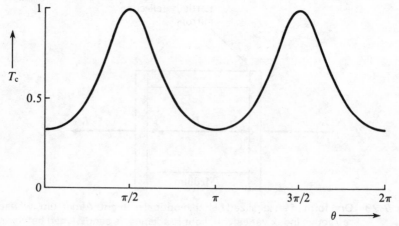

Fig. 7.30 Transmission of a Fabry–Perot cavity according to Eq. (7.14) assuming that $F^2 = 2$ and $\delta_0 = \pi/2$.

However, if I_i is now increased to the point where θ is comparable to δ_0, then the transmission of the cavity starts to increase. This implies that I_c also increases (from 7.15) and leads in turn to a further increase in θ and a corresponding increase in T_c, etc. The cavity thus 'switches' to a near-resonant state with high transmission. Once there it can be held near resonance with a smaller I_i because of the resonant magnification factor.

Optical bistability with characteristics like those described above has been observed in many different physical systems. One of the simplest of these consists of a 0.5 mm thick crystal indium antimonide (InSb) cooled to 5 K [7.17]. The natural reflectances of the crystal faces by themselves (36%) are sufficient to form a suitable Fabry–Perot cavity. When light of 5.3 μm wavelength from a CO laser is used, then optical bistable behavior can be observed. Other semiconductor materials have also been used, one example being zinc selenide, which can operate at room temperature using the output of an Ar ion laser ($\lambda = 514$ nm). In this particular case, however, the devices are basically interference filters and not Fabry–Perot etalons. Other possible types of device have included laser diode structures incorporating electrical feedback (rather than optical feedback as in the Fabry–Perot devices).

Optical bistable devices with switching times as low as a few picoseconds and with switching energies of a few picojoules have been demonstrated. With characteristics such as these it becomes possible to think in terms of *optical computers*. Suppose for example that we could form a 100×100 array of such devices on a 100 mm^2 chip of GaAs. A switch cycling rate of some 10 GHz would enable some $100 \times 100 \times 10^{10}$ or 10^{14} switching operations per second to be carried out (the fastest conventional computers operate at some 10^{10} operations per second). If we further assume a switching energy of 1 pJ per element, then the heat loading is $10^{14} \times 10^{-12}$ or 1 W mm^{-2}, which is acceptable (though only just). Of course although a large number of switching operations are possible per chip they are essentially operating in parallel. Parallel computing, that is the handling of many separate data channels simultaneously, is as yet in its infancy; however, it would seem that optical computers are best adapted to this type of architecture. Certainly there are some types of computing problems such as image processing which seem well suited to such techniques.

7.1.9 Free-space communication

So far in this chapter we have concentrated on optical communication using optical fiber waveguides. In certain circumstances free-space communication may be perfectly viable. Such systems can be easily set up and costs are considerably less than if fibers are used. A typical example would be a link

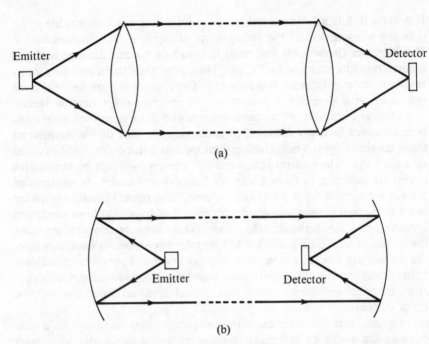

(a)

(b)

Fig. 7.31 Two simple types of free-space transmission system using (a) lenses, and (b) concave mirrors.

between nearby buildings in an urban environment. An obvious disadvantage is that adverse atmospheric conditions such as rain or snow may introduce severe distortion or even render the link completely inoperable. Even when conditions are favorable the signal will be attenuated by both absorption and scattering processes in the atmosphere. The former arise from the presence of molecular constituents such as water vapor, carbon dioxide and ozone. Strong absorption occurs around the wavelengths of 0.94 μm, 1.13 μm, 1.90 μm, 2.7 μm, 4.3 μm and 6.0 μm. Between these values lie the so-called *atmospheric windows* where losses are determined by scattering. Fluctuations in the absorption and scattering tend to modulate the signal strength and so amplitude modulation is not usually satisfactory.

The simplest systems consist of LEDs or semiconductor lasers and silicon photodiode detectors coupled together by a suitable lens or mirror system such as shown in Fig. 7.31. The use of lasers with much smaller beam divergences (e.g. Nd:YAG, CO_2) of course greatly simplifies the problem of beam collimation. Normally the extra difficulties involved in modulating such lasers would not make the effort worthwhile. However, a possible future use for such systems is in deep-space communications, where the low beam divergences are useful in view of the large distances involved (see Problem 7.12).

7.2 **LASER PRINTING**

It has been found possible to incorporate lasers with advantage into two main types of printing processes, namely electrostatic printers and printing plate generation. Laser electrostatic printers have seen a very rapid growth over the last few years. A key factor in this has been the rapid expansion of information processing and the increasing availability of personal computers. They offer a much higher printing speed (up to 100 pages/minute) and a higher quality than impact printers and are beginning to approach the latter in terms of cost. The basis of all laser printers is a rotating drum with a photosensitive surface. A film of cadmium sulfide (or sometimes selenium) a few tens of microns thick is laid down on an aluminum substrate with a transparent dielectric protective layer on top. In operation the photosensitive layer is first of all electrostatically charged with a corona discharge (see Fig. 7.32). Then a modulated laser beam is scanned repeatedly across the (rotating) surface. Where the beam strikes the surface the CdS becomes conducting due to the phenomenon of photoconductivity, and hence the charge can leak away from these regions. Thus as the drum rotates a 'charge' image is produced on the drum surface that reflects the irradiance pattern of the scanned laser beam. Next the drum surface passes under the 'developing station' where it comes into contact with charged black plastic particles (the *toner*). These adhere to the uncharged parts of the drum surface (being repelled from the charged regions since they have the same polarity of charge as the drum surface).

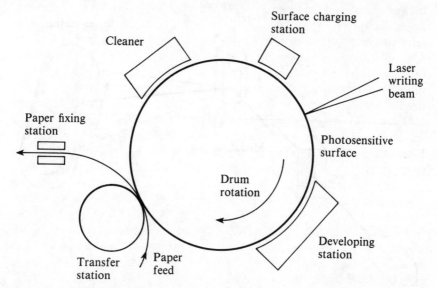

Fig. 7.32 Schematic diagram of a photoconductive drum assembly used in a laser printer.

Thus the charge pattern now becomes a *real* black and white image. This image must now be transformed to paper and this is again achieved by electrostatic attraction. The paper is charged before coming into contact with the drum surface at the *transfer station*, and toner particles are attracted to it. Before use the image must usually be more permanently *fixed* onto the paper. The details of the fixing method used depends on the nature of the toner: for example, heat may be used to 'melt' the particles into the paper's surface.

The most commonly used beam scanning system utilizes an HeNe or Ar ion laser, a modulator and a rotating polygonal prism (Fig. 7.33). Holographic scanners (Sec. 6.5.2) have sometimes been used in place of polygonal prisms. Omitted from Figure 7.33 (but equally important) are the collimating and focusing optics. The HeNe laser is used because the standard photosensitive materials are highly sensitive to its output and also because of the excellent beam quality which generally necessitates only a single lens to focus it to the required spot size. However, it cannot be internally modulated at the high speeds required and so an external modulator is also required. Both acousto-optic and electro-optic modulators are suitable, but the acousto-optic method is often preferred because of its freedom from thermal drift and its ability to operate with unpolarized light. In addition it is less costly and does not require a high-voltage power supply.

A recent competitor to the HeNe laser is the GaAs/GaAsP semicon-

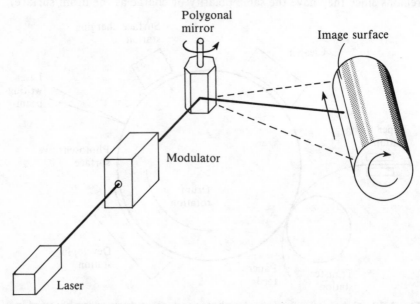

Fig. 7.33 Laser printer beam-scanning system utilizing a rotating polygonal mirror.

ductor laser. Comparable CW power outputs can now be obtained with much simpler power-supply requirements. Modulation is easily carried out by varying the drive current and this obviates the need for an external modulator. Laser diodes are now available which operate at wavelengths down to 720 nm or less, so that they are nearly as efficient as the HeNe laser in causing photoconductivity. In any case adding proprietary materials to the CdS can increase its peak sensitivity to 700 nm. The biggest problem with diode lasers is their wide beam divergence, so that the optical requirements as far as collimating and focusing are concerned are then much more stringent. This tends to some extent to offset the advantages gained from not requiring an external modulator.

Other developments have concerned the photoconductive material itself; organic photoconductors for example show good photosensitivity, are relatively cheap and have a response that can be extended into the near infra red. However, they are quite soft mechanically and often involve hazardous (e.g. carcinogenic) materials. Another promising possibility is amorphous silicon, which has almost ideal physical properties but which is relatively expensive to manufacture.

In the area of more conventional print media the laser has been introduced into automated character- and document-scanning equipment and photolithographic platemaking equipment. In a typical set up a low-power HeNe laser scans across the original picture. A photosensor picks up the reflected radiation and provides an intensity-modulated signal for the platemaking system. In the latter a modulated laser beam (Ar ion or HeCd) is scanned across an ultra-violet sensitive plate which is then developed chemically.

7.3 OPTICAL DISK SYSTEMS

In recent years *optical disks* have been used increasingly for entertainment, educational programs and general audio-visual communications [7.18]. In the field of data storage direct optical recording systems are becoming popular as computer peripherals, where the combination of very high information capacity and rapid random access makes optical disks an attractive alternative to other forms of computer memory store. The high information capacity, long shelf life and long storage life are leading to applications in archival storage.

In all the optical disk systems, such as prerecorded audio disks (compact disk or CD), video disks (often called laser vision or LV) and data-storage disks, we shall assume that the information is recorded or *written* onto the disk and played back or *read* optically. In practice a variety of lasers such as argon ion, HeNe, HeCd, and AlGaAs semiconducting laser diodes have been used as the light sources for writing and reading. There are, in fact, alternative methods of writing the disk – for example electro-mechanical cutting – and also for reading it – for example capacitative pick-up. We shall not, however, consider these further.

The main advantage of optical disks over other systems such as conventional audio disks and magnetic tape systems, apart from the high storage density, is the absence of physical contact between the reading head and the information storage medium, which prevents wear. Furthermore, in the case of an optical disk a transparent film may be deposited over the information stored to protect it from damage.

As with conventional audio gramophone records the information is stored in a spiral, called the *track*, on the surface of the recording disk. In practice with optical disks, however, there is often neither a groove nor indeed a continuous line present but only *marks* forming a broken spiral line. These marks are small areas giving an optical contrast with respect to the surroundings. They are most commonly depressions or *pits* formed in the surface of the disk. (See Fig. 7.34) As a consequence the reflectance will change along the track according to the distribution of the pits, which represents the information stored.

To read the stored information an optical pick-up converts the variations in reflectance into an electronic signal. A lens within the pick-up focuses a low-power laser beam to a small spot of light on the track and also redirects the light reflected from the disk to a photodetector (Fig. 7.35). The output of the photodetector varies according to the distribution of pits along the track and gives an electrical signal which enables the original audio, video or data signal to be regained.

Audio signals are stored digitally on the disk. Sound samples are taken at the rate of 44.1 kHz and the sound level of each sample is converted into a numerical value which is represented in a binary codeword of 16 bits. Additional bits for error correction are then added and a bit stream at 4.3218 MHz is stored on the disk. 'Zeros' are represented by a low photo-signal and 'ones' by a high-level photosignal, so the track will consist of pits and spaces of discrete lengths. Video signals, on the other hand, are stored in analog form because digital storage requires too high a bandwidth. The composite video signal (with color and irradiance information) is frequency modulated (FM) around a carrier frequency of 7.5 MHz and sound added as a duty cycle modulation. This causes the center-to-center distance of the pits to vary according to the FM content and the ratio of pit length to space length to vary according to the sound content. In optical memories data is stored in both analog and digital form and while initially the disks were nonerasable progress is being made in the field of erasable storage media (see Section 7.3.4). To be useful in electronic data processing a storage peripheral must be capable of retrieving stored data with a final error rate of the order of 1 in 10^{12}; optical disks have met this requirement.

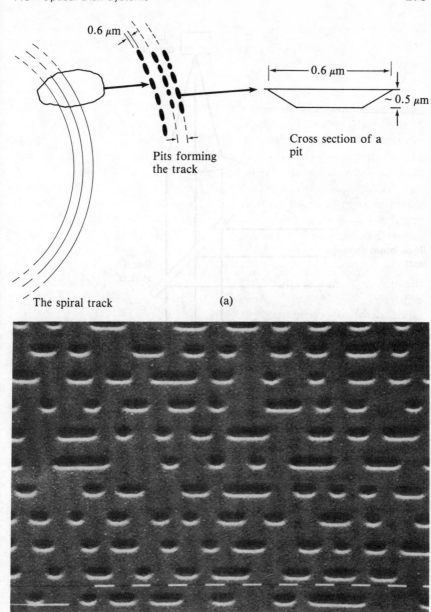

(a)

(b)

Fig. 7.34 (a) Schematic of a typical optical disk. The precise 'geometry' of a pit depends on a number of factors including the storage mode and readout technique employed. (b) Scanning electron micrograph of an optical disk (From G. Bouwhuis, A. Huijser, J. Pasman, G. Von Rosmalen, K. Schouharner Immink, *Principles of Optical Disc Systems* (1985). Courtesy Adam Hilger Ltd).

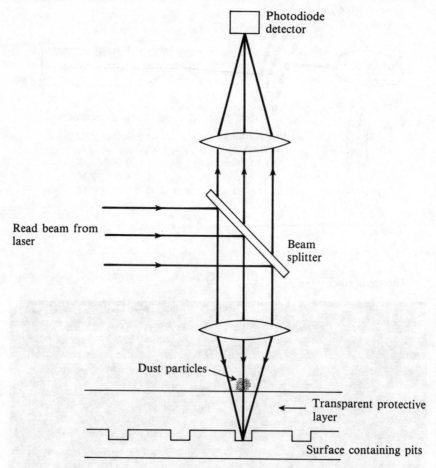

Fig. 7.35 The basis of readout from an optical disk. The read beam from a laser is focused onto the surface containing the pits. Particles of dust on the protective layer are not in focus and do not affect the readout process.

The high information density achieved with optical disks results from the very small spot size to which a laser beam may be focused. We saw in Section 3.6 that the diameter of the spot is given by $(4/\pi)\,\lambda F$. In terms of diffraction limited spots the minimum diameter of a spot of light formed at the focal point of a lens is about $\lambda/2NA$, where NA is the numerical aperture of the lens ($NA = n\sin\theta$, where n is the object space refractive index and $\theta = \phi/s$, ϕ being the diameter of the clear aperture of the lens and s the lens-to-object distance). Consequently the information density is of the order of $(NA/\lambda)^2$.

Example 7.7   Information density

Let us calculate the information density which may be achieved using an argon ion laser ($\lambda = 457.9$ nm) and a lens with a numerical aperture of 0.8.

The minimum spot diameter $= \dfrac{\lambda}{2NA} = \dfrac{457.9}{2 \times 0.8} = 0.29 \ \mu m$.

The information density, allowing about a spot diameter between spots, is then $(NA/\lambda)^2 = 3 \times 10^{12} \ m^{-2}$. A typical disk may carry information in a region having an outer radius of 145 mm and an inner radius of 70 mm, that is, over an area of about $5.0 \times 10^{-2} m^2$. Therefore this disk can store $3 \times 10^{12} \times 5 \times 10^{-2} = 1.5 \times 10^{10}$ bits of information.

7.3.1   Recording

To a certain extent the recording process depends on whether the disk is to be replicated in large numbers for the consumer market or is essentially a one-off for storage purposes. Most disks, whatever their purpose, contain information recorded in the form of a height profile. Because of this, replication of the disk is relatively simple and therefore inexpensive.

Recording information from, for example, a video tape into the surface relief pattern is called mastering. In this process a master disk is produced and this is used to form *stampers*, which in turn are used to generate large numbers of video disks by injection-molding techniques.

In a typical mastering process, the master disk, which is a flat glass substrate, is coated with a thin layer of photosensitive material (photoresist) about 0.12 μm thick. The surface relief pattern is then recorded by exposing the resist to a focused laser beam, the irradiance of which is modulated in accordance with the information to be stored using a fast acousto-optic or electro-optic modulator as illustrated in Fig. 7.36. The exposed areas of resist can now be dissolved away leaving holes or pits in the resist. This process is very similar to the familiar techniques of photolithography used in the mass production of integrated circuits.

The master disk is rotated at an angular frequency of 25 Hz under the focused laser beam, which is scanned radially outwards, thereby producing a spiral track of pits. Using, for example, a 25 mW HeNe laser beam with a lens of NA of 0.65 it is relatively simple to produce pits which are 0.6–0.8 μm wide with a track spacing of 1.6 μm. Pits can be formed at the rate of several million per second, their spacing and length being of the order of a micron as illustrated in Fig. 7.34.

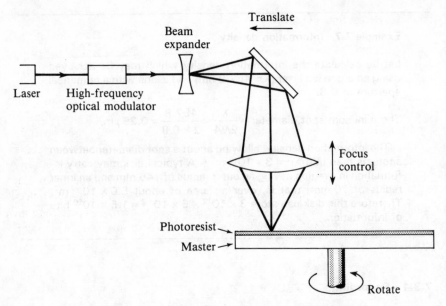

Fig. 7.36 Schematic diagram of laser beam recorder.

The recorded master disk is now inspected and if satisfactory it is used to form a negative of the surface relief called a 'father'. This is fabricated by electroplating the master with nickel. The nickel father is then separated from the master and subsequently used to form a family of stampers. This is done by growing mother positives by further electroplating with nickel after chemical modification of the surface of the father. In turn each mother is used to form several negative sons, which are used in mass replication. In, for example, the 2p process (from photopolymerization) developed by Philips for video disk replication [7.19] the replica substrate is 1.2 mm thick and its surface is coated with layers of the 2p laquer, an aluminum layer to form a reflective coating and a protective coating (Fig. 7.37). Two disks are then glued together to form a double-sided video disk.

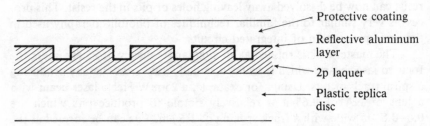

Fig. 7.37 Diagram of replica disk formed using the Philips 2p replication process.

7.3.2   Recording media

As mentioned in the previous section, the pits have dimensions of the order of microns and accordingly the recording material must have a very high resolution and, to minimize the required laser power for writing, it should have high sensitivity. Preferably the recording material should allow for real-time recording and allow instant retrieval (reading) of the stored information. That is, there should ideally be no processing steps between writing and reading. In addition to photoresists, metal films, particularly those based on alloys of tellurium, have very good resolution and high sensitivity. In this case a pulse of laser radiation creates a pit or hole in the metal film through a process of ablation or melting, thereby again altering the reflectance of the film. As the hole-burning process is a thermal rather than an optical effect, the laser wavelength is not critical, so any laser which can deliver the required power can be used for writing.

Example 7.8   Laser power required for writing on metal film recording media

Typical writing speeds are 10 million pits per second. Let us assume for simplicity that the pits are rectangular in shape with the following dimensions: width $0.6\ \mu m$, length $2\ \mu m$ and depth $0.15\ \mu m$. The density of tellurium is $6.24 \times 10^3\ kg\,m^{-3}$ while the thermal properties of tellurium are:

Thermal capacity $202\ J\,kg^{-1}\,K^{-1}$
Boiling point $1200\ K$
Latent heat of fusion $0.14 \times 10^6\ J\,kg^{-1}$
Latent heat of vaporization $0.89 \times 10^6\ J\,kg^{-1}$

The total latent heat required to melt then vaporize tellurium is then $1.03 \times 10^6\ J\,kg^{-1}$ and the thermal capacity term, which is $2.4 \times 10^5\ J\,kg^{-1}$ can be ignored in comparison.

The heat required to form a pit is thus the mass of a pit times the latent heat, that is,

heat required $= (0.15 \times 2.0 \times 0.6)\ 10^{-18}$

$$\times 6.24 \times 10^3 \times 1.03 \times 10^6 = 1.16 \times 10^{-9}\ J.$$

If the writing speed is 10^7 pits per second, then the required laser power is $1.16 \times 10^{-9} \times 10^7 = 11.6\ mW$. Clearly this is a minimum laser power as we have made no allowance for the light reflected from the metal film (which is wavelength dependent). This, however, does decrease when the metal melts (see Section 5.1) and in addition our assumption that the pits have a rectangular shape leads to an overestimation of the mass of material to be removed, so our estimate of the laser power requirement may not

be too much in error. It is noteworthy that this power requirement
can now be met by laser diodes.

Pure tellurium has a low melting and boiling point but it is rather
unstable in that it rapidly oxidizes and degrades under conditions of high
humidity. Alloying it with selenium and antimony improves the stability.
Techniques have been developed to protect the tellurium alloy from contamination by the atmosphere. These include the air sandwich and the antireflection trilayer structure. In the former (Fig. 7.38) two transparent
plastic or glass substrates each with a 30 nm thick film of tellurium alloy on
one face are sandwiched together with a 1 mm air gap between them and
hermetically sealed. The recording light then passes through the substrate
and vaporizes a small region of the film to form a hole. The read beam is
strongly reflected by the unpitted surface but is not reflected when it enters
a pit.

In the trilayer structure shown in Fig. 7.39 a layer of dielectric is
formed between a very reflective layer such as aluminum deposited on the
substrate and a semi-transparent layer of tellurium alloy. The dielectric and
tellurium layers together have an optical thickness of $\lambda/4$, so that the three
layers form an antireflection structure tuned to the wavelength of the write
laser. The write beam again forms holes or pits in the tellurium so that when
the read beam encounters such a hole it passes straight through the dielectric
to the aluminum layer and is strongly reflected, whereas the unpitted areas
reflect very little light. Thus the optical contrast of the trilayer is very high.
The sensitive tellurium alloy can be provided with a transparent plastic
overcoat which is so thick that it does not affect the antireflection process.

An alternative to pit formation by ablative processes, which can give
rise to problems of contamination by the ablated material, is bubble forma-

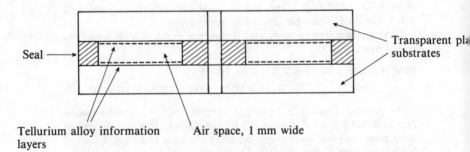

Seal

Transparent plate
substrates

Tellurium alloy information
layers

Air space, 1 mm wide

Fig. 7.38 Schematic diagram of an air-sandwich optical disk. Recording light
passes through the substrate and vaporizes small regions of
tellurium to form a hole. The sealed space provides a protective
environment for the tellurium.

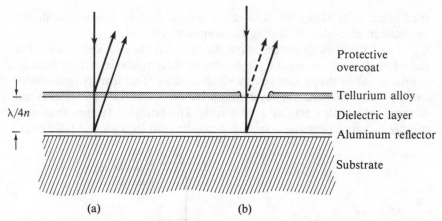

$\lambda/4n$

Protective
overcoat

Tellurium alloy

Dielectric layer

Aluminum reflector

Substrate

(a)   (b)

Fig. 7.39 Principles of the trilayer structure. In (a) the path difference between the beams reflected at the tellurium alloy and aluminum layers is half a wavelength, so that destructive interference occurs between the two beams shown and very little light is reflected. (b) shows that where holes have been formed the antireflective structure has been destroyed and the reflected beam is strong.

tion. In this case the sensitive layer consists of a polymer–metal bilayer as shown in Fig. 7.40. Upon irradiation the metal is heated by the laser beam. This heat is transferred to the polymer which decomposes at a few hundred degrees celsius. The resulting gaseous emission separates the two layers and deforms the metal into a bubble with a diameter of the order of the laser spot size. The bubble which has a permanent character acts as a scattering center for light on read-out.

Optical disks formed by creating pits in thin metal films or bubbles in metal–dielectric bilayers have been used for replicating many copies. The disks with bubbles are particularly good for replication purposes as the bubbles are quite robust. Both types of disk are useful in another respect, namely that they can be used for direct effect recording or optical direct

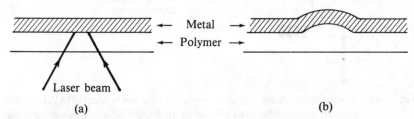

← Metal →
← Polymer →

Laser beam

(a)   (b)

Fig. 7.40 Bubble formation. In (a) laser beam vaporizes the polymer and the resulting gas pressure creates a bubble in the metal (e.g. titanium). (b) The bubble acts as a scatterer for light on readout or it can be used to disrupt the antireflective nature of a trilayer structure.

read after write (DRAW). This on-line data storage is essential in the application of optical recording for computer systems.

The DRAW facility stems from the fact that the heat delivered to the recording medium, to form a pit, bubble or other readable surface feature, is minimized so that it can be quickly dissipated. This usually necessitates using a very thin sensitive layer supported on a substrate for mechanical strength which also acts as a heat sink. The readable feature thus very rapidly becomes permanent so that it can be read by a second laser beam

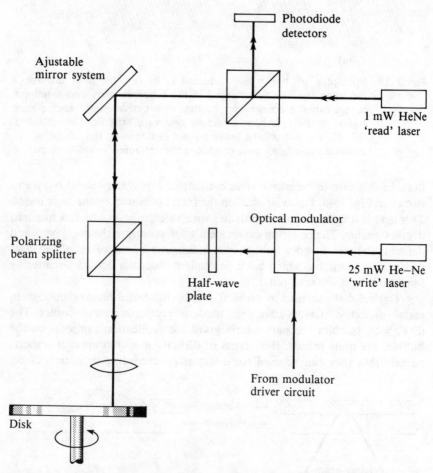

Fig. 7.41 A simplified diagram of a direct-read-after-write (DRAW) optical disk recorder. The read and write reflected beams have an angular separation and different polarizations so that reflections from the write beam do not interfere with the read (and tracking) beam. It is necessary to be able to move most of the optical system so that the beams may scan across the disk.

only 10 μm downstream from the write beam. In many systems, such as that shown in Fig. 7.41, two lasers are used. One of about 25 mW output, provides the write beam, while the other, of about 1 mW output, provides a beam for readout purposes. Clearly the read beam should be of sufficiently low power to avoid damaging the disk. Precautions must also be taken to ensure that reflections of the write beam do not interfere with the read (and tracking) beam. This is achieved by angular separation of the beams (not shown in Fig. 7.41) and different polarizations. In other systems the same laser is used to provide both the write and readout beams. DRAW enables stored information to be monitored as it is written and if necessary corrections can be made to it.

The recording processes described so far provide permanent features on the optical disk and as a result the data should be readable without error for a long period of time – an important feature for archival storage. Storage lifetimes in excess of 10 years have been claimed, while 30 years is the goal for some applications.

7.3.3   Data readout from optical disks

Figure 7.42 shows the basic arrangement for readout. A laser beam, usually from a laser diode because of size considerations is focused through the substrate onto the reflective layer of the disk. The focusing lens is a microscope-type objective lens, and to scan the whole disk, is mounted together with the laser in the readout head on a carriage below the disk. Part of the reflected light, which is modulated by the relief pattern of the disk described in Section 7.3.1, is gathered by the same lens and is directed to the photodetector. Light is strongly reflected from the areas where there are no pits (often called 'land') and is largely scattered by the pits so that the output of the detector varies as the beam follows the track. In digital storage, for example, a change in the level of the reflected signal represents a transition from a pit to land or vice versa. These transitions are, in fact, used to represent ones, while the path length between transitions, on either pit or land, represents a certain number of zeros, as illustrated in Fig. 7.43.

The use of reflected rather than transmitted light offers a number of advantages. For example, since the disk is approached from one side only the player construction is simplified and the number of optical components required is thereby reduced. A protective coating needs to be present on only one side of the information layer and the relief structure can be shallower than in transmission; both these points simplify mass replication of the disks. Finally focus control is made much simpler and dirt and scratches on the protective surface are separated from the information layer and are thus out of focus, thereby removing their effect on the playback signal.

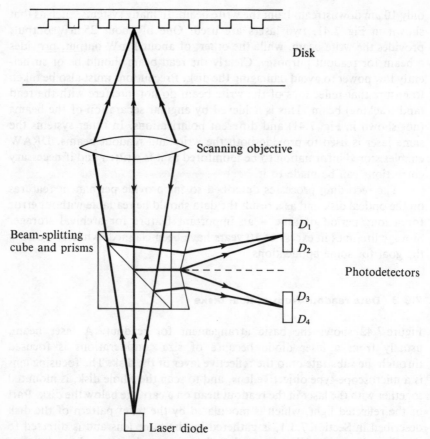

Fig. 7.42   A schematic drawing of a small (30 mm high) optical readout head.
The two prisms deviate the light reflected from the disk to the four
photodetectors. In addition to providing the required optical 'signal'
(by summing the output of all four detectors) the detector outputs
can be used for focus control and accurate tracking of the spiral
track.

Optical signals are also required from the disk to control the vertical
height of the readout head, that is, to ensure that the laser beam remains
focused on the information layer, and to ensure that the laser beam
accurately follows the spiral track of data prints. Focus needs to be maintained accurate to about 1 μm while tracking should be correct to about
0.1 μm. Inevitably vibrations and eccentricities of the disk mean that servo-
control of the readout head is required to ensure that these allowed errors
are not exceeded. The signals required for focus and tracking have been
obtained in a variety of ways, some of which are described in Refs. 7.18.

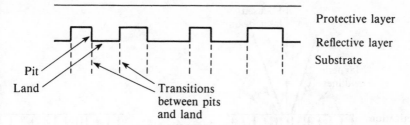

Pit
Land
Transitions
between pits
and land

Protective layer
Reflective layer
Substrate

001001000100010000010010000100000100   Binary representation

Fig. 7.43 Digital storage. A binary 'one' is represented by a land–pit or pit–land transition: the number of 'zeros' is defined by the path length (either pit or land) between transitions.

7.3.4 Erasable optical disks

It was mentioned earlier that the recording processes described to date form permanent features but for many applications such as computing and in updating stored information an 'erase', rewrite facility would be beneficial. Materials which can be used for erasable optical disks include magneto-optic materials, thermoplastics and chalcogenide films for permanent storage and photochromic, photoferric and photoconductive materials for limited storage lifetime. As an example of these let us consider Curie point writing, which is probably the most common method. With reference to Fig. 7.44 the write laser beam heats up a small region of a thin film of vertically magnetized ferromagnetic material (for example GdTbFe) to a temperature above its Curie point so that the region will lose its permanent magnetization. If the region is allowed to cool down in the presence of an external field orientated antiparallel to the initial magnetization, then regions with reverse polarization are formed – see Fig. 7.44(b). Readout in this case is usually accomplished by the Kerr magneto-optical effect, in which a beam of polarized light reflected from a magnetized surface has its plane of polarization rotated by an amount depending on the strength of the magnetization and the direction of the magnetization relative to the direction of the light beam. We see then that a polarized laser beam suffers different rotations depending on which part of the film it is reflected from. The amount of rotation is only a few tenths of a degree and it is usually necessary to use a sensitive differential detection technique based on passing the reflected light through a polarizing beam splitter and comparing the two light levels produced [7.20].

Erasure and rewriting simply consists of heating the film on the disk above the Curie point again in the presence of an appropriately directed external magnetic field. Clearly the laser used for readout must be of

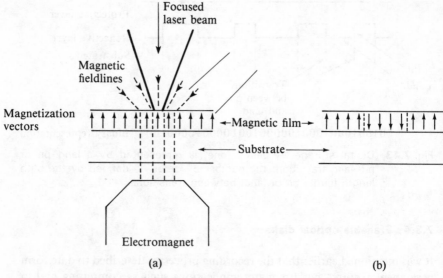

Fig. 7.44 Magneto-optical recording. (a) A focused laser beam raises the local temperature of the magnetic film (e.g. gadolinium terbium iron) above the Curie point in the presence of an external, magnetic field directed opposite to the magnetization of the film. (b) When the heated region cools it has the opposite magnetization to the neighboring regions.

significantly lower power than the write laser to avoid the danger of destroying the stored data. There is much current interest in the field of erasable optical disks and several multilayer systems are currently being evaluated [7.21].

Optical disk systems are increasingly being used in mass storage systems. The Megadoc system [7.22], for example, comprises 64 disks in which access time on any one disk is ~ 150 ms while load time for a given disk is 20 s. The capacity of such a system is in the region of 10^{12}–10^{14} bits, which can be retrieved at random within a few seconds. To put this in perspective the contents of this book could quite easily be stored on about 20 tracks occupying a width of about 32 μm of a disk having a diameter of about 0.3 m.

PROBLEMS

7.1 Given that a TV channel requires an analog frequency bandwidth of 4 MHz, estimate how many such channels can be transmitted, in principle, using a light beam of wavelength 0.8 μm, assuming (a) analog and (b) digital modulation (using a 14-bit number) of the beam. Explain why, as yet, such numbers cannot be achieved.

7.2 Calculate the critical angle for a glass–air interface where the glass has a refractive index of 1.55.

7.3 A step-index fiber with a core diameter of 200 μm has core and cladding refractive indices of 1.46 and 1.40 respectively. Calculate the following quantities: numerical aperture, acceptance angle, expected bandwidth–distance product and the total number of modes able to propagate at a wavelength of 0.8 μm.

7.4 An optical power of 100 W is launched into an optical fiber of length 200 m. Given that the power emerging from the other end is 50 W, calculate the fiber attenuation (ignore end-reflection effects).

7.5 Sketch the refractive index profile across a graded-index fiber when the profile parameter (γ) takes the values 1, 2, 4 and 10 and where $2\Delta = 0.1$.

7.6 In the region of 1 μm an approximate expression for the refractive index of pure silica is:

$$n^2 = 1 + \sum_{i=1}^{3} \frac{A_i \lambda^2}{\lambda^2 - B_i^2}$$

where $A_1 = 0.696\ 166\ 3$, $B_1 = 0.068\ 404\ 3$,
         $A_2 = 0.407\ 942\ 6$, $B_2 = 0.116\ 241\ 4$,
         $A_3 = 0.897\ 479\ 4$, $B_3 = 9.896\ 161$.

Evaluate expressions for $dn/d\lambda$ and $d^2n/d\lambda^2$ and hence plot graphs of these quantities over the wavelength range 0.8–1.6 m (a short computer program may be found useful for this purpose). Show that $d^2n/d\lambda^2$ becomes zero at about 1.3 μm. Also verify that at $\lambda = 1$ μm the approximations assumed in the derivation leading to Eq. (7.10) are valid.

7.7 Estimate the material dispersion (expressed as a bandwidth–distance product) expected from a single-mode silica-based fiber when used in conjunction with a laser which emits at 1.2 μm and which has a bandwidth of 2 nm.

7.8 It has been suggested that if a material can be found where the onset of the infra red lattice absorption band is at a higher wavelength than in silica, a much lower ultimate fiber attenuation will be possible. Estimate from Fig. 7.14 what minimum attenuation might be possible at a wavelength of 4 μm assuming Rayleigh scattering is the dominant loss mechanism. Would this figure allow for an unrepeated transmission across the Atlantic?

If such fibers could be developed, what other problems would need to be tackled?

7.9 Plot the expected frequency response of a photodiode operating in the photoconductive mode where the diode has an effective capacitance of 20 pF and a 50 Ω load resistor is used.

7.10 One of the problems involved with optical fibers is that of splicing them together without incurring too much loss of optical power. In simple splicing systems the two fiber ends are simply 'butted' together. Investigate the expected loss from such systems as a function as the sideways displacement of the fibers away from perfect alignment. Assume that the coupling efficiency is directly proportional to the area overlap of the two fiber ends.

7.11 Show how equations 7.14 and 7.15 may be solved by graphical methods and hence derive the transmission characteristic for a Fabry–Perot-based optically bistable device where $F = 1$ and $\delta_0 = \pi/2$.

7.12 One of the problems of signal transmission over very large distances is that of the spreading of the beam due to diffraction. In this respect compare the beam spreading expected from the following two systems when operating over a distance of 1.3×10^9 km (about the distance from Saturn to the Earth): (a) a radiofrequency transmitter operating at 10 GHz and using a 4 m diameter antenna and (b) a laser system using a wavelength of 0.6 μm and an initial beam diameter of 100 mm.

7.13 Estimate the maximum scanning speed possible in a laser printer which has a resolution of 0.05 mm and a laser power of 5 mW. Assume that the minimum energy density required to activate a photosensor site at the laser wavelength is 3×10^{-3} J m^{-2}.

REFERENCES

7.1 K. C. Kao and G. A. Hockham, 'Dielectric-fiber Surface Waveguides for Optical Frequencies', *Proc. IEEE*, **113**, 1151–1158, 1966.

7.2 H. Taub and D. L. Schilling, *Principles of Communication Systems*, McGraw-Hill, New York, 1971, Chapter 5.

7.3 J. Tyndall, *Royal Institution of Great Britain Proceedings*, **6**, 189–199, 1870–72.

7.4 A. C. S. van Heel, 'A New Method of Transporting Optical Images Without Aberrations', *Nature*, **173**, 39–41, 1954.

7.5 H.-G. Unger, *Planar Optical Waveguides and Fibres*, Oxford University Press, Oxford, 1977, Chapter 4.

7.6 F. A. Jenkins and H. E. White, *Fundamentals of Optics* (4th edn), McGraw-Hill, New York, 1980, Section 13.5.

7.7 M. Born and E. Wolf, *Principles of Optics* (6th edn), Pergamon Press, Oxford, 1980, Section 13.5.

7.8 T. Miya, Y. Terunuma, T. Hosaka and T. Miyashita, 'Ultimate Low-loss Single Mode Fibre at 1.55 m', *Electron. Lett.*, **15**, 106–108, 1979.

7.9 J. Wilson and J. F. B. Hawkes, *Optoelectronics: An introduction*, Prentice Hall, London, 1983, Section 7.2.10.1.

7.10 M. J. Howes and D. V. Morgan (eds.), *Optical Fibre Communications: Devices, Circuits and Systems*, John Wiley, Chichester, 1980, Section 2.3.

7.11 (a) H. Ishio, J. Minowa and K. Nosu, 'Review and Status of Wavelength-division-multiplexing Technology and its Applications', *J. Lightwave Technol.*, **LT-2**, 448–463, 1984.
      (b) G. Winzer, 'Wavelength Multiplexing Components – A Review of Single-mode Devices and their applications', *J. Lightwave Technol.*, **LT-2**, 369–378, 1984.

7.12 G. H. Sigal, Jr. and D. C. Tran, 'Ultra-low Loss Optical Fibres: an Overview', *Proc. SPIE Int. Soc. Opt. Eng.*, **484**, 2–6, 1984.

7.13 J. Wilson and J. F. B. Hawkes, *Optoelectronics: An introduction*, Prentice-Hall, London, 1983, Appendix 5.

7.14 D. W. Smith, 'Coherent Fiberoptic Communications', *Laser Focus*, **21**, 92–104, 1985.

7.15 R. G. Hunsperger, *Integrated Optics: Theory and Technology* (2nd edn), Springer-Verlag, Berlin, 1984.

7.16 F. A. Jenkins and H. E. White, *Fundamentals of Optics* (4th edn), McGraw-Hill, New York, 1980, Section 14.9.

7.17 D. A. B. Miller, S. D. Smith and A. Johnston, 'Optical bistability and signal amplification in a semiconductor crystal: applications of new power effects in InSb', *Appl. Phys. Lett.*, **35**, 658–660, 1979.

7.18 (a) G. Bouwhuis, J. Braat, A. Huijser, J. Pasman, G. Van Rosmalen, K. Schouhamer Immink. *Principles of Optical Disc Systems*, Adam Hilger Ltd, Bristol, 1985.

   (b) Jordan Isailović, *Videodisc and Optical Memory Systems*, Prentice-Hall, New Jersey, 1985.

7.19 (a) H. C. Haverkorn, Van Rijsewijk, P. E. J. Legierse, G. E. Thomas, 'Manufacture of Laservision Video Discs by a Photopolymerization Process', *Philips Tech. Rev.*, **40**, 287–297, 1982.

   (b) J. G. Kloosterboer, G. J. M. Lippits, H. C. Meinders, 'Photopolymerizable Lacquers for Laservision Videodiscs', *Philips Tech. Rev.*, **40**, 298–309, 1982.

7.20 (a) M. Mansuripur and G. A. N. Connell, 'Signal and Noise in Magneto-optic Readout' *J. App. Phys.*, **53**, 4485, 1982.

   (b) M. Mansuripur, 'Disk Storage: Magneto-optics Leads the Way', *Photonics Spectra*, October, 59–62, 1984.

7.21 (a) M. Mansuripur, 'Disk Storage: Magneto-optics Leads the Way', *Photonics Spectra*, October, 59–62, 1984.

   (b) M. Mansuripur and G. A. N. Connell, 'Laser Induced Local Heating of Moving Multilayer Media, *Applied Optics*, March, 1983.

7.22 J. de Vos, 'Megadoc, a Modular System for Electronic Document Handling', *Philips Tech. Rev.*, **39**, 329, 1980.

Appendix 1

Solutions to Problems

Chapter 1

1.1 0.27 mm
1.2 0.8, 1.0
1.3 3.66×10^{-19} J or 2.29 eV
1.4 0.53×10^{-10} m; 2.17×10^{-20} J or 13.58 eV
1.5 2018.1 K, 5.2×10^{-6} m
1.6 60.57%, 5.01 m^{-1}
1.7 0.37 m^{-1}
1.8 4.39×10^5 m^{-3}
1.9 1.28×10^9 Hz
1.10 0.12 m^{-1}
1.11 1.31 m^{-1}; 6.49×10^{22} m^{-3}
1.12 51.9 MHz; 1.

Chapter 2

2.1 0.923, 0.471
2.2 Internal angle 61.2°, rod inclined at 57.6° to the vertical
2.3 117.9°
2.4 78%
2.5 0.25%
2.7 Material $\lambda_g (\mu m)$
    GaAs   0.861
    GaP   0.549
    CdTe   0.827
    InP   0.919
    SiC   0.413
2.8 2.5×10^{11} W m^{-2}
2.9 1.27
2.10 275 nm
2.12 46.7 mm, 7.7 nm.

Chapter 3

3.1 10, 20
3.2 1.2 MHz
3.3 1.2×10^9 Hz
3.4 2.54×10^8 W m^{-2}
3.5 2.95×10^{-4} m, 7.42×10^{-4}, 6.82×10^{-3}
3.7 1.38 mm
3.8 2.37×10^7; 5 m; 122.5 m
3.9 5.34×10^{19}
3.11 1.34×10^{-12} s.

Chapter 4

4.2 1 580 278.13, 3 160 556.26; 3×10^8 Hz
4.3 0.06 mm
4.4 0.010 5 mm
4.5 $2.049 \times 10^{-5}\,^\circ\text{C}^{-1}$ or $7.514 \times 10^{-6}\,^\circ\text{C}^{-1}$
4.8 0.123 m s^{-1}
4.9 $0.21\,^\circ$C
4.11 1.68 GHz; 853 MHz.

Chapter 5

5.1 7.8×10^{-3} s
5.5 172 mm s^{-1}
5.7 0.011 s
5.8 0.57 mm diameter
5.9 157 mm, 3.4 mm
5.10 17.59 MeV
5.11 $0.001\,77$ m^3 ($= 1.77$ litres).

Chapter 7

7.1 (a) 9.4×10^8, (b) 3.36×10^7
7.2 40.2°
7.3 (a) $NA = 0.414$
     (b) $\alpha_{\max} = 24.5^\circ$
     (c) 2.6 MHz km
     (d) 52 926
7.4 15 dB km^{-1}

7.7 630 MHz km

7.8 4×10^{-3} dB km^{-1}

Across the Atlantic this would give ~ 22 dB loss overall

7.12 (a) 1.2×10^7 m (b) 9500 m

7.13 4.2×10^4 m s^{-1}, 35 pages s^{-1}.

Appendix 2

Physical Constants

Rest mass of electron	m	$= 9.110 \times 10^{-31}$ kg $= 0.000\,549$ u
Charge of electron	e	$= 1.602 \times 10^{-19}$ C
Electron charge/mass ratio	e/m	$= 1.759 \times 10^{11}$ C kg^{-1}
Avogadro's constant	N_A	$= 6.022 \times 10^{23}$ mol^{-1}
Planck's constant	h	$= 6.626 \times 10^{-34}$ J s
	$\hbar = h/2\pi$	$= 1.055 \times 10^{-34}$ J s
Boltzmann's constant	k	$= 1.381 \times 10^{-23}$ J K^{-1}
Speed of light (in vacuum)	c	$= 2.998 \times 10^{8}$ m s^{-1}
Permittivity of a vacuum	ε_0	$= 8.854 \times 10^{-12}$ F m^{-1}
Permeability of a vacuum	μ_0	$= 4\pi \times 10^{-7} = 1.258 \times 10^{-6}$ H m^{-1}
Stefan-Boltzmann constant	σ	$= 5.670 \times 10^{-8}$ W m^{-2} K^{-4}
Rydberg constant	R_H	$= 1.097 \times 10^{7}$ m^{-1}

Appendix 3

Laser Safety

Most practical lasers emit radiation that is potentially hazardous. The degree of the hazard is related to the output characteristics of the laser, the way in which it is used and the experience of the operator. The types of laser and the ways in which they are used are, as we have seen, many and varied. It would therefore be unreasonable to suggest that all laser applications require the same degree of control. Accordingly, systems of classification of lasers have been introduced which are given below.

Any classification must be operable and consistent with our knowledge concerning the injuries which laser radiation can cause. The mechanism by which laser radiation causes damage is similar for all biological systems and may involve thermal, thermo-accoustic and photo-chemical processes. The degree to which any of these mechanisms is responsible for damage depends on the parameters of the laser source such as wavelength, pulse duration, image size and power, and energy density.

One of the principal characteristics of laser radiation is its beam collimation. This, together with a high energy content, can result in large amounts of energy being transmitted to biological tissues. The primary event causing damage is the absorption of the radiation by the biological system. Absorption occurs at an atomic or molecular level and is thus wavelength specific. Thus it is primarily the laser wavelength which determines which tissue is liable to be damaged. Absorption of radiation leads to a rise in temperature which may then disrupt molecular bonds and hence impair the function of the molecule. The rise in temperature is related to the length of exposure and the irradiance of the beam, and this leads to the notion of a radiant exposure or dose measured in joules per square meter. Exposure to Q-switched or mode locked lasers can cause a very rapid rise in temperature of the tissue so that liquid components may be converted to gas leading to a rupturing of cells. In general, the interrelationships between damage mechanisms and exposure are very complex (Ref. 1), and we shall not pursue them here.

Probably the most vulnerable part of the body, as far as laser radiation is concerned, is the eye. This is mainly because the eye lens will focus incident collimated laser radiation to a small point with a radius of the order of the wavelength and with a corresponding high energy density. The hazards are wavelength dependent so that radiation in the ultraviolet and infra-red regions, which is absorbed by the cornea, represents a danger to the cornea, whilst radiation in the visible and near infra-red represents a retinal hazard. The increase in irradiance from the cornea to the retina is given approximately by the ratio of the pupil area to that of the image formed on the retina. Typically the pupil may expand to a diameter of 5 mm with a corresponding retinal image of $10-20 \, \mu m$ diameter. Thus the irradiance increases by a factor of between 2×10^5 and 5×10^5. A laser beam of $50 \, Wm^{-2}$ incident on the cornea then represents an irradiance of about $25 \, MWm^{-2}$ on the retina. About five percent of the radiation falling on the retina is absorbed in the pigments within the rods and cones and this may be sufficient to cause a burn and a loss of vision.

In general terms, skin can tolerate a great deal more exposure than can the eye, though blisters, ulceration and scarring of the skin may occur for high levels of irradiation. Again the hazards are wavelength dependent, being more pronounced for ultraviolet radiation. Any organization which uses lasers would be advised to draw up a Safety Code of Practice, which should be based on an accepted classification of lasers. The classification accepted in the UK and Europe is described below. There are slight differences in the classification used in the USA. These classifications and related information on laser safety are given in considerable detail in the various publications cited in Reference 2.

Laser Classification based on BS 4803:

Class 1   Output power is so low as to be inherently safe.

Class 2   Such lasers operate in the visible part of the spectrum and their output power is limited to 1 mW for continuous wave (CW) operation. Such lasers are not inherently safe but some eye protection is afforded by the natural aversion response of the eye, including the blink reflex. Hazards can be controlled by relatively simple procedures.

Class 3A   These lasers operate in the visible part of the spectrum (400 nm to 700 nm) and their output is limited to 5 mW for CW operation. Some protection is still provided by the aversion responses. Direct intra-beam viewing with optical aids may be hazardous.

Class 3B   These lasers operate in any part of the electromagnetic spectrum between wavelengths of 200 nm and 1 mm. Their output power is limited to 500 mW for CW operation. Direct beam viewing could be hazardous and must be avoided. Likewise specular reflections may be hazardous but diffuse reflections will not generally be so. Under no circumstances should the beam be viewed with optical aids.

More detailed control measures are necessary.

Class 4 These lasers also operate within the wavelength range 200 nm to 1 mm and their output power exceeds 500 mW. Not only is viewing of the direct beam and specular reflections hazardous but, in some cases, viewing of diffuse reflections may also be hazardous to the eye. In addition, there is also a risk of skin burns from the direct beam and from first order specular relections.

The beam from such lasers is also capable of igniting flammable material so that care must be taken to minimise the risk of fire.

The use of Class 4 lasers requires extreme caution for safety both of the user and of other persons who may be present. If possible the system should be totally enclosed.

N.B. It is stressed that the above table is intended as a guide only and that laser users should consult the publications given in Reference 2. The American *Standards for the Safe Use of Lasers* Number Z136 issued by the National Standards Institute should also be consulted.

Each laser device should carry an appropriate label and notice of warning (ref. 2.a Part 2 p.3).

The safe use of lasers often involves the provision of safety interlocks and warning light on access doors to rooms where lasers are being used, together with beam stops and enclosures. Materials which act as diffuse reflectors should be used wherever possible. Protective eyewear should also be available for use with Class 3B and Class 4 lasers. Bearing in mind that the protective medium will not afford protection over the whole spectral range care must be taken to ensure that the eye protection has the correct spectral response to match the laser being used.

Finally it should be remembered that most lasers are high voltage devices (several kV) often capable of delivering large currents and therefore care must also be taken in this respect.

REFERENCES

1. McKinlay A. F. and Harlon F. Biological Bases of Maximum Permissable Exposure Levels of Laser Standards Part 1: 'Damage Mechanisms' *J.Soc Radiol Prot* **4** (1) 1984.

2(a) British Standard, 'Radiation Safety of Laser Products and Systems' – 3 parts BS4803 1983.

(b)   American National Standards Institute, 'Standards for the Safe Use of Lasers', *ANSI* **Z136** 1980.

(c)   International Electrotechnical Commission, IEC Standard 'Radiation Safety of Laser Products, Equipment Classification, Requirements and Users' Guide', Publication 825 1984.

(d)   'Safety in Universities Part 2:1 Lasers'. The Committee of Vice-Chancellors and Principals of the Universities of the United Kingdom, 1978.

(e)   Rockwell, R. J. 'Analysing Laser Hazards' *Lasers and Aplications* May 1986 p. 97.

(f)   Kaufman J. and Tucker R. 'Laser Absorbers for Eye Protection' *Lasers and Applications*, October 1985 p.69.

(g)   Winban D. C. 'Dispelling Myths about Laser Eyewear', *Lasers and Applications*, March 1986 p. 73.

(h)   Rockwell R. J. 'Controlling Laser Hazards', *Lasers and Applications*, September 1986 p. 93.

(i)   Wolbarsht M. L. and Sliney D. H. 'Laser Safety Standards Move On' *Lasers and Applications*, April 1987 p. 97.

Index